CHRISTMAS 1989

TO DAD

Another piece in the
historical puzzle that
created the world
as we know it,
including you!!

LOVE,

Brian

SHADOW OF HEAVEN

SHADOW OF HEAVEN

THE LIFE OF LESTER PEARSON

VOLUME ONE: 1897-1948

JOHN ENGLISH

LESTER
&ORPEN
DENNYS
PUBLISHERS

FIRST EDITION

Canadian Cataloguing in Publication Data

English, John, 1945–
Shadow of heaven: The life of Lester Pearson.

Includes bibliographical references and index.
ISBN 0-88619-165-3 (v. 1: bound). –
ISBN 0-88619-169-6 (v. 1: pbk.)

1. Pearson, Lester B., 1897-1972. 2. Canada – Politics and
government – 1963-1968.* 3. Canada – Politics and government
– 1957-1963.* 4. Canada – Politics and government – 1935-
1957.* 5. Prime ministers – Canada – Biography. I. Title.

FC621.P43E54 1989   971.064'3'0924   C89-094173-4
F1034.3.P43E54 1989

The Publisher wishes to acknowledge the support
of the Ontario Arts Council.

Except where otherwise indicated, all pictures
are from the Pearson family.

Design by Gordon Robertson

Typeset in 11 pt Galliard by The Coach House Press

Printed and bound in Canada by Gagné Ltée for

LESTER & ORPEN DENNYS LIMITED
78 Sullivan Street
Toronto, Canada   M5T 1C1

To Paul Martin

CONTENTS

PREFACE

THE book's title, the cover photograph notwithstanding, comes from Book V of the great epic of British Protestantism, *Paradise Lost,* which Milton published in 1667, three centuries before Lester Pearson's most memorable year as prime minister, the year of Canada's centennial when the nation tried to come to terms with its past and define itself anew. That definition was modern and secular and Lester Pearson, in his public career, gave it clarity. "What if earth," the angel Raphael asks Adam, "Be but the shadow of Heav'n, and things therein / Each to other like, more than on Earth is thought?" Raphael offers this vision of an earth that mirrors heaven just before he describes to Adam how Satan's pride caused the wars of heaven. Raphael's history emphasizes, as Milton himself did, the imperative and the danger of free human choice, the essence of British liberalism, and the interdependence of all creatures, the foundation of Pearson's internationalism. During his lifetime, Pearson and the British Canadian Protestant tradition became increasingly secular. In his public life, he never spoke of God or called upon him to explain or justify his ways. He deplored and sometimes feared those who did. Nevertheless, Pearson's thought, language, and ethics bear heavily the weight of the tradition that Milton represented long before. His biography reflects the transformation of that tradition in this century.

Lester Pearson has not been easy to know. He had a Victorian reserve that made revelation about one's private life difficult.

In writing this biography, especially on those occasions when I had to divine Pearson's private thoughts and motives, I often recalled Virginia Woolf's comment about her sighting of a kingfisher on a cold September day that awakened a special feeling in her. No biographer, she rightly warned, could ever know that important fact about her life in the late summer of 1926 and no biographer should pretend to do so. Like Woolf, Pearson left abundant written material, but he also leads his biographer through some mazes that have no end. I believe I can fairly claim to have reached the end of some mazes that have confused earlier wanderers and to have clarified the route to understanding his thoughts and actions. I never met Lester Pearson, but the wit and ebullience that mark his letters and life have made him a wonderful companion. At the mention of his name, nearly all of his friends immediately smile, and the doses of bitterness are very few.

His family has been extremely supportive of my work. His children, Geoffrey and Patricia, have shared their memories, letters, and photographs. They have been exceptionally candid and generous and have not requested the change of a single sentence of the manuscript for this book. It has been a model relationship for a biographer to have, an example as rare as it is commendable. Fred Pearson and Pamela Phillips have also been very helpful, as has Maryon Pearson's brother, Herbert Moody.

The progenitor of this biography was a project to publish some of Lester Pearson's papers that I undertook some years ago with Bob Bothwell. The papers were collected but a publisher could not be found. Ardath Francis collected most of these papers of which I have made extensive use in the writing of this biography, and I am much indebted to her for her work. I have also used notes that Bob Bothwell and I compiled for other projects and would like to thank Bob for his help and his wise counsel throughout. Jack Granatstein has also shared some of his material with me. The Massey Papers were taken from Massey College to the University of Toronto Archives and immediately sealed to researchers. In a spirit of scholarly dissemination and subterfuge, Jack showed me the notes he had taken in Massey College. Norman Hillmer has given me many documents, and he and Ben Greenhous corrected several errors in the manuscript.

I would also like to acknowledge the help of numerous archivists, especially Roy Maddocks, Peter Robertson, and Maureen Hoogenraad at the National Archives of Canada. Jane Barrett, the librarian of the Canadian Institute of International Affairs, shared her unrivalled knowledge of the literature on Canadian foreign policy with me. There is a listing of other archives in the "Notes on Sources". Although space prohibits my listing all the archivists who were so helpful to me, I must record here my thanks for the unfailing courtesy they showed me. I also received material from several private sources, and Mrs. Kenneth Kirkwood and V.C. Wansbrough were particularly helpful. The University of Waterloo library helped with interlibrary loans, and head librarian Murray Shepherd gave me an office for the duration of the project. In Ottawa, Constantine Brancovan often provided me with a summer room, complete with the gin and tonics he so cherishes.

The Killam Foundation granted me a senior research fellowship, which freed me from my teaching duties. The Social Sciences and Humanities Research Council supported my research costs. The Killam Foundation and the Council are remarkable institutions that do not command the praise and support they merit. Without them, we would have a much poorer country. The Centre on Foreign Policy and Federalism at Waterloo, which has been supported by the Donner Canadian Foundation, has also given me much assistance in the project, as has the history department at Waterloo. The department's greatest assistance came through the exceptional skills of Gail Heideman, who input the entire manuscript. I also owe a great debt to Irene Sage Knell, who helped with research, advice, and the organization of my chaotic office. Irene Majer, Neeta Logsetty, Kathy Sage, John Shewchuk, Karen Trussler, and Ellen Yachnin provided assistance at various times. Jim Howe spent the best part of two summers in the microfilm room for me. I owe all of them a great debt.

I began my relationship with Lester & Orpen Dennys badly when, after Louise Dennys and Malcolm Lester called to invite me to lunch to discuss a possible book on Pearson, I went to the Royal Ontario Museum restaurant and they went (correctly) to the Art Gallery of Ontario restaurant. Forgiving my provincialism, they rescheduled our lunch and did not lose enthusiasm for the project. I have never regretted my decision to publish with them. Their success in Canadian publishing is the result of their genuine concern for their product; they are model publishers. Beverley Beetham Endersby has transformed many graceless passages into readable English and has done so with a sense of charity towards one whose commas often fail. Gena Gorrell has cheerfully harrassed me when I've missed deadlines and has ably assisted in putting the final touches on the manuscript.

Work on this manuscript began just before the birth of my son Jonathan. He and my wife, Hilde, have often missed me as I laboured over its pages. My parents and Hilde's parents have helped with babysitting and many other tasks. I deeply appreciate their generosity and patience. John Holmes died just before this manuscript was finished. John, who, uniquely, could make a gathering more serious yet happier, taught me through deed and word more about Lester Pearson than anyone else. I miss him.

CHAPTER ONE

BEGINNINGS

God was in His Heaven and Queen Victoria on her throne.
— Lester Pearson on the surroundings of his birth[1]

THE CENTURY was old but the country still young when Annie Bowles Pearson gave birth to her middle son, Lester Bowles, in the Methodist parsonage in Newtonbrook, Ontario, in the early morning of April 23, 1897. The air Lester first breathed was British-Canadian and Protestant, an air very different from that lingering today above metropolitan Toronto, which has smothered the Victorian hamlet of Newtonbrook beneath its steel and concrete. A few weeks after Lester's birth, that village of small homes, backyards, vegetable gardens, and picket fences joined in the grandest celebration of British imperial history, the diamond jubilee of Queen Victoria's glorious reign. Victoria, Queen and Empress, Defender of the Faith, beloved mother, and devoted wife, was the glory of her time, in the imperial heart of London, the many palaces of the British Raj in India, the exotic court of the Sultan of Zanzibar, and Reverend Edwin A. Pearson's modest pulpit in Newtonbrook Methodist Church.

Loyalty to Queen Victoria, who gazed upon her Canadian subjects from postage stamps, dinner plates, silver spoons, and imposing statues in city parks, did not conflict with Southern Ontario's increasing pride in the young Dominion of Canada. For Lester's father,

I

Edwin, British loyalty, Canadian nationalism, and Methodist faith were stems of the same plant whose foliage grew ever more brilliant. The pages of his scrapbook are filled with clippings about the triumphs of his Empire, his nation, and his church. A few days after Lester's birth he clipped Rudyard Kipling's tribute to Canada's past loyalty and future greatness in the Empire:[2]

> Carry the word to my sisters –
> To the Queens of the East and the South
> I have proven faith in the Heritage
> By more than word of the mouth.

For Edwin Pearson and his parishioners, the British heritage of Shakespeare, the King James Bible, Wesley's hymns, and, not least, the British navy was their own. Newtonbrook lay along the upper reaches of Yonge Street and reflected in its outlook both the countryside to the north and the provincial capital of Toronto a few miles to the south. Known widely as "the city of churches" and, more questionably, as "Toronto the Good", the capital had recovered from a period of economic stagnancy and was well prepared to reap great profits from the "great Canadian boom" that was just beginning. Many who reaped those profits were Methodists who had come to Toronto and its opportunities from the small towns and farms of Southern Ontario. They kept their strong religious attachment, and from their eminent positions in the city's political and economic affairs, they deeply influenced the values of the city. For example, Joseph Flavelle, the greatest butcher of the Empire, whose vast packing plants may have given Toronto the nickname "Hogtown", was the Sunday-school principal of Sherbourne Street Methodist. George Cox, Ontario's leading financier, and A.E. Kemp, an important manufacturer, guided, respectively, the Mission Society and the Music Committee. They were, Flavelle later wrote, part of "a community of Methodists who in one generation passed from being mostly poor people to those who are comfortably off, and in some cases very well to do." They taught in Sunday schools, prayed before meals, and urged temperance and a Sabbath without work, games, drinks, or even streetcars upon Torontonians and Canadians. But if they did no business on Sunday, they did plenty of it, and with incredible enthusiasm and success, on the other days. Their business practices might now land them in jail and would certainly cause a public stir, but late-Victorian Canada imposed restraint and censure mainly upon social, not economic, behaviour. Its capitalism was rugged, and it thrived.[3]

Industrial capitalism was transforming the landscape of Southern Ontario, taking young men and women from the farm and placing them in factories, where the realities of time and work were much different. The workers clustered in industrial pockets, and the crowding spread sickness, especially tuberculosis, and caused resentment, especially towards those factory owners who erected imposing Victorian mansions on the hills above the city. The difference between rich and poor, city and country, past and present, troubled many Methodist ministers, and some turned towards a "social gospel" that dreamed of a new order to build a heaven upon earth. The pace of change was both disturbing and exhilarating. On the one hand, many of the traditional beliefs seemed threatened; on the other, future possibilities seemed so much greater than they had to the mainly European peasant ancestors of the rich and poor of late-Victorian Ontario. Toronto's population grew from 96,196 in 1881 to 208,040 in 1901, by which time street railways threaded its thoroughfares, telephone and electricity wires hung above them, and even a few motor cars made their hesitant way among horses, buggies, and pedestrians. Within a decade of Lester's birth, Marconi sent the first wireless message across the Atlantic, the Wright brothers flew at Kitty Hawk, Henry Ford founded his motor company, and Freud published *The Meaning of Dreams*. Modern times had come, and Newtonbrook's Methodists were not immune to its chill winds, which would sway the foundations of Christian faith and British loyalty in the new century.

Certainly Edwin Pearson and Annie Bowles had had few doubts about the future of God or the British Empire when, at age twenty-two, they'd first met on a late Sunday afternoon in November 1890, in

a Methodist church in Orangeville, Ontario. "Ed" was a probation-
ary Methodist preacher, moving from one Southern Ontario town to
another to fill in for an ailing pastor or simply an absent one; his
father was an Orangeville minister, and Annie's, Thomas Bowles,
was the sheriff of Dufferin County, a figure of some renown in the
small community, partly because of the vigorous sermons he
delivered as a lay preacher on Sunday mornings but mainly because
he added a cocked hat and a judicial sword to the sheriff's traditional
uniform of pin-stripe trousers and cutaway coat. Although the families were acquainted, such familiarity did not breed informality
between Ed and Annie. When Ed returned to Collingwood from
Orangeville, he carefully declared his interest in Miss Bowles. "Dear
Friend," he wrote, "I do not altogether relish the way this letter
opens [but] I am loathe to write 'Dear Annie' lest it draw your wrath
down upon my head." Ed had suggested to Annie on that November
Sunday that they correspond, and she had agreed, although neither
offered any reason why they should. A lot was left unsaid. The few
moments and brief conversation they had shared were enough, until
Christmas when they could "have many long chats, and [could] then
explain everything". In fact Ed really had little to report: Collingwood was dull and in decline; nothing ever seemed to happen there.
After a few similar musings, Ed, probably with some frustration,
concluded: "Well there is a great deal that I feel like saying, but I cannot, for I must remember that I am not sufficiently acquainted with
you to know what you would consider proper and what improper."

Annie's reply, which also began "Dear Friend", offered some
encouragement – perhaps more than Ed had expected. With some
embarrassment she confessed that she did not know what to say to a
friend of the opposite sex of such short acquaintance. She nevertheless granted Ed "liberty to begin your letters in the future as you
intimated" and she admitted that she was granting this "liberty" even
though she "didn't know under the circumstances [if] it would be
either improper or a violation of Etiquette". She promised to write
every Friday morning to Ed, who, in that age of Saturday post,
would receive her letter the following day. He could reply on Mon-

day, when the church news would be freshest. After some scattered reports of Orangeville events, Annie closed her letter with more boldness than Ed's "Sincerely Yours", declaring she would remain "Your Irish Friend".[4]

And Irish they certainly were, but not the music-hall type of those days: roistering, belligerent, sentimental, Catholic, and poor. Although both families had lived in overwhelmingly Catholic parts of Ireland, they were Methodists, a faith with a strong evangelical tradition, but evidence suggests that their Irish-Catholic surroundings forced them to mute their Methodist enthusiasm. The Pearsons came from Dublin and had lived in a section of town called the Coombe, or Liberties, where the seeds of many of the Irish rebellions had been planted. The area lay outside the control of the city government, and fugitives often found a haven there, as did skilled and prosperous artisans who wanted to shun civic regulations of their trade and lives. In 1795, one such artisan, Samuel Pearson, a linen-draper, married Charlotte Anderson in St. Catherine's Church, a historic structure on whose steps Robert Emmett and his companions were hanged eight years later, thus signalling the end of the dreams of reform and Catholic emancipation of the United Irish.[5]

With Nelson's victory at Trafalgar, the rebellions that had fed on the hopes of French support ceased. Even those Dubliners who celebrated Nelson's triumph, as Wesleyan Methodist Samuel Pearson almost surely did, were to face unhappy days in the aftermath of Trafalgar and the British decision to close down the Irish Parliament in 1801. Dublin's Irish peers abandoned College Green for London's Westminster, and they and their prosperous kin sold their city mansions to whoever would buy. The enlightened Georgian Ascendancy of the eighteenth century, which had bestowed exquisite city squares and grand public buildings upon Dublin and a good livelihood upon the linen-drapers and weavers, gave way in the nineteenth century to a declining city and an increasingly desperate population.

Samuel Pearson trained his son Marmaduke to become a linen-draper, but a poorer Dublin could not afford elegant linen. As the wealthier Protestants left for England or for newly prosperous

Northern Ireland, Dublin's proud artisans lost both status and wealth. The narrow alleys of the Liberties teemed with beggars, and the stench drove away all visitors. One by one the great Dublin artisans' trades collapsed as Britain turned to free trade and opened its markets to imported goods. The indigent crowded the streets, and gloom lurked in almost every Liberties household by the 1840s. In 1842 Marmaduke Pearson married Catherine Pritchard, and the Methodist newly-weds took up residence on the appropriately named Wesley Terrace. Although the Pearsons' home was better than most in Dublin, the area surrounding it was, in the words of an 1844 report, "an intermixture of putrid lanes, and dense niduses of diseased, ragged, starving poverty, or of bold shameless stenchy vice". Soon the famine struck, and death came even more quickly to the young; in 1847 Marmaduke and Kate Pearson and their three children fled Ireland for New York. Two years later they returned to British soil, settling in Toronto.[6]

Annie's family, like Edwin's, were of the conqueror's race, but by the nineteenth century as much Celtic as British blood flowed through Bowles veins. Though the first Bowleses in Ireland were probably members of the dreaded constabulary who forced English rule upon the Celts, their Englishness had given way to Irish ways by the fourth generation. They had become, a family historian claims, "warm-hearted, hospitable, sociable, highly emotionalized, a bit irresponsible, impetuous, hilarious and blessed with a high disregard of consequences" – in short, "thoroughly Irish". The adoption of things Irish did not include religion: they married their own or made their spouses Methodists, which the Bowleses themselves had become after John Wesley's great Irish crusade. In the nineteenth century, as religion became more closely linked with Irish politics, the Methodist Bowleses in Catholic Tipperary probably felt even more isolated.[7] And, as always in Ireland, there wasn't enough land. Whatever the motivation, Charles Bowles left Kilkenny in 1826, with his new bride, Nancy Barrie, and his possessions piled upon a donkey cart, and set out for Canada. He stayed for a year in "Muddy York" and then headed northwest, to the Township of Chinguacousy in what later became Peel County. As the Bowleses prospered, their religious commitment intensified. The Irish Bowleses had not been noted for such fervour previously, but in the new world the church became the centre of their lives.

Their experience was not unique. In the isolation and primitive conditions of life in the Upper-Canadian frontier, evangelistic Methodism flourished. Passion came above reason; the truth as it was in Jesus had to be felt, not deduced. R.P. Bowles recalled his and Annie Pearson's grandmother confessing her sins at a Methodist class meeting.

> I can see her yet, rising slowly as her turn came. Soon there was a suppressed sob. Then her right hand began to move up and down waving the end of her shawl with the regularity of, but much more slowly than, the wag sign at a railway crossing. With her handkerchief, her left hand wiped the tears from her eyes. Then in a wailing, weeping voice that threw zero into my bones, she began her confession. She was a great sinner ... but she was sure the Lord had forgiven her, and here her voice, in a crescendo of sobbing and weeping, high-pitched itself into an Irish wail.[8]

Nancy Bowles's devotion and emotion passed on to her three sons, who became lay Methodist preachers.

Local, or lay, preachers far outnumbered ordained Methodists in Upper Canada. The Bowleses began their ministries in the Caledon Hills region, north of Brampton, but their reputations spread widely. What they lacked in education, they made up in fierce conviction. Two of the brothers remained on the farm, but Thomas Bowles, Annie's father, gradually took to town life, which in those days was markedly different from rural life. He wore city dress (when not in his sheriff's garb), played croquet on well-tended lawns, and urged education upon his children. The quality of his faith also changed. He bore his witness, not at fervent class meetings as his mother had, but in well-reasoned scientific and historical arguments that often touched upon the problems of this world more than on the promise of the next.[9]

The Bowleses and the Pearsons had come to Canada as farmers and small merchants, but by the 1870s the young were turning away

from the land and account books towards the town and the professions. Marmaduke Pearson's dry-goods business at Yonge and Rich-
mond streets in Toronto flourished, as did his sons; three of them
entered the real estate business, one became a civil servant (thanks,
no doubt, to the strong Conservative attachments of the Pearson
family), and Marmaduke Jr., who was ordained in the Wesleyan
Methodist Church in 1862, became an eloquent preacher and a
renowned administrator. As Methodism outgrew its simple, rural
origins, his eloquence and business skills assured him of a successful
career. The simple wooden box church was replaced with the stone
or brick Gothic edifice with long rows of polished oak pews, a sono-
rous organ, and sermons that spoke to the mind as much as the heart.
Methodism did keep up its itinerant tradition, and Marmaduke
moved on, after three or four years, to a new charge. Each time the
congregation swelled as Marmaduke's good works and convincing
arguments converted more Canadians to the Methodist faith, which
had long since abandoned its aversion to ostentation and material
success while retaining its commitment to evangelism. When Marmaduke left a congregation there were warm farewells, accompanied
by a gold purse or a gold watch, or a new gown for Mrs. Pearson.
When, for example, he left Ottawa in 1882, the congregation gave
him a bound volume of Topley's *Views of Ottawa* and the princely
sum of $150. In his parting remarks, Marmaduke expressed his
delight with the rapid decline of the church's debt and "concluded by
congratulating the congregation on the possession of the Divine
blessing, of which he said the manner in which matters had gone of
late was ample proof". He came to know the new captains of indus-
try, such as the Masseys and Flavelles, and the redoubtable Sam
Hughes* even asked why such a fuss should be made about the 1897
visit to Toronto of a Catholic cardinal when the visits of the dis-

---

* Hughes, an Orangeman, was a member of Parliament and a vigorous defender of
Protestant causes. He later became minister of militia and defence in Robert
Borden's government in 1911 but was fired in 1916 for insubordination. The Catholic
vicar general in Hughes's constituency in the early 1890s denounced Hughes as a
"vicious dog".

tinguished Rev. Marmaduke Pearson, superintendent of the Toronto Methodist Conference, were ignored.[10] Certainly the wedding of Edwin and Annie was not ignored.

How far away was the one-room shack in the wilderness and the stench of Dublin's Liberties when Annie wed Ed on a July afternoon in Orangeville in 1892. Toronto papers called it a "fashionable" wedding. Flowers surrounded the altar where Marmaduke, Rev. R.P. Bowles, and the local pastor presided. Annie, "one of [Orangeville's] loveliest daughters, wore a beautiful bridal gown of white souri silk trimmed with duchesse lace and a long tulle veil caught up with orange blossoms."[11] It was reported that the bride was the "recipient of a number of costly presents" from as far away as Denver and New York, but the "handsomest" of all was her father's gift, a grand piano. The bride and groom took the evening train to Toronto, and there the lake-boat to Cleveland, Detroit, and Chicago for their honeymoon.[12]

Lester Pearson remembered his father as "a modest minister, not an embattled evangelist", one "who led his flock rather than harried it". Ed Pearson seems a simple man, his demeanour, "saintly". To him, "sincerity and simplicity were good, pomp and pretence suspect."[13] In his own times, however, he was not so simple as his son recalled, and his ministerial style reflected the great changes in contemporary Methodism as it adapted with some difficulty to an increasingly urban, industrial, and commercial society. In the 1890s and the early twentieth century, Canadian Methodism tried to come to terms with higher criticism of the Bible and with the demands for social regeneration through the building of a heaven on earth. Lester Pearson wrote of his father that "the man was the message", and perhaps he was, but in a more complicated way than Lester suggested. In 1892, when Ed finished his last courses at Victoria College prior to ordination, Professor George Workman lost his position at the college for investigating the Scriptures too closely. The Methodist journal, *The Christian Guardian,* in historian Ramsay Cook's words, "was determined to scotch the serpent of liberalism at every opportunity — and there were several."[14] Indeed, error abounded. While some Methodists moved from scientific criticism of the Bible to criticism of society, Ed shunned the theological and political conflicts of the day – eventually if not at the beginning. At Victoria College, he was an active member of the Liberal-Conservative party, taking part in spirited debates on such questions as the rights of labour. He first tried law but quickly lost interest in the subject, although not in disputation. When he entered the ministry, he committed himself fully to the intensity of debate at divinity school. In one of his early sermons at Davisville, where he served just after Lester's birth in 1897, Ed came down firmly on the side of a traditional view of sin. "I am getting heartily sick," Ed declared, "of the definitions and thoughts of sin seeming to prevail in many quarters today. Sin is 'that abominable thing' hated by God; then why trifle with it and call it mere error, or disharmony, or using the language of a present day writer, 'a ripple on the ocean of God's love'?" The sources of danger were everywhere: "the modern drama, the imaginative literature of the day, the doctrine of necessary evil, presented by the modern evolutionist ... and the modern newspaper", which played "fast and loose with sin and crime". The "high class Toronto theatres", which had Ibsen's "new women" and new thoughts, got strong criticism from Ed. The "preachers" too bore responsibility, "for perhaps a hundred sermons are preached telling that God is love for one saying God is a consuming fire". Small wonder that a newspaper reported, when Ed became a minister, that he would make "an intelligent, manly clergyman, and a fearless exponent of the doctrines of the church".[15]

The sentimental modernism of so many young preachers was not for Ed. Perhaps his devotion to sports, which his son saw as a contradiction in his character, was, in fact, an expression of the muscular side of his Christianity. It was Ed's contemporary, the famed evangelist and former baseball player Billy Sunday, who declared that Jesus Christ was "no dough-faced, lick-spittle proposition".[16] Ed's style was less aggressive, but, like Sunday, he shunned the intellectual cloisters of Christianity. He lost his interest in the angry debates among theologians and philosophers. Family legend has it that Ed Pearson had only three or four non-theological books in his library, and that he was a dull preacher whose amiable soul and sporting interests captured the hearts but not the minds of his congregation. If so, he chose the image. He, unlike all but a few contemporaries, was a university graduate, with first-class honours standing in English literature from the University of Toronto and a solid record in his study for the ministry. However, Ed, unlike some other famous Methodists, such as J.S. Woodsworth, accepted rather than challenged the political and religious orthodoxies of the day. His obituary in the Methodist *New Outlook* aptly suggested that his ministry had been "an example of the belief that Christianity is not a exotic in human life" and, even more perceptively, that Ed "had evidently studied to preserve a becoming consistency between a cheerful naturalness and the sacred character of his holy calling".[17]

Ed lived, as he once said, "in an age characterized by rush, fret, and friction" and his role was to protect his flock by swaddling it in the secure cloak of Christianity.[18] The Masseys and the masses alike drew strength from his messages. At Centennial Methodist Church in Toronto, Ed's congregation grew from 220 to 550 between 1904 and 1907. The evidence of such devotion inspired the millionaire Methodist Chester Massey to come forward with tens of thousands of dollars to build a new Tudor-Gothic church with eighty-one-foot spires, electric lighting, and very comfortable pews.

Each Sunday hundreds of worshippers watched as Ed's family passed them on their way to the front pew reserved for the minister's family. The three Pearson boys – Marmaduke, the oldest by three years; Lester; and Vaughan, a year younger than Lester – stayed only three years in any area, but, as minister's sons, they were immediately known in the community. As Lester later said, the children of a Methodist parsonage were always under close scrutiny.[19] Communities were smaller then, and radio and television non-existent. Thoughts and hopes centred on nearby streets and dwellings, and celebrities lived around the corner, not in Hollywood, New York, or London (except, of course, for the Royal Family). As the Pearsons moved from Newtonbrook to Davisville (both now part of Metropolitan Toronto), to Aurora, back to Toronto, and then to Peterborough, Hamilton, and Chatham, home was much the same in each place. The origins were British, the culture Anglo-Canadian. Red-brick parsonages, churches on the main corners, clapboard town halls, a few saloons (one was too many for the Methodists), and a clear sense of where everyone fitted marked such towns. The militia marched resplendently to church on some Sundays; the fraternal lodges came forth on others. The school system had common standards and limits, and except for the teachers and students, little changed. The familiar red readers lay in every desk. Classes began with the Lord's Prayer and "God Save the King", and the teacher worried little about implanting the values of Anglo-Canadian society in the children's minds. At home, Annie, even more than Ed, reinforced the values of school and church. Ed was gone so often, to church meetings, to civic gatherings, and to call on the lame, the halt, and the grieving, that all family tasks fell to Annie. Although Anglo Ontario was changing rapidly, the imposing structures of family, church, and school made the young Pearsons' world seem "simple and reasonably serene".[20] In the summers, the children went to their cousins' farms. Here, too, there was church every Sunday: Junior League at ten, morning service at eleven, Sunday school at half-past two, and evening service at seven. Then, on Wednesday nights, there were prayer meetings and occasionally revival meetings where the faithful pledged their faith, though much less exuberantly than Ed's grandmother had done in pioneer days not so long before.

Lester had fond memories of his childhood, although he does use the term "conscripted" to describe his church attendance. Otherwise, "The air was pure and the skies clear and blue. We did our own work, and made our own fun, together.... No one we knew suffered from tensions.... We had little money, but our greatest pleasures cost us nothing." Yet the Pearsons had much more money than most Canadians; they had good silver, fine dishes, and some help for Annie with the household tasks.[21] And the air was certainly not clear in Hamilton, already Canada's steel capital when the Pearsons arrived in 1910.[22] Yet a parson's son's world was enclosed by the special position the parson occupied in Anglo Ontario in those days. Lester's world seems especially sheltered. Most Canadian men worked six-day weeks; most wives had many children; and most people had just enough education to read the newspaper. In a church that had once prized simplicity, the ostentation of so many prominent Methodists led some ministers towards a demand that greater equality, if not simplicity, be returned. Ed Pearson responded differently. As time passed, Ed Pearson's Methodism became a civics lesson,[23] one in which the traditional values of the Anglo-Canadian home and church were upheld. His strong denunciations of sin increasingly belonged to the past. He became ever more a counsellor, guiding his flock through the treacherous pathways of modern life. In Hamilton, for example, he prided himself on the basketball court he built for "working girls" to use at lunch-time and in the evening hours. He did not try to remake society. He favoured individual acts of kindness. As time went on, he became ever more amiable; whenever he took on a new charge, the local newspaper always mentioned his pleasant manner; and his obituarist deemed him one of "the most lovable ministers of the United Church of Canada". Religion became morality and, in his own words, "The whole scheme of Christianity was to reproduce Christ. The credentials of any man's Christianity was his likeness to Jesus."[24]

Ed was more like Jesus than most. By all accounts this gentle and good man took in strangers, cared for the sick, and gave solace to the weary. His children, his wife, and his congregations adored him. His heroics on the lacrosse and baseball fields neatly complemented the increasingly gentle image Ed developed. The scorn for sin and its denial that he expressed in the 1890s gave way to a clearer focus upon the New Testament's gospel of brotherly love. Yet, for Ed Pearson's congregations, his Christian message was inoffensive, although he did try to exalt those of lower degree. In the smaller cities and towns that he loved most – Peterborough and Chatham above all – the distances between rich and poor were not so obvious as they were in Hamilton and Toronto, and his ministry thrived in the church, in the school, and on the playing field. "There are some people," he preached in 1907, who "would crush out all amusement, and there are those who will pursue everything from which pleasure is derived." He chose the middle way, one that led straight to the ball field and away from the tavern.[25]

Ed's strong opposition to drink – a sin that could not be over-looked by any Methodist – was equalled by his opposition to those forces that threatened his beloved British Empire. In 1900 he attacked those who cheered on the Boers against the British in the South African War. British freedom, he averred, closely adhered to the doctrine of brotherly love; the "Kruger oligarchy" forswore that doctrine in denying British freedom. His congregation "thoroughly endorsed" these sentiments.[26] In 1909, Ed visited the British Isles and saw the British fleet off the Isle of Wight, then celebrated the glorious twelfth in Ireland by crossing the Boyne to Drogheda and witnessing the Orangemen's parade in Belfast.[27] He had no doubts about Canada's duty when Britain went to war in 1914.

Ed Pearson moved in the mainstream. In the new century, how-ever, what became significant most often lay outside that stream. Les-ter wrote in his memoirs that, in his parents' home, there was not "much intellectual or artistic stimulus". In Britain, Ed made pilgrim-ages to Wordsworth's and Shakespeare's homes, and in Canada, that great work of literature, the King James Bible, was a daily compan-ion. However, at home, the Pearsons clung to the traditional intellec-tual props, and the "stimulus" of "modern" cultural life was absent. Those modernist icons of pre-war days such as Freud's *Meaning of Dreams,* Picasso's *Les Demoiselles d'Avignon,* and probably even Schweitzer's *Search for the Historical Jesus* found no place in the Pear-son home; there the "things" of the twentieth century – the radio, the telephone, and the motor car – were accepted, but not the thoughts.

Marmaduke Jr. (who, understandably, soon became known sim-ply as Duke), Lester, and Vaughan thus left their family's faith behind. Lester rarely attended church, spared his children Sunday school, and never publicly professed his religious feelings for most of his life. At the age of seventy-one, he denied a charge that he was an agnostic, claiming that he remained "true to my early teaching of divine guidance by a divine being" and, further, that he believed "in the Christianity of my home". The answer is obviously oblique. When his colleague Charles Ritchie declared that the one thing he could thank God for was his own creation, Lester quipped waspishly, "Oh Charles, thank your parents."[28] That and much more Lester Pearson certainly did. Although ministers' sons are often rascals, and Duke sometimes was, Lester was a model child. He always stood near or at the top of his class. He was a leader; the earliest extant document in Lester's handwriting is a 1904 notice for "A Nice Concert" at W.G. Graham's, in Aurora, with two cents' admission except for children-in-arms, who were free. C. Graham was the "Tresurer"; Duke Pearson, the Secretary; and Lester, Duke's junior by three years, the President. From Aurora, Lester went to Central Public School in Peterborough where an inspiring teacher, R.F. Downey, woke his intellectual curiosity. Lester maintained this curiosity as he passed through the Peterborough and Hamilton collegiate institutes. High marks, then as now, do not command the affection of one's classmates. Lester still reflected such embarrassment in his memoirs written six decades later, especially when he claimed that he was "mentally retarded" in science and mathematics and "only the most concentrated application made it possible ... to pass any examinations in them." Hardly. At Peterborough Collegiate Institute in 1910, for example, he received the highest grade in algebra, 100, and his arithmetic mark was 75, not outstanding but much better than the class average of 61. It is quite true, however, that his best subjects were those where his remarkable memory could assist him: English grammar, Latin, and, most of all, history. His lowest marks were always for penmanship: in 1910 he received only 17 out of 50, which certainly was a dismal performance but not enough to undermine his first-class standing. In Hamilton, the pattern persisted, and there another fine teacher, "Mike" McGarvin, whetted his appetite for history, an appetite already created by the romantic imperial tales of G.A. Henty and Rudyard Kipling, which carried the young British Canadian far beyond the imaginative boundaries of pre-war Ontario into an exotic and challenging world, but one still solidly within the British domain.[29]

Lester excelled, but he was no bookworm. The regimen of the church and Annie's well-organized household gave Lester an appreciation of time that most adolescents lack. He studied piano on Grandfather Bowles's grand, and the Methodist hymns of his youth stayed in his memory all his life. At the musical recital held by Miss Wilhelmina Gumpricht, ACTM, he displayed much cleverness "as one of three boys among twenty girls". Far more Hamiltonians and fellow classmates noticed his cleverness on the baseball diamond.

All the Pearson boys were athletes, and Vaughan was perhaps the best. They played rugby, lacrosse, hockey, and baseball, the sports of Southern Ontario in the first decade of the century. Athletics bonded the Pearson family together. Lester's strongest childhood memories were of Ed preaching on Sunday and playing centre field on summer evenings. Their separate scrap-books abound with press clippings detailing their athletic prowess, sports items outnumbering all others. One suspects that sports took similar precedence in male conversation in the Pearson family, providing a link between generations that religion and politics did not. Lester's strongest memory of his grandfather Marmaduke was of Dominion Day in 1913 when the two of them went off to a Toronto Maple Leafs baseball game at Hanlan's Point. Marmaduke enjoyed every hit through Lester's eyes for he could no longer see the ball himself. Baseball was the most popular sport in small-town Ontario, one that lacked the class distinction of cricket or the moral unsavouriness of horse-racing. It was the people's sport, and the Pearson boys definitely wanted to be part of that motley crowd.

Those who knew Lester Pearson well warn anyone who writes about him not to forget sports, which were genuinely important to him whether he played or watched. Through sports he worked out aggression and frustration; his sporting prowess belied the "sissy" image that his background suggested; and he competed in a way that showed how much he liked to win. Historians and others have made much of the transition from cricket to baseball in Canada, seeing it as an indication of creeping Americanization and of an increase in the regimentation and competition of sports that reflected the country's maturing capitalism. Such weighty matters aside, for Lester Pearson the "game" was fun, the best part of the Sunday-school picnic coming when his triple bounced over the left-fielder's glove and his toss to first finished the double play. Baseball won him favour; it became a lifelong part of what he was. Tales of the days when Duke played right field; Lester, second base; and Vaughan, shortstop, enlivened many Pearson family hours – for Duke, Lester, and Vaughan, if not for the others, who had heard the saga of "the boys of summer" once too often.[30]

Annie went to few games, and she was, of course, not a public figure. She left no school marks, no sermons, only a few tributes from former congregations and a few words from her sons. Memories of her are not consistent, but all who knew her claim her influence was great. In Lester's memory, "Mother, who worked so hard and was often unwell, was the centre of our little group, its soul and its solace." She definitely pushed her boys forward, in a way in which Ed, whom she thought too "easygoing", perhaps did not.[31] When the sons wrote home from the war they addressed most letters to Annie, and they reported those details that she liked to hear. Some remember her as a strong personality, a touch censorious.* She was an excellent artist; her heirs still display her paintings. Her grandchildren recall her generosity, hard candies, and gentle wit. The few of her letters that remain are well written, and laden with advice that was generally sensible. Annie's family was more intellectually inclined than were the Pearsons, with a distinguished lineage (the poet John Greenleaf Whittier was an ancestor), and a romantic tinge. Some Bowleses became missionaries in China; others, for example, the Rev. R.P. Bowles, Annie's favourite cousin, flirted with socialism and spiritualism. Annie, however, had little time for books. The daily rounds of household duties, the demands of Bible-study classes, women's circles, and the myriad other activities of a parson's wife

---

* Her grandson Fred Pearson recalls how his grandmother rudely interrupted him as temptation loomed in the form of an attractive young female on the front porch of her Toronto home in the 1930s. She had, he recalls, little patience with youthful wild spirits and ordered the "hussy" home.

probably left her few moments in which to indulge her own interests. She made the family's clothes, drew water from the backyard well, and her hands were never idle.[32]

Piano lessons, paper routes, prayer meetings, church, and school also made Lester's life at home full of routine. In summer, some relief came when the boys left for a Bowles farm in Chinguacousy Township. Country and city then seemed far apart, and Lester had many arguments with his country cousins about the "comparative importance of the 'city bug' and the 'country bug' in national development". We do not know whether Annie's frailty or the contemporary belief that farm life was healthy for young boys in a way that city or even village life was not was the reason for these rural summers. Lester quickly discovered that the "country cousins" knew more about the "facts of life" than he did. His initial lessons in the mysteries of sex came from observing farmyard behaviour. Ed and Annie did not encourage interest in or knowledge of the opposite sex, and when that interest exploded, as it did for Lester at the age of fourteen at a Junior League meeting when his heart began to palpitate in the proximity of a young girl, they emphasized that the objects of Lester's affection should be Methodists. And in the early years, they always were.[33]

From a later perspective, Lester Pearson's memory of carefree days in a loving family seems strange, considering the numerous restrictions he faced and the intense regimen of church and home. When he later said that he didn't "recall very much in the way of discipline", he reveals how much his comments derive from his perception of the child-rearing methods of the time.[34] In the nineteenth century, bourgeois families believed that restrictiveness could create those qualities most prized in a child and, later, in an adult. The child, Methodist leader Nathaniel Burwash argued as late as 1882, shared man's fall with Adam. By the turn of the century, however, psychologists and Methodist preachers were emphasizing that restrictions bred resentment and an inability to choose freely as citizens in a democratic and urban society must do. The model for the parent became ever less the

Old Testament Jehovah and ever more the loving Jesus who taught by example.

Lester Pearson's early years coincided with this shift as middle-class Canadian families adapted to the new concept of childhood. His upbringing thus bore traces of both the restrictive past and the indulgent future. A modern authority has characterized parents as belonging to one of three groups: authoritative, authoritarian, and permissive. Lester's parents fit most closely the first category; they were controlling, yet affectionate and willing to encourage autonomy in their children. Ed and Annie, like most of their middle-class Methodist flock, "came to locate a special trust in childhood and accepted a responsibility to nurture the young for the benefit and advancement of society."[35] Ed and Annie were far from permissive, but they did possess that twentieth-century perspective of the child that acknowledges and supports emancipation from its parents.

Lester's months on the farm, hours in the church, daily prayers and anthems, and childhood friends had little obvious impact on his later life. He was to lead an urban, secular, and international life that carried him, by his own admission, far away from his early days. Yet his devotion to his parents endured. He truly loved them, never denouncing their ways because he recognized they had given him autonomy. One of our most perceptive students of childhood has written: "My own image of life is that of a traveler whose knapsack is slowly filled with doubts, dogma, and desires during the first dozen years. Each traveler spends the adult years trying to empty the heavy load in the knapsack until he or she can confront the opportunities that are present in each fresh day."[36] Thanks to Ed and Annie, the Pearson boys left home bearing light knapsacks.

CHAPTER TWO

THE WARS

I realize that I do not remember it so clearly after all. History remembers it and I remember it as history.

— Vernon Scannell[1]

SIXTEEN-YEAR-OLD Lester Pearson graduated from Hamilton Collegiate Institute in 1913 and acquired his first blue serge suit, which he topped off with an Edwardian bowler hat. Childhood had passed into adolescence. It was to be Lester's last summer on the Bowles's farm in Chinguacousy Township; his college years would begin in the fall. Lester's parents hoped he would become a Methodist minister. His scholastic success, his apparent oratorical abilities, his athletic skills, and, not least, his amiability marked him as a worthy heir to family tradition.[2] There is a family photograph dating from that time that captures the pre-war sense that everything was in its place and would work out. The Pearson family appear solid, people of substance. The boys are becoming men. Annie's hair is now grey; Ed's is thinning, his evenings of roaming centre field having obviously been taken over by lawn bowling. Marmaduke, in his clerical collar and old-fashioned spectacles, squints at the photographer. The only visible relics of his early athletic renown are his massive hands. Duke's head, tilted, stares insouciantly into the camera; a faintly smiling Vaughan looks away. Lester, his pants well pressed and his jacket off, inspects the photographer, his curiosity obvious.

That curiosity was broad, coming from Lester's quick mind and limited experience; as he says in his memoirs, his parish was his world and extended no farther than "an area of not more than fifty miles around Toronto".[3] Ed's itinerant ministry had taken the family on a circuit around Ontario's thriving capital, landing them briefly in the city's centre. The family had prospered with the city, Ed's salary rising from $600 in 1897 to $900 in 1904, $1,400 in 1907, and $1,700 in 1911, and the parsonages became ever more comfortable.[4] On the lawns lay bicycles and ball gloves; inside the house was the clutter of the pre-war middle-class household. In this early age of consumption, the Pearsons worked hard to keep up. The boys had paper routes (Lester delivered the eccentrically Conservative *Toronto World*), worked in shops, and took advantage of the half-price or free services offered to the clergy and their children. The tastes of the minister of one of the largest and richest churches in Hamilton, and his family's, reflected those of the parishioners. Sometimes the temptation of easy money was strong. Lester's earnings from his morning paper route for the *World* vanished when Ed, on the "advice of one of his wealthier parishioners", invested it in an ill-fated asbestos mine. Lester commented: "My father laid up for himself, I know, much treasure in heaven, but he was singularly inept, as no doubt a minister of the Gospel should be, in making two dollars out of one on earth."[5] It nevertheless says something about Ed, and the age in which he lived, that he tried.

Ed's political activities had not survived his college days, but his support for the Conservative party had. During a 1909 visit to Britain, he and thousands of others saw the British fleet pass King Edward VII and Czar Nicholas II off the Isle of Wight. In 1911, with Lester in tow at Hamilton's YMCA, he cheered Sir George Foster as the old Tory war-horse denounced those who favoured the Reciprocity Treaty with the United States and those who opposed Canada's making a direct contribution to the British navy.[6] Lester probably understood little of, but definitely shared, his father's political views. At the heart of pre-war Canadian Conservatism was the belief that Canadian interests were most fully realized through active participation within the British Empire. This imperialist sentiment did not undermine Canadian nationalism; indeed, it probably reinforced it.[7] Anglo Canadians, the Pearsons among them, saw the attachment to the British crown as an indispensable part of Canada's nationhood. Shakespeare and Queen Victoria were as much a part of Canada's heritage as were John A. Macdonald and the CPR. This breathtaking assertion was simply taken for granted in most homes, including the Pearsons'.

It was also "taken for granted" that Lester would follow his father and brother Duke to Methodist Victoria College, in the University of Toronto. The college had left Cobourg for Toronto in 1890 and had established itself on the northeast side of elegant Queen's Park Crescent. The splendid Romanesque college fitted well among the mansions of the *haute bourgeoisie* surrounding Queen's Park; some of the grandest of them now housed prominent Methodists such as Joseph Flavelle. These richly panelled halls were not closed to young Methodist collegians, who went to tea and meetings there. Lester took a room with Duke in the newly constructed Late Gothic Revival Burwash Hall, which mimicked in appearance, if not in collegiate ambiance, the Oxbridge style its donors, the Massey family, had come to cherish.* Vincent Massey himself had just returned from Balliol College at Oxford to become dean of the men's residence, where he tried to impose, in his words, "more dignity" on the raucous Canadian collegians. He failed. "Civilization," he lamented to a friend, "is a slow process but I am satisfied that we are making some progress." Indeed, there was hope: he reported that the "rather fearsome crudity" of the undergraduate was being "softened".[8]

The scraps of initiation programs, social notices, and *Varsity* clippings Lester saved from his first year suggest that the softening process had some way to go. The wit came from the music hall, not from

---

* At Victoria College in 1911 the faculty chairs included the Hart Massey Professor of the English Bible, the Eliza Phelps Massey Professor of Oriental Languages and Literature, and the J.W. Flavelle Associate Professor of Oriental Languages and Literature. The Gooderhams had also endowed two chairs, no doubt to expiate the many sins attached to their whisky business.

23

Balliol's high table, and the athletics were those of Toronto's Hanlan's Point more than of Eton's playing fields. Initiation practices were probably not as rough as in Ed's days at Cobourg, where he had led a protest against "hazing", calling it immoral.[9] Women now suffered along with the men, but the violence had become mainly verbal, not physical. *The Varsity,* Toronto's student newspaper, breathlessly chronicled how "Freshies [were] put through Sausage Mill" on the first weekend in October. The "Sophs" erected a gravestone marked "The Class of 1917", daring the "Frosh" to tear it down; of course, they tried. The skirmishes were regulated by a newly organized student council, which "intervened once or twice to prevent practices not strictly upright, such as using clubs, throwing bottles of paint, etc." The gravestone demolished, the initiation came to an official end at "The Bob", a social named in honour of a long-departed Victoria janitor. There "Froshs" and "Sophs" shrieked collegiate songs at each other from opposite ends of the Burwash dining-hall. "Softened" or not, such deportment almost certainly horrified Vincent Massey, who was soon to fight another battle when Vic's undergraduates, Lester among them, refused to wear academic gowns to dining-hall as Oxford tradition dictated.[10]

Lester did not betray his rebellious side in his early letters home. In one of the two letters he wrote to his mother during his first two days at Victoria, he confessed that he felt "fresh and [had] made some bad blunders". Still, the meals, at least by his standards, were "fine", and he renewed acquaintance with many students he had known at one of the schools he had attended. (All but three in Lester's "room" at Hamilton Collegiate Institute had "come down" to the university.) All of his professors were "fine men" who knew him as "Duke[']s brother or your son", and A.J. Bell, the John Macdonald Professor of Latin Languages and Literature, even recalled having taught Annie. He reported that the professor of religious knowledge was an especially "fine fellow" and that he was not taking French, German, or biology, although he did enquire whether Annie thought he should take the last. Cryptically he added, "I have had a talk with R.P."[11] The Rev. R.P. Bowles, who had presided at Ed and Annie's wedding, was now Victoria's chancellor.

Toronto had almost four hundred thousand souls, Ontario well over two million by 1913; but those who shared the privilege of university life were an élite. The advantages of membership were already clear to Lester and most of his classmates, and would remain so for most of their lives. When, for example, Lester became so overwrought in a first-year examination in his hated algebra course that his nose began to bleed, forcing him to leave the examination hall, he was taken to Professor Alfred Tennyson De Lury, the head of the mathematics department. Lester pleaded for extra marks because of the shorter time he had had to write the examination. The distinguished mathematician responded:

"Pearson. Is your name Pearson?" And I said: "Yes." And he said "Would you be any relation to Ed Pearson?" And I said: "... that's my father." He said "Oh, Ed, how's he getting along?" It transpired they'd been friends at college and played baseball together or something like that. So I tried to get him back on to my dilemma and I reminded him that I was in trouble. "Oh, don't worry about that, my boy ... you couldn't help your nose bleeding."

But De Lury could help Pearson, and the young collegian subsequently received the highest mark he ever achieved on a mathematics examination.[12]

Lester earned a "first" in his modern history course, although his standing overall was a "second". In extra-curricular pursuits, he made his mark, despite his relatively small stature and his age, in lacrosse, rugby, and hockey, sports in which his natural quickness gave him an advantage, but not enough of one to make him a campus hero.[13] He ventured forth to a few theatres, although we don't know whether he followed Ed's injunction that if "the show going on is not going to elevate your morals, leave the opera house at once".[14] Certainly he did not taste liquor nor did he take those evening strolls to the city's sordid areas that an earlier Toronto undergraduate and future Liberal prime minister, Mackenzie King, was inclined to take. In the summer of 1914, when Lester went home to his father's new charge at Park Street Methodist Church in Chatham, his path seemed clear.

The Ladies' Aid of Park Street Methodist placed bouquets of

roses, nasturtiums, and gladioli in every room of the parsonage to welcome the Pearsons in 1914. Lester, Duke, and Vaughan played ball during that first, very hot summer, when, according to *The Chatham Daily Planet,* many parishioners fainted during church services. The beaches of nearby Lake Erie were crowded and, again in the *Planet*'s words, "Many a Young Leander spent the whole afternoon in the water or else lying on the sand and basking in the sun." Reading the papers of those summer days, one can only agree with the famed British tourist of 1913, Rupert Brooke, that there was "a fine, breezy, enviable healthiness about Canadian life".[15] Brooke also found in Ontario a genuine "British feeling", misused by party politicians but none the less "real". "It will remain, potential of good, among all the forces that are certain for evil."

When war was declared against Germany in August 1914, the Pearsons believed, every bit as much as Brooke did, that the British side represented good. There were no doubts, even if a few of Ed's Methodist colleagues were uneasy about shucking off the pacifist robes they had donned in peacetime. Ed's Christianity was practical, not theological, and he quickly committed himself to the patriotic efforts of his congregation and city. He urged young men to enlist and church women to join the Red Cross or the Imperial Order Daughters of the Empire. All church services now ended with "God Save the King".

When Duke and Lester returned to Toronto in September, they immediately joined the University Officers Training Corps, which Vincent Massey, short of stature but long on British patriotism, commanded at Victoria College, Lester becoming Massey's orderly and a bugler in the corps band.* Massey's task was difficult; as Duke recalled, the Victoria undergraduate took "a cordial dislike to early reveille and to the creation of a social order built upon military rank".[16] Nevertheless, each passing month brought a more martial

---

* According to an unpublished memoir by Dr. William Dafoe, Vincent Massey's brother Raymond, later a distinguished actor, attracted much attention as a Burwash Hall resident because of the gleaming new Hupmobile he parked nearby.

air to campus life, but not enough to disturb the normal frolics of the fall term. The campus reflected the country in the first six months, as Canadians expected the war to end soon with, of course, a British victory.

Lester, now a self-confident second-year man, came second in an oratorical contest; his topic was "Bismarck". On the football field, however, he dropped a punt behind his team's line, and Victoria lost the cherished Mulock Cup. At Christmas Duke and Lester returned home and tried to persuade their parents to let them enlist even though Lester was only seventeen and Duke only 5 feet, 1 inch. On January 3 Lester heard Ed pray for an early end to the European war at both morning and evening services and, the next day, he left for Toronto.[17]

Lester began a brief diary on January 1, 1915, which reflects, as he relates in his memoirs, his "growing uneasiness about remaining at college while the war was on". It also reminds us how young Lester was and how little Canadian university life demanded intellectually. "A very busy day," he wrote on January 19. "Didn't do much in the morning but in the afternoon I went to a lecture at 3, Varsity basketball at 4, Vic basketball at 5, hockey at 6 and our skating party at 8. Took Miss Jenner home."* Even more striking was the entry for three days earlier: "Grandpa died today. Got word early this morning. A great shock to me. Father, mother and Vaughan came down from Chatham. It was very sudden. I skated and played hockey this afternoon. Was at [the Literary Club] tonight. A very exciting meeting." Other entries are similar, although complaints about military drill become more common, as do notes on female partners at various gatherings. He slept in on Sunday mornings, went to shows, and even played pool.[18] On St. Valentine's Day, 1915, he asked his parents about enlisting in the Eaton Machine Gun Battery. Two weeks later Duke told him he was enlisting with the 25th Battery, Canadian Field

---

* Pearson and most other undergraduate males rarely referred to the female undergraduates by their first names. In his early diary the references to female students are always as formal as the one to Miss Jenner.

Artillery, and within a fortnight he was gone. "Things" seemed "very lonely"; the room they shared at Gate House, Burwash Hall, was "deserted", and "everything [seemed] broken up". Duke wrote regularly, but, to Lester, the war itself was still far away, although the growing number of students who were signing up gave the war effort a disturbing immediacy. Lester's mind was not on his work but on the duty to go to war: on April Fool's Day he missed a history test, but he managed to get it "fixed up". The following day, Good Friday, he "didn't do a bit of work". Instead, he played handball and baseball and went to a show. Most of the examinations were hard, and he despaired about the results. However, he did well in all subjects, except economics, which remained a mystery to him throughout his life.

In 1915, Lester clearly lacked emotional maturity, but he did possess exceptional intelligence, an asset that he endeavoured to conceal beneath a casual approach to his studies. Sports mattered most; in the atmosphere of Victoria in wartime, a civilian man's mettle was established on the rugby field, not in the classroom. In his second year away from the manse, Lester had begun to take his religious duties less seriously, perhaps guiltily since when he slept in on Sunday morning he sometimes tried to make an afternoon service. His interests, unlike those of many of his fellow students, were clearly directed towards this world rather than the next. Only when parents or relatives were near was he a dutiful church-goer. On April 23, he celebrated his eighteenth birthday "by doing little work & much play" and buying a new suit. Three days later, his diary has its first reference to the battles raging on the Western Front: "Papers full of great Canadian victory at Yser. George Smith of Chatham & Harry McGuire of Orangeville wounded." In April the Canadians heroically held their own line and that of French colonial troops who fled the dreaded poison-gas attack the Germans launched upon the Ypres salient. The casualty lists filled long columns in Ontario's newspapers, and in Victoria's classrooms the call to duty became irresistible. On April 23 he enlisted.[19]

A friend, Pierce Congdon, had interrupted Lester's studying of

Plautus and Terence in the college library to tell him that there was a vacancy in the University of Toronto Hospital Unit. The great advantage of that unit was the fact that it would be going overseas almost immediately. Lester's parents reluctantly consented, no doubt encouraged by the news that the hospital unit was non-combative. By late afternoon, Lester was in khaki, private #1059 in the Canadian Army Medical Corps. The next day he returned to Plautus and Terence and, in his own words, "did pretty good" in the examination. That night, however, he felt "kind of depressed".[20] He had every right to be.*

Ed, Annie, and Vaughan came down to Toronto to bid farewell and to give Lester $25 collected from Chatham friends. The last days were a whirlwind as Lester said goodbye to friends and family, crammed for his final examinations, and learned to carry stretchers, keep in step, and salute officers. The unit's departure was delayed, and Lester's stomach acted up but not so much that he could not share some "jolly times" with Ed, Vaughan, and his friends. Finally, at 11:00 a.m., on May 15, he left Union Station for Montreal. By 11:00 p.m. he was aboard an old cattle-boat, the *Corinthian,* that was to take them to England. Lester took his place, a very cramped one, in steerage in the hold, where he and the other privates were "jammed together, living, eating, sleeping side by side on boards almost touching each other". The food was dreadful and quite literally dirty. W.A. "Billy" Dafoe, who became Lester's closest friend and later one of Canada's most prominent physicians, recalled that one of the first dinners in the mess consisted of partially cooked tripe that was green on one side. This "offering", Dafoe claimed, was "liberally sprinkled with the dust and dirt off the ceiling", shaken onto the plates as the troops marched on the deck above. Lester was sick most of the way, perhaps from the sea and the food, perhaps simply from fear. German

---

* Lester passed his medical on April 27, 1915. The Defence department report gave his height as five feet, eight and a half inches. His complexion was described as fair, his eyes green, and his hair dark brown. The only blemishes were "two hairy moles" below his left ear.

submarines had sunk three unarmed ships, including the *Lusitania,* within the past month. On May 24, the *Corinthian* neared Britain and the danger zone where German submarines lurked, and Lester admitted in his diary for the first time that he was "kind of scared".[21]

Lester's fears were legitimate for the war had become a deadly stalemate. The Germans had failed to reach Paris in the initial attack of August 1914 and had dug their trenches, daring their opponents to challenge them. With the machine gun, heavy artillery, and barbed wire, the defence had many advantages, the offence few, at least until the tank and the airplane tipped the balance in 1917. The Germans turned their offence towards Russia and inflicted great defeats in which hundreds of thousands died in a few weeks. Winston Churchill, the First Lord of the Admiralty, persuaded the British government to open a second front in the Balkans in April 1915, but the Gallipoli landing was disastrous as Turkey, Germany's ally, slaughtered the troops when the British failed to expand the initial bridgeheads. The mood of Britain turned serious and often bitter. The war would not be over soon, and many more would die.

Yet the romance of England and war still enchanted Lester, and the weariness and terror that we now associate with the First World War were still far away as the *Corinthian* took its berth at Plymouth Harbour at 9:00 a.m. on a beautiful midspring day. The historic harbour town where Drake had bowled as the Armada approached was as green and quaint as Lester's favourite author, G.A. Henty, had promised it would be; and in the evening, as they disembarked, moonlight bathed the blessed land. On May 28, Lester arrived at Shorncliffe, a "great camp" where he and "thousands" of other Canadians strolled the town streets that Friday night. Like all English Canadians at that time, Lester found much that was familiar on English streets but also much that was exotic. The experience must have been similar to exploring Grandmother's attic: every box's treasures brought a shock of recognition, being at once a part of you and entirely new. Lester, already steeped in the lore of the English countryside, was able to add to his knowledge since his hospital work was relatively light; the extent of that knowledge astonished the newly arrived Duke for whom he acted as tour guide through south-west England.

Lester dreamed of winning the Victoria Cross, but his daily lot was bedpans and ministering to a grumpy sergeant's lumbago.[22] Lester and the other privates dwelt in "spotlessly clean" long wooden huts. They slept on boards ranged along the sides of the huts and ate off board tables in the centre. Shorncliffe was only a few miles from Dover, and the daily early-morning march took the young Canadians along the white cliffs, then glistening in the June sun. Drill followed in the afternoon; fatigue struck at night. The YMCA or Salvation Army tents rescued the weary, offering a desk to write letters, a dry canteen, a chequer-board, and a piano. On weekends, Lester's affection for Britain grew into fascination and even veneration. His infatuation with London, which throughout his life was his favourite city, began with his first leave on June 12, 1915. Along with ten other "boys" from Varsity, as its alumni called the University of Toronto, Pearson took a third-class train to Charing Cross, which the impressionable young Anglo Canadian thought was "the quietest and most unusual large station ... in the world". English railway practice was a metaphor for English life generally. There was, at the great Charing Cross station, an "utter lack of turmoil and sense of quiet orderliness". "It could not be like that in America," Lester piously wrote. "There if anything or any person is famous it must appear so or the fame would soon be gone."

The fame of London's monuments could never be questioned. After checking into the Regent Palace, just off Piccadilly Circus, where a room and a regal breakfast of porridge, cream, bacon, poached eggs, toast, strawberries, and coffee cost only 6 / 6 ($1.60 Cdn.), Lester breathlessly scurried from sight to sight. The young Canadians were treated like heroes because their countrymen had saved the day at Ypres. A tolerant guard at Westminster Abbey even let Lester sit in the Coronation Chair, read the King's Bible, and pat the Stone of Scone. In Parliament, he heard Prime Minister Asquith speak, but on the whole he found the Commons "like our Provincial House, and about as undignified". The British Museum, however, entranced the budding historian and already devout anglophile. He spent fifteen minutes in the Library's Manuscript Saloon, reverently poring over Captain Scott's last scribbles on his tragic Antarctic mission, which ended with a scrawled: "For God's sake tell England to take care of our dear ones." "The secret of Britain's greatness," Lester solemnly concluded, "lies in that self-written obituary of a great and noble soul." Their leave over, the young heroes returned to camp, where Lester continued to perform "very menial tasks for recruits sick with mumps, measles and other unheroic diseases". However, the monotony was occasionally broken – one NCO reacted to a Pearsonian medical initiative by stating that if Lester had been a medical student he would have had him shot. Most often Lester spent the nights uneventfully, "perched at one end of a bed listening to a story of blood and carnage, the low monotone of the raconteur broken now and then by a cry from one of the wounded dreaming of the nightmare ... of Ypres or the senseless deep babbling of another fighting his battles over again." When he left the hospital and walked along the cliffs in the moonlight he could hear the faint roar of Flanders guns not so far away and yearned to be there.[23]

Duke went over to France shortly after he arrived in Britain on August 20, 1915, but Lester stayed behind.[24] A few days after Duke's arrival and a brief leave in Scotland, a land and a people that enthralled him, Lester learned that he and the University of Toronto Base Hospital were being sent east. Lester formed part of the advance party, which, acting on the orders of a confused yet fussy British lieutenant, managed to load the supplies on the wrong ship. The incident, Lester recalled later, illustrated what prompted the rank and file's favourite question: "How do you ever think we can win this blinkin' war with a gang like that running it?"[25] He had learned that blind respect for authority was not always wise or warranted, and the moral certitudes of adolescence were fading quickly. Things were no longer simply black or white. When Lester took on a quartermaster's position looking after supplies, he soon ended his grumbling about meals, for, he wrote, "I soon became an adept in making away with the odd hospital delicacy, having a feast with some of my cronies, and writing the missing articles off the books as lost in transit." Ed and Annie would surely have disapproved, but Lester did not have "any qualms of conscience in seizing the opportunity to acquire any little thing surreptitiously from a negligent government".[26] Lester was "one of the boys", and they had quickly lost faith in "the brass".

The supplies were finally loaded onto the right ship, the *Min-newaska,* which in terms of cuisine and accommodation was much superior to the *Corinthian.* Nevertheless, Lester became seasick before the lights of Plymouth faded, this time recovering quickly. His letters home, like earlier ones about his London and Scottish trips, appeared on the first page of *The Chatham Daily Planet.* Whether Lester was aware that some of his letters would receive such wide circulation is unknown. What is clear is his parents' pride in their middle son and Lester's devotion to them. As the *Minnewaska* passed by "grim and majestic Gibraltar", Lester reassured his parents that the voyage was safe and he was secure: "I have felt perfectly great ever since the first day and am thoroughly enjoying things.... Every day we get lectures on diseases etc. that we will have to combat. You needn't worry about me as we are alright. All one needs is to use care. Half of the deaths ... are caused by needless actions, so I am going to be careful as I think too much of you dear people at home and I want to see you again too much to run any chance." Lester would have fun but would not be foolish or be pushed around. One story he did not tell his parents or *The Chatham Daily Planet* was about the time when he received "number 2 field punishment" because he refused to join a parade of naked men being washed down publicly on board ship. He later told a British radio audience that he "thought it was unbecoming to my dignity as a recent Canadian civilian to obey such an indelicate order."[27] A lot was left unsaid, but early lessons endured.

New lessons accumulated quickly. At Malta, the *Minnewaska* took on coal: "Maltese labourers, very low specimens of humanity, carried the coal in large baskets from the scows up inclined planks to the bunkers." Once on board they fought over "scraps" from the table. What Lester saw in Malta and later in Egypt punctured his romantic image of the Empire's outposts. Alexandria's native quarter exceeded his vivid imagination's bounds. The quarter's pungent smells, crowded streets, many tongues, and "multitude of beggars" with their "never ending wail for backsheesh [*sic*]" contrasted starkly with the modern part of this ancient city, which, to Lester, seemed not unlike Hamilton except that most business was transacted in French. There was, he said, "too much cosmopolitanism" in Alexandria. This remarkable conclusion no doubt derived from the defensiveness that comes from encountering the new and exotic. His letter home, duly printed on the front page of *The Chatham Daily Planet,* betrays the doubts he felt: "My I have appreciated Canada since I left it and I think we are easily the best as well as the most civilized." Alexandria, in his view, was "one of the worst places in the world", a place where "the word morality is [not] known". But, Lester rather sanctimoniously continued, the city was "no temptation to me who has been brought up in as good a home as I have. All it serves is to make one hate evil and to appreciate everything that is good." What the Alexandrians thought of the No. 4 General Hospital Corps marching through their main street, singing "O Canada" and "The Maple Leaf Forever", cannot be imagined.[28]

From Egypt, Lester's unit moved on to Salonika in Macedonia, landing there on November 12. That ancient city's minarets glistened in the morning sun, reminding the young Canadians of the many battles that had raged on the Macedonian plains and hills beyond since Alexander the Great, whose arch overlooked the city, had set out to build his empire more than two millennia earlier. There were no battles in 1915, for Greece was neutral and the British and French, fresh from defeat in the Dardanelles, were protecting their position by keeping the Bulgarians from their German allies. Still, danger lurked nearby. The Greeks almost opened fire on these first Allied troops, and the telephone lines from the German, Turkish, and Austrian consulates hummed with the news of the Allies' arrival. The "hospital" was makeshift, several tents, their floors spread with straw, with patients grabbing at each other as they wailed throughout the night.[29] The cold came quickly and fiercely in that first Macedonian winter, and soon those wounded in battle were outnumbered by cases of frost-bite, pneumonia, typhus, and blackwater fever. Cold winds lashed the canvas tents, roads became seas of slime, German Zeppelins hummed ominously above; for Lester, the "last illusions of [war's] adventure and ... romance were destroyed."[30]

However, many illusions remained. Lester boasted to his parents and, through them, to all of Chatham of the valour of the French aviators, the stolid courage of the British "Tommies", and the "jauntiness" of the "crazy Canadians" who loathed rank, knew no fear, and shared a kind of closeness they had never known at home. They played football while Zeppelins dropped bombs, and taught the Tommies the intricacies of baseball. Most of all, Lester yearned to be on the Western Front. The troops at Salonika had little obvious purpose after November 1915. Britain's hopes of constructing a Balkan alliance of Rumania, Bulgaria, and Greece had collapsed, and Churchill became a strong advocate of using the troops at Salonika elsewhere. He wrote to a friend in December 1915: "I do not like holding Salonika, even if it is not impossible as many declare.... The Balkans must be left to stew in their own bitter juice."[31] For Mike, Salonika was "horrid" because that desultory Balkan campaign had no heroes. In France and Flanders, they could be found everywhere.

In the absence of heroics, Lester looked after the stores, a tedious yet, as he admitted, cushy job. He broke the boredom by learning French and wandering about the area. Occasionally he strayed into dangerous zones without realizing it. The many historic events that had occurred around Salonika were now commemorated in rubble, broken Turkish daggers, and piles of stones. Philip of Macedon's ancient capital had become an unidentifiable ruin. The outstanding feature of the scenery, in Lester's opinion, was "its unending monotony. Vegetation simply did not seem to exist and as far as the eye could see there was nothing but a great expanse of rocky soil tunnelled here and there by narrow, deep gulleys."[32] Mount Olympus towered in the distance, but Zeus, if he was still there, looked with no fondness on the benighted land below.

Lester's reaction to the Macedonians he encountered on the Monastir road just outside Salonika is especially interesting. Their homes, he claimed, "were hardly fit for animals and the inmates appeared about as hopeless as their homes". They were "a treacherous, deceitful lot who thought nothing of killing a man for a drachma," he wrote.

> They had been bred to hate, had lived to fight and had died in ignorance of any better existence. Their religion little better than a superstitious paganism, their education a farce, their life only a struggle for survival, what could one expect? Whether a beneficent government and a good educational system might not regenerate such a people is an open question. The pessimist would say, no, that they were too far gone for any hope of improvement. The optimist would assert that they could be changed in a generation. As I wandered through their towns and gazed into their hovels, I was inclined to agree with the former view. Later I had reason to change my belief.

Lester's values remained unchanged. He believed in a Christian god, modern progress, education, and, not least, the war that defended those values.[33]

In Salonika, the war was being waged against disease and the elements. As the fierce winter became a stifling summer, malaria spread through the ranks of the British troops and then through the hospital unit that tended them. Daily potions of quinine saved Lester from the dreaded malaria, although he later claimed that he had hoped for a mild but permanently curable attack that would require his return to Britain. His health unfortunately endured, as, among the increasingly depleted ranks, his even more apparent athletic prowess attested. A nurse later recalled how popular he was, not least because he seemed so "boyish" in that dismal, ancient place. His exuberant spirits on the playing field and in the mock all-male concerts masked a deep-seated fear that his war effort was to be no more than sorting tin cans in Salonika. He told his parents in March 1916 that he thought that the war would end in that year, a judgment shared by Duke, now at the Front in France.[34] When Vaughan arrived in France in June, Lester felt that he was serving neither God nor the Empire as fully as he should be.

Sheriff Thomas Bowles and Jane Bowles, Lester's maternal grandparents. Thomas added "a cocked hat and a judicial sword" to the sheriff's traditional pin-striped trousers and cutaway coat.

Rev. Edwin A. Pearson – "a modest minister, not an embattled evangelist" – and Lester, "a son than whom there is no better", in 1898.

Ed and Annie Pearson with their boys in 1903. Lester is wearing the ruffles.
Marmaduke Jr. was three years older, Vaughan a year younger. "Although
ministers' sons are often rascals, and Duke sometimes was,
Lester was a model child."

The family gathers around Ed's father, Rev. Marmaduke Pearson (seated):
Annie, Duke, and Ed, standing; Vaughan and Lester on the ground.

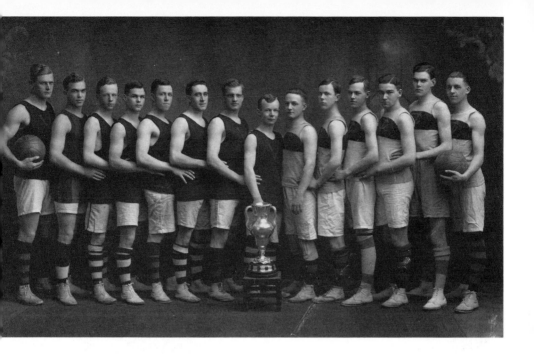

ABOVE: The Victoria College basketball teams in 1915. The shortest player is Duke; Lester is the second to the right of him. Captains James Wear (far right) and A.M. Horner (far left) would both die at Courcelette the next year, on Sept. 15 and 16 respectively.

LEFT: Lester (left) and a friend, packed for war. Lester sailed to England in May 1915 as a private in the Canadian Army Medical Corps. (NAC PA-110821)

Lester in Salonika in 1916, and (above) with his Varsity pals there: left to right, Pierce Congdon, Sandy English (no relation to author), Lester, and "Smitty". The hospital was makeshift, the wounded were outnumbered by victims of typhus, pneumonia, and blackwater fever, but despite the grim surroundings Lester led his unit's hockey team to the championship of the Macedonian front. (Above, NAC PA-117622; left, NAC PA-119893)

He had to get out, and he had learned how to pull "strings in a good cause". In his memoirs, he recounts in considerable detail how he persuaded his father to use his friendship with Canada's eccentric minister of militia, Sir Sam Hughes, to secure him an infantry commission that would take him to France. Ed wrote to "Sir Sam" and asked for a transfer and a promotion for Lester, "a son than whom there is no better". "Does it not seem to you eminently fair," Ed asked Sir Sam, "that his ambition to do a bigger 'bit' than he has been doing should be gratified?"[35] The task was simple, for Sir Sam was always willing to do a favour for a fellow Methodist and, by the fall of 1916, neither regulations nor even the prime minister could restrain him. Hughes commanded the Canadian authorities in London to ask the War Office to order the headquarters of the Mediterranean Expeditionary Force to order the authorities in Salonika to send Lester back to England immediately. Even though Prime Minister Borden fired his most erratic minister in November, Hughes's order had effect. On February 10, 1917, Lester got his orders to return to England to qualify for a commission in the Canadian infantry, but, to Lester's frustration, the "brass hats" took a month to sort out the formalities. There was some modest reward: Private Pearson became Acting Corporal Pearson, without pay. The promotion entailed absolutely no duties.[36]

In the meantime, Lester led his unit's hockey team to the championship of the Macedonian Front, and he became sentimental about leaving his "pals". After two years on that desolate Macedonian plain, Canada "seemed ... a scene of a bygone shadowy life", and his experience "had been so narrow, so hemmed in, so untouched by the outside world, so ignorant of its happenings ... that [the soldiers in Salonika] had become a self-contained little group." Even Lester's language about his "pals", "boys", and "chums" betrayed an intimacy that his prose never again reflected. As did Rupert Brooke, who died on his way to the Eastern Front in 1915, Lester found in war a feeling of fellowship, "a fine thrill, like nothing else in the world".[37]

In 1917, Lester returned to a Britain where war was no longer a thrill. The British war effort, having survived the slaughter of the

Battle of the Somme in late 1916, had become mired in the mud of Passchendaele. Bitterness overcame some soldiers, including soldier-poets Robert Graves, Siegfried Sassoon, and Wilfred Owen. For them the war had become, in Sassoon's words, "a hopeless, never-shifting burden". Yet, it remained one the Empire's sons must bear, and the views of the war poets were not shared by most Englishmen, or by Canadians such as Ed and Annie Pearson, who took great pride in their three sons in uniform.[38] When Ed and Annie left Chatham in the spring of 1917, the congregation of Park Street Methodist Church expressed its own pride in the way that the Pearson family had responded so nobly to "the call of our country". At the departure ceremony Ed was overcome and found speaking difficult, but he did express his belief that "it must be because of three soldier sons of the parsonage that he and [Annie] were being so kindly treated."[39] There were no doubts about the rightness of the war in Chatham and none yet in the minds of the Pearson boys.*

Lester arrived in Britain after a perilous journey through the submarine-laden Mediterranean. A bit wealthier than most corporals, he bribed the ship's barber to permit him to spend the nights in the padded comfort of the barber's chair. At Marseilles, the passengers disembarked and took a train so crowded that the humans and horses had to sleep in shifts. After four days they reached Le Havre, where the usual confusion kept them overnight on louse-infested blankets, but the next day Lester arrived in London and headed directly to the Regent Palace on Piccadilly, where he and his travel-

---

* In an October 1916 service, Ed led the congregation in paying tribute to seven Park Street members who had lost their lives in battle. He read a letter from a soldier to his mother, which declared it was "a noble privilege to die in this war, when we die for women like you". Ed strongly approved the sentiment: "It sounds better than 'I will not stand up to be shot at' which I heard a young man say, with a cigarette in his mouth, as he stood watching the Kent Battalion's homecoming the other day." Park Street Methodist took the lead in "Patriotic Services" in Chatham. A typical service was that of November 12, 1915, which began with a sermon on Nurse Edith Cavell ("Her Soul goes marching on") followed by patriotic hymns ("Be a Volunteer", "Flag of the Free", "After the Fray", "The Battle Hymn", "God Bless Our Native Land", and, at the service's end, "God Save the King").

ling companions quickly shed their filthy uniforms (for the first time in fourteen days) and headed for the bath-tub. The next day, March 27, 1917, the three Pearson boys met for the first and last time during war. They had only an hour together at the convalescent home where Duke was recovering from his wounds, and they used it to celebrate their reunion, not to lament their lot.

The London to which Lester returned offered various pleasures he was quickly learning to appreciate. The women looked different, their skirts shorter, their lipstick brighter, but a three-day leave gave little chance for dalliance. A rumour spread that the "Huns" had landed at Dover, and Lester was recalled to the great military base at Shorncliffe. There, he received the welcome news that he was to report to a cadet battalion that was training at Oxford's Wadham College. Delighted, he reached Oxford on March 30, and became an officer cadet in D Company, No. 4 Officer Cadet Battalion. There, in Matthew Arnold's "sweet city with her dreaming spires", the home of so many of Britain's lost causes, Lester spent four lovely months during the war's worst year.

Although few of Lester's letters from this period were saved and they were no longer front-page news in Chatham, we know that he felt guilty about not being in France, where Duke and, as of June, Vaughan were. He was in a colonial company, the Afcananzacs, which was made up of three South Africans, fourteen New Zealanders, three Australians, and twenty-seven Canadians. The company commander was Captain J.M. Morrell, scion of a distinguished brewing family and, in Pearson's words, "a typical stage-type Englishman, slightly over middle age, very unmilitary in appearance but very serious in his attempt not to be...." He worked the rough colonials hard, making them rise at 6:30 and drill at 7:15 and at three other times during the day. There were lectures and examinations, with such questions as "How do you teach trigger pressing?" and "What do you understand by 'Fire Direction'?" Lester did well in the examinations, but his deportment in the drill sessions suffered in comparison with that of the veterans from the Front. However, on the playing field he continued to impress all. On a track-and-field day, he managed to set a record, throwing a cricket ball a remarkable 114 yards. The feat gained him a mention in the London *Times,* a step up from *The Chatham Daily Planet*.

Pearson's platoon commander for part of the period was Robert Graves, a fine soldier and poet who had become thoroughly repelled by the meaningless deaths on the Western Front and who himself had been reported dead and, impishly, had had *The Times* print a correction, which "informed his friends" that he was recovering from wounds in London. Graves commanded his platoon toughly; while he hated the war and spent his spare moments at Garsington, the country estate of Philip and Lady Ottoline Morrell, where Britain's most famous conscientious objectors, including Aldous Huxley and Bertrand Russell, did "agricultural work" for wartime service, he was not a pacifist. Lester's verve attracted him, but there is no evidence that Graves ever shared his doubts about the war with his cadet.[40]

That summer Annie was having problems with the war, too. Vaughan's departure in 1916 had been difficult for his parents. They had discouraged him from enlisting, but Vaughan told them that the pressure to enlist at the university was too intense to resist, even though he knew it was "pretty hard" on his parents. In June 1917, just before the Pearsons left Chatham for Guelph, Ed felt compelled to write to Sir George Perley, the minister of overseas military forces in London, asking for Lester's return.

> I have gladly given my three sons – all our children – and they have enlisted as Privates from Toronto University. The youngest is about to go to France; the eldest is at Bexhill-on-Sea taking a Commission after a year at the front and a casualty which incapacitated him for three months. Their mother is brave but broken in spirit and by her urgent wish I write to ask if you could have my middle son [Lester] returned on furlough or returned to complete training or revert to the Flying Corps and train here. Can we not in view of our sacrifice and the fact that our boys are all overseas, two for over two years and one a year, reasonably ask you to show some special favor to us.

This time there would be no "special favour". Sir George Perley replied in early July:

> The need of men is so urgent that we have had to reduce to the minimum the number returned to Canada, and the circumstances in which a man can be permitted to return must be very grave indeed. I am very sorry not to be able to accede to the request of a family which has given so generously to the Cause, and whose sons have done so splendidly, but unfortunately my personal feelings in the matter cannot be allowed to interfere with any duty.

Sir George expressed hope that Annie would soon find "relief from anxiety". However, only the war's end seemed likely to bring that relief.[41]

Lester completed his training at the end of July, and the Afcananzacs had a raucous final evening that mocked the formality of the cadet program. By mid-1917 the noble traditions exalted in 1914 at Oxford had given way to a cynicism about rank, competence, and even heroism. One wonders how the officers and cadets laughed at the skit "Night Ops by the Remnants". The following evening, August 2, the cadets celebrated their "liberation" with dinner at Frascati's in London. Afterwards Lester did the London rounds of "teas, meeting old friends, shows, dinner at the [Trocadero], supper at the Savoy, and then another show." Late-Edwardian Toronto must have seemed very far away.[42]

The Afcananzacs dispersed Lester, now a lieutenant, to the 4th Canadian Reserve Battalion at Bramshot, where Duke happened to be stationed. Each commanded a platoon of "Tommies", and both were soon bored. In his memoirs, Lester indicates that he had wanted to join the Royal Flying Corps (RFC) when he first tried to escape Salonika. Flying had certainly intrigued him ever since a French aviator had taken him for an aerial jaunt about Macedonia in February 1916, and Ed had mentioned the Flying Corps as a means of having Lester return to Canada. In a contemporary memoir Pearson writes: "Finally Duke decided, I really had very little to do with it, that we had both seen enough of foot-slogging and that we were to transfer to the air." Duke's decision to join the Royal Naval Air Service may have had something to do with the Scottish nurse to whom he had become engaged. Lester's aims were romantic in a different sense.[43]

Like so many young men of that day, Pearson was fascinated with speed and flight. Moreover, the airmen of the First World War were its heroic gladiators, "Knights of the air" Lloyd George called them, testing their individual mettle in a war where individuality was submerged in the trenches. Billy Bishop and Manfred von Richthofen, the "Red Baron" and his famous Circus, were already part of the popular lore of wartime, and their "hits" were counted like Babe Ruth's home runs. The frailty of the wood and linen Sopwiths whose exposed pilots fought the elements and the enemy emphasized the romance of it all. By 1917 the aerial duelling had become much more deadly as the pilots' hand-guns had been replaced with machine guns. The mounting casualties were robbing the RFC of its strength, and, in the summer, the training period was drastically shortened so that new pilots could replace those who had fallen. Lester was willing to face the danger of air war, but he would not be reckless. When General Arthur Currie, "the portly Commander of the Canadians", addressed Canadian officers in the summer of 1917, he "kept repeating the phrase that 'some of your officers will rest on the field of honour'". Lester thought that Currie "gazed fixedly" at him every time he uttered that phrase. It obviously shook him, since he wrote: "I wasn't desirous of qualifying just then for a cross on the field of honor." Those common phrases – "field of honour", "mother's pride", and "God's children" – no longer resonated for Lester as they had in 1915 and 1916, even though he chose the most dangerous area of service – the Royal Flying Corps, where life expectancy had come to be measured in months.[44]

After some delay, which caused Lester to detest "brass hats" even more, he reported to the School of Aeronautics at Reading on October 10. The course crammed a year's training into six weeks. For the first time, Lester had no friends around him; but, as always, he made them quickly. He took pleasure and pride in having a place in the officers' mess, where he enjoyed the food, but not the drinks: Lester's mess bill clearly indicates that he, unlike so many others, did not break the abstainer's pledge all young Methodists made.

Other Methodist tenets survived as well. The Methodist Church in Canada officially supported the government's decision to introduce conscription, a decision which caused a breakdown of the party system as most English-Canadian Liberals joined with the Conservative government to support the use of compulsion. French Canadians and Sir Wilfrid Laurier objected strongly to the "breaking of the promise" of no conscription. The election of December 1917 was the most bitter in Canadian history. Lester wrote to his parents on December 4, thirteen days before the Canadian general election fought on the issue of conscription, declaiming the "anti-conscriptionists" as "detestable", and saying that they were giving Canada "a bad name". Quebec, he especially resented, and he was going to cast his first ballot "on the right side with those who are trying to keep Canada in the proud position in which her army has placed her and against those traitors who would drag her from that position".[45]

In late November, Lester began to fly. He was, in his own words, thrilled, imagining himself as "Sir Lester, knight of the azure blue", a hero for modern times. In fact, "Lester" had become "Mike" at flight school; his squadron commander considered the former too sissified for a pilot. "Mike" stuck with him; henceforth it will with us.

One day, Mike and his instructor at the Hendon training base had their engine "cut out" at about seven hundred feet. Remarkably, both escaped with "a good shaking ... up and some cuts". Mike was not intimidated by the event; a few days later, on December 15, he took his first solo flight. In describing his initial "jumpiness", he told his mother that, just as he was told he would fly solo, he "got a letter from you mother and I think you must have known it would arrive just at that time, for it was full of just the advice I needed then, re keeping calm, cool and collected." Half the credit for his making the flight therefore belonged to Mother. The other half was awarded to Wrigley's spearmint gum, which, for Mike, was the best help in keeping his wits.[46]

Mike Pearson lost his wits one evening just before Christmas, when he decided to spend a night in nearby London, contrary to camp rules. He met up with some cronies and, as usual, they ended up at Mike's favourite haunt, the Trocadero. There, in the middle of a grand repast, an air-raid warning sounded. Mike, knowing that his absence might now be detected and severely censured, quickly hopped a bus for the Hendon base. He tells the story well: "I found myself rolling along the Edgeware [*sic*] Road on a bus going too fast especially as both the bus lights and the street lights were off. A bomb exploded all of half a mile or more away. The driver had had enough. He stopped and told his few passengers to get out, as he proposed to do, until the all-clear sounded." Mike obeyed, and as he walked behind his bus to cross the road, was promptly hit by another bus, coming in the opposite direction with its lights off. There, on London's Edgware Road, his active service ended, in his own words, "ingloriously".[47]

The Cabells, an American family in London's Regent's Park who befriended the Pearson boys, cared for him at Christmas, and gradually his health returned. He was put on leave and waited for a medical board to decide what to do with him. Vaughan was still in the trenches in the aftermath of Passchendaele; Duke was flying a Sopwith Camel. Word of Mike's future finally came: he was to return to Canada "on the first ship". On April 6, just before his twenty-first birthday,[48] he embarked for home. His war was over.

This story of the accident and its aftermath follows that told by Mike Pearson in his memoirs. There is some confusion, and the sources for the period are scarce. There are no letters home after early February 1918, and the retrospective diary that Pearson created in February 1919 from his letters to his parents ends abruptly in December 1917, just before the accident. His memoir's account of 1918 and, for that matter, the first part of 1919, is brief. There are, nevertheless, some intriguing fragments.

On April 8, 1918, *The Guelph Mercury* noted that Lieutenant Pearson was coming home on leave. "He returns to Canada," the *Mercury* reported, "largely owing to an injury received which has largely shattered his nerves". In a medical-board report of August 10, 1918, Pearson is described as "unfit" for flying or observer's duties, but "fit" for ground duties. His disability, the board reported, occurred in December 1917, and was "attributable to the Service". It was the result of an "airplane crash" *(not* a bus accident), and the board was "uncertain" whether the disability was permanent. That disability was "neurasthenia" – a "generalized anxiety syndrome that had been found [before the war] primarily in private hospital rooms and exclusive sanitaria" and was most common among officers.[49] That is the polite description; to soldiers of the time, it simply meant, as the *Mercury* said, that his nerves were shattered.

In 1919, Pearson filled out the University of Toronto "Roll of Service" and a questionnaire for *Acta Victoriana,* a Victoria College publication. In both cases, he indicated that he had been injured at Hendon aerodrome, not on London's Edgware Road.[50] Two letters from the period also present some contradictions. On January 6, 1918, Mike reported to his parents that he was out of the hospital but not strong enough to work. Nevertheless, "headquarters" had attached him to another unit. That, he added, "doesn't look like getting back, does it[?] Please don't be too disappointed if nothing happens. I am really perfect physically so I think, after all, it is my duty to go to France." On February 3 he wrote again, just before he went before his medical board: "I don't expect leave but will try. Frankly, were it not for you two I wouldn't want to go back till it was all over." If he did go home he would feel he was "running away just at the moment of danger when the Hun is about to strike his last great blow". Still, he wanted to look at other possibilities: "How about instructor in the flying corps in Canada?" He asked Ed how such instructors were appointed. Ed found out quickly. Mike, in the judgment of his doctors, had no alternative to teaching. His personnel file contains medical records that make it clear that the bus accident injured his pride more than it did his body. His "incapacity", to use the doctor's term, was due to "partial loss of function of the nervous system". He could neither fight nor fly.[51]

Mike says nothing in the memoirs about the specific nature of his injury. What he says about his outlook during the six weeks he waited for the medical board's report does bear upon the evidence. Those weeks, he wrote a half-century later, were "a time I shall never forget. It was then that I became an adult." With a friend, Cliff Hames, Mike spent hours trying to get "some understanding of what we were being asked to do; to bring some reason to the senseless slaughter. For what? King and country? Freedom and democracy? These words sounded hollow now in 1918." Mike and Cliff, also the middle son of a preacher, "came closer together in that short time than I have ever been with any person since, outside my family." In Mike's wartime scrap-book there is a clipping: "Second Lieutenant Clifford R. Hames of the 62nd Squadron, Royal Air Force, England, was killed on April 25 [1918] in an airplane accident" – nineteen days after Mike landed at Saint John.[52]

The official historian of the Canadian Army Medical Corps of which Mike Pearson was a part was Sir Andrew MacPhail, philosopher, physician, and McGill professor, and he would have rejected the questions Mike and Clifford Hames were asking. His capacious mind embraced the traditional values of his society, and these were reflected in the history he wrote in the early 1920s. In his history he criticized the leniency shown to soldiers "suffering, thinking they suffered or pretending to suffer", from "neurasthenia". Such afflictions, in his opinion, were symptoms of "childishness and femininity".

Robert Graves, who knew the trenches and the war better than did MacPhail, later said that anyone who spent more than three months under fire could be considered neurasthenic. Similarly, anyone who spent three months waiting to fly in France underwent an unimaginable strain. Somehow in those months Mike lost his zeal for battle. After three years of waiting to go to France and three months preparing to fly, his emotional strength had been drained from him. His situation was not unlike the one soldiers faced at the Front: the static state of trench warfare, where the men sat waiting for shells to explode, was characterized by an increasing degree of nervous tension. When there was movement, the incidence of war neurosis dropped drastically, even though the danger and the casualties were greater.[53] For Mike, perhaps, the waiting simply became intolerable. The uncertainty of his fate and the time he had to consider it while he was exempted from military drills caused him to see himself and the external world differently. He would never fight again. Freedom and democracy, King and Country would regain meaning for him back home, but that meaning would never be quite the same. And neither would he.

CHAPTER THREE

RENEWAL

Friends were parted. Life seemed large and empty. You had to earn a
living. It was not easy to begin again....

– Charles Carrington on 1919[1]

ONE LATE-SUMMER day in 1918 Mike met "Billy" Dafoe, who
had shared the lice in Salonika's tents and who had also
returned early from the war. The two of them persuaded two young
women to join them for a walk along the remoter reaches of the
Grand River, near Brantford, Ontario. The water shimmered in the
summer heat, and it seemed natural to think of swimming. Mike bet
Billy and his female friend that they would not go in. He even offered
to find a suit for the young woman and did so, borrowing one of the
tank suits men wore in those days. She took the dare, donned the
suit, which covered her in a loose fashion, and Billy stripped to his
undershorts. They swam there, a few miles from the country club,
and Mike lost ten dollars he could not spare.

Certainly Mike and Billy could not have imagined that 1918 swimming scene in their pre-war Victoria College dorms or even in their
tent on the wind-swept Salonika plain where such fantasies surely
flourished. The war had blurred the strong images of responsibility
and authority that had supported Ontario Methodist culture and
Anglo-Canadian social relations. Methodist moral values seemed
triumphant. The bars were closed, and the "ideal of service" so

cherished by Methodists flourished as women took up factory jobs and replaced men at harvest time in the country. Women, the moral sex, now had the vote, and the country's politics could finally be cleaned up. Yet by midsummer 1918 the triumph of Methodist values in civic life could not conceal how the war had undermined the consensus that had given the pre-war church its strength. Rich and poor no longer sat so comfortably together in Methodist pews. Sir Joseph Flavelle, the former Sunday-school principal who had become head of the Imperial Munitions Board and a baronet, unfairly became "His Lardship", a businessman who publicly proclaimed his service but who privately craved his profits. The war radicalized the clergy, and in October the Methodist General Conference passed the most radical program ever accepted by a major Canadian church. The rich were separated from the poor, the young from the old. Toronto was dry; but women's skirts were shorter, cigarettes more common, and young Methodists not so willing to stand at attention morally. Mike, Billy, and the young women were part of the "younger generation", the offspring of society's traditional guardians, who, in the flux of post-war social change, now sought out experiences that both generations saw as new and even naughty. The seeds for this rebellion were planted with the poppies in Flanders Fields. They germinated later.[2]

"Disillusion," Mike Pearson's contemporary and fellow warrior Charles Carrington wrote in 1930, "came in with peace, not with war; peace at first was the futile state."[3] What we know of Mike Pearson's life after he returned home from the war in April 1918 shows many traces of this futility. The dutiful son and soldier who had chronicled his passage into war for the patriotic readers of *The Chatham Daily Planet* and who had craved the danger of the Front and the romance of the air kept no record of his home-coming. The unusually articulate teenager had become a mute young adult, leaving only fragments with which to reconstruct this period in his life. Nevertheless, like cuneiform tablets, those fragments are revealing.

To a later generation familiar with the war-weariness of Remarque and Hemingway, Mike's return home after he failed to become one of Lloyd George's "Knights of the azure sky" rings with the truth born of fiction. This familiarity can be deceptive, for the images drawn from the literature of the post-war generation blot out the everyday reality of the returned soldier's lot. Once home, Mike did not reject the world of his father and mother; in fact, his reunion with Ed and Annie at Toronto's Union Station in April 1918 was "the happiest emotional moment" of his twenty-one years.[4] He would have sensed no disapproval. After all, Annie had begged for his return in mid-1917, when her own emotional health had broken down, and Ed, we know, had worked to get his middle son back to Canada. In short, Mike had every reason to expect understanding, and the continuing deep affection he showed his parents indicates that he got it. His brothers at the Front were equally understanding. When Vaughan wrote to Mike in midsummer 1918, he strongly encouraged him to stay in Canada. After all, Vaughan added, Mike had been "away for three years", and he owed the war nothing more.[5] Mike's failure to reach France, no doubt an overwhelming disappointment in 1915, mattered less in 1918 to a society and a family weary of war. Still, his values and self-confidence were obviously shaken by the war, and he, like those shell-shocked veterans of France, needed time to heal his wounds.

Mike Pearson was welcomed home, but the image of what he thought he would become was shattered along with his emotional stability. The medical-board examiner's May report on his condition is unlike earlier and later ones. He told the board that he had headaches every day, that sudden noises upset him, and that he slept lightly and woke often. During the day, he said, he became very drowsy and was unable to stay still for long. To the doctors on the board, Mike appeared "quite pale" and was "very nervous and fidgety in his actions". His lips and facial muscles "trembled" when he spoke, and "he could not remain in one position for more than a minute at a time". Even in September 1918, when another medical board examined him, Mike was nervous, and he stuttered when questioned. The tremor in his face and fingers had disappeared, but he told his examiners that "sudden noises" still made him "jumpy" and that he continued to have nightmares about "flying and crashing". Somehow in the next year this broken human being regained the emotional equilibrium that later generations would remember. How he did so remains cloaked in history's shadows, but we know that his family and friends (but not their Methodist faith) were important aids in the reconstruction.[6]

The military also helped the process. After a brief retreat to his parents' parsonage in Guelph, Mike reported to Royal Air Force Headquarters in Toronto, where the RAF operated a training centre for Canadians and Americans who wanted to join. The medical board had declared him unfit, recommending his discharge from active service. When Mike met with RAF commanding officer Colonel Cruickshank, he was told, "almost accusingly", that he would have to be returned to the Canadian Army, which presumably would discharge him. Despite his faltering nerves and frequent nightmares, discharge was unthinkable to Mike. His strong reaction to the news caused a change in Cruickshank's estimation of him. Sensing that he was not dealing with a mere "slacker", Cruickshank asked if Mike might be interested in joining the staff of No. 4 School of Aeronautics at the University of Toronto. Mike quickly agreed, but was forced to admit that his knowledge of aircraft and flying was limited. "Well," Cruickshank said, with a sigh, "we will have to make you an instructor in aerial navigation." As Mike later commented, "Aerial navigation was somewhat rudimentary in those days but not more so than my teaching of it."[7] It did not really matter. German morale had suddenly collapsed in the late summer of 1918. By September Mike's students knew that they, too, would never reach the Front. The war would soon be over.

Mike spent the last months of the war in Burwash Hall at the university. The residence halls were virtually empty, since nearly all of the men at Victoria were still in khaki and in Europe. Those housed in Burwash were airforce veterans, some recovering from crashes, others, like Mike, trying to restore their mental balance. In Mike's memory, life there was "pleasant and the going was easy". He saw it that way because he had to. In fact, the world around him in Toronto in 1918 and early 1919 was in turmoil. The streets swarmed with the war's casualties; housing was scarce; and workers were organizing to demand greater equality and rights.[8] Tempers were short. Rioters smashed a Greek-owned café on College Street when the owner allegedly mistreated a returned soldier. Other nearby stores were destroyed, and only when Mayor Tommy Church threatened to read the Riot Act on August 7, 1918, five days after the troubles began, did peace return to the streets. At the university, professors were recoiling from the anti-Quebec and pro-war hysteria of the election of December 1917, and were flirting with new political alternatives, including socialism. The Methodist Church, which had proclaimed the sanctity of the British and Canadian cause in the war's first months, was now asking probing questions about the war and about the kind of Canadian society that had fought it.

In defining what part he would play in post-war Canada, Mike Pearson faced several choices. He could join the raucous band of returned soldiers clustering together in veterans' groups and striving ever more ineffectively to recapture the camaraderie of wartime. However, their anger, their wobbly politics (sometimes supporting established order, at other times denouncing it), and their focus on the past were not to Mike's taste. Neither were those – whether politicians, as was Arthur Meighen, or professors, as was George Wrong – who called for a reassertion of traditional Anglo-Canadian values to counter the disorder and decadence of post-war life. We will see later that Pearson's British experience did influence his view of the need for tradition and for cultural models. He feared anarchy and distrusted revolution. The most famous North American expatriate of the time, T.S. Eliot, moved from a similar set of beliefs to a denial of the values of humanitarianism and liberal democracy in favour of a classicism in which the weak individual soul found discipline and order in collective and traditional authority symbols. In a certain sense, Donald Creighton, Pearson's future academic colleague, fellow son of the Methodist manse, and, much later, his bitter critic, reflected Eliot's approach in Canada. For Mike, however, Creighton's and Eliot's paths offered little temptation. His wartime experience had been essentially liberalizing. His distrust of the "brass hats" created an enduring suspicion of specious claims of authority.[9] His own fears and doubts, which surely contributed to his breakdown in 1918, strengthened his tolerance for human frailties; the censorious note he struck in some of his early letters home – for example, his horrified and priggish reaction to Alexandria – finds few echoes in his post-war life. He became suspicious of dogma and of deterministic views of the human predicament. He later remarked about his wartime experience: "I got hurt before I got a chance to get killed – that's about what it amounts to."[10] There is a touch of conservative fatalism in the remark; more importantly, there's a strong dose of liberal rationality.

The RAF treated Mike better than it did most unfit flyers, probably because, despite his emotional problems, he excelled on the rugby field. In the fall of 1918, as more soldiers returned and young male students appeared once again on campus, games began. Mike had grown in the three years since he left Varsity. (He had weighed 140 pounds and stood 5 feet, 8½ inches, in April 1915 when he enlisted; in September 1918, he weighed 155 pounds and stood 5 feet, 10½ inches.) Football was not yet a sport for behemoths, and Mike's size was considered an asset. In 1918 Canadian rugby was similar to American football, although the Canadian game retained most of the traces of its British public-school origins. Speed and agility still mattered most, and Mike had both in abundance. The RAF team had several American members who had come to Toronto to enlist before the United States entered the war, and they and Mike were the "stars" in Varsity Stadium that fall.

In his memoirs, Mike says little about what he did or felt that fall. He, of course, recalled that "never-to-be-forgotten day", November 11, 1918, which "saved the rest" of his generation, and on which he and hundreds of thousands of others took to Toronto's streets to embrace, to remember and forget, and, above all, to share "the almost incredible relief of the present". The news came to Toronto at 3:00 a.m. when Eaton's "wildcat siren" awakened the city. *The Globe* reported what followed on November 11: "At a little after 3 o'clock a procession, mostly of women munition workers, paraded Yonge

Street, cheering, wildly beating tin pans and blowing whistles. By the time a crowd began to gather all along Yonge Street, motor cars came tearing down the street, reckless of all speed laws, tooting their horns and awakening the entire city." Seventy thousand Torontonians had served; ten thousand would never return. They were missed, but that fall, Mike, like most young Torontonians, lived for the present, not the past or future, and the present was sports.

Mike's scrap-book and his father's are filled with breathless accounts of his rugby heroics. The RAF team battled city and other military teams, and Pearson was invariably the "Fliers star". He played quarterback, a position that, in those days, before the forward pass dominated Canadian football, required kicking and running skills as well as quick wits. When the student officers played civilian teams, military rivalries were forgotten. Mike played each Saturday and practised all week. His doubts about flying vanished as he darted about the rugby field. In one game against the Ontario Rugby Football Union "Beaches" team, Mike, playing alongside the American collegiate football hero Gene Lockhart, brought his team back from a 12-to-1 half-time deficit. Alas, the Beaches lead was too great, and the game ended 12 to 10. The reporter blamed Lockhart, who "muffed and fumbled atrociously and gave Pearson, whose punting and all round play featured, but little assistance". Reading this account must have been marvellous therapy. In the military championship game, however, Lockhart returned to his own Canadian Officer Training Corps (COTC) team and, unfortunately for Mike, to his usual form.

The crowd poured into Varsity Stadium, where fans' cheers had not echoed for two years. Some wore cloth masks to ward off the influenza that was striking down so many in the fall of 1918. The cheerleaders assembled beside their teams, ready with doggerel for every triumph and tragedy. Mike Pearson was a special target for COTC cheerleaders, who grudgingly admired his talents. The most personal of their cheers asked

What'll we do with him boys; what'll we do?
What'll we doo-doo-yoo-dee-yoo-dee-do-do-do?

Will we get the Pearson boy?
Sure we will, and then, oh joy,
Goodbye RAF.

They rarely got the "Pearson boy", who quarterbacked with verve and grace. His punts consistently forced back the "mudcrushers", as the COTC team was rudely dubbed, but, alas, the "Fliers" halfbacks did not soar above the "mudcrusher" defence. Lockhart repeatedly swept around and over the defence, and only Mike could catch him, but he could not do it often enough. The "Fliers" fell 11 to 9, but Mike could hold his head high.[11]

Sports, then, were Mike Pearson's sanatoria; the crowd's cheers the sedatives for his jangled nerves. The medical boards had told him he needed rest, and he had found it, paradoxically, in physical exertion. Athletics had never been so popular or so idealized as in the post-war era. Newspaper sports sections swelled to accommodate society's new heroes, victors not at Verdun or Passchendaele, but at Yankee Stadium, the Montreal Forum, Soldiers' Field, and even Varsity Stadium. In Mike's view, the Americans went too far. No longer was "the game" the thing; the gate was everything, even at the most august of American universities, Yale and Harvard, where the football receipts could amount to a million dollars per year in the early 1920s. Mike strongly disapproved of such trends and of the rise of professionalism in athletics. Nevertheless, his feelings for sports were every bit as enduring and profound as those of America's most celebrated sportswriter, Grantland Rice, who made the mortals of the North American playing fields into Leander and Hercules. The camaraderie of the clubhouse was the closest Mike could come to those treasured memories of wartime male friendships. As well as restoring Mike's shattered confidence, sports became ever more important as a family bond after the Pearson sons came back from the war. The family's best athlete, Vaughan, returned home in 1918, the emotional wounds of the war years deeper and more lasting than his physical ones. "Cutey" Pearson, as a Chatham sportswriter had dubbed him in his teens, never recovered his balance, except on the baseball diamond, where he rarely missed a play. He stayed a bachelor, absorbed in the memories of his youthful exploits. Mike and Vaughan eventually moved far apart, but sports bonded them to the end. The same was true of Duke, who married his Scottish nurse, Connie, in December 1918 (Mike assured Ed and Annie that she was a "splendid girl" though they must have noted that Duke was married in a Church of England parish church in Northumberland).[12]

In a later decade, Mike's athletic prowess might have brought him fortune as well as fame. But in 1918 his horizons were more limited. First, he had to complete his degree, which the University of Toronto in an act of patriotic generosity decided he could do in a single term from January to May 1919. The university granted him, and others, a year's credit for wartime service, but the abbreviated 1918-19 term was occasioned by the flood of returning students in numbers that the university was ill-prepared to handle. At Christmas, Mike went home to Guelph, where he heard Ed pray for those who had fallen and for an enduring peace.[13] Then, in early January, he enrolled for his final year at Victoria.

Victoria's graduating class of 1919 comprised forty-four women and only seventeen men, although as undergraduates the class had been more balanced. Few of his old friends were around, and his old roommate, Duke, was still in England, awaiting authorization to return. Nevertheless, cousin R.P. Bowles was still chancellor, and many of the faculty were familiar, although distinctive in ways that Mike seemed to overlook. Pelham Edgar, Douglas Bush, and E.J. Pratt were already fine scholars of English literature, and C.B. Sissons, a historian with a special interest in contemporary events, was having a significant influence in Ontario politics as a close adviser to the farmers' movement, which, to everyone's astonishment, would form the province's government in 1919. Mike attended a few of the political gatherings on campus in that most tumultuous political year, but he left only one odd mark. He headed the "Progressives" in their successful challenge in the Victoria Union Literary Society's debate on contemporary Ontario politics.

Academic pursuits did not really interest Mike. In truth, he had not fully recovered from his emotional collapse in 1918. A medical board examined him in April 1919 and found him still nervous and "easily excited by noises". Although he was now getting eight hours of sleep per night, dreams of flying and crashing still troubled him. He told the board that his memory was good, but that he was "unable to concentrate on work or sit still during lectures". The board thought he needed six months before he would fully "recover", but it recommended no further treatment.[14]

Intellectually, the University of Toronto and Victoria College asked little of Mike Pearson. Naturally, they gave him little as well. He performed adequately in his examinations on his return, but rightly saw that sports and social events could benefit him more than the crowded post-war classrooms. Since winter had ended the rugby season, Mike turned to basketball and hockey, where he was less skilled physically but where his cleverness made him a team leader. His prowess on the playing field led to his election as class president, and he represented his year at the final class dinner. In the 1919 year-book photograph, the serious-looking adolescent who had left in 1915 has clearly become a man. He wears his prized lieutenant's uniform, his hair is swept back, the hazel eyes try to penetrate, the chin juts forward, and the caption reads "Justly famous". Beneath the caption a short essay explains how the neurasthenic war veteran had become class president: "Since he first came to Vic 1915, Lester has shown himself to be an all-round man. In sports a leading figure; an equally good student, heading his course. One of the first to go to war. After a varied experience in England, Egypt, and Salonika, he nearly became an aviator, but an accident brought him back to Canada and to Varsity." Among the many sad tales of broken warriors, Mike Pearson's seems an especially happy one.[15]

Mike continued to draw his generous RAF pay of about $90 per month until mid-April, when he was discharged. His commanding officer wrote to the Air Ministry, London, that Pearson, though "medically unfit for flying", had served at the School of Aeronautics, where "his services were of great value". What these services were was not mentioned. This highly honourable discharge eased the transition to civilian life, as did the more than $700 of accumulated pay that Ed had held, pending Mike's return.[16] No longer the poor parson's son, Mike could afford to live off campus at the Delta Upsilon fraternity house on Bloor Street and to dine with whatever meagre elegance Toronto could muster. On March 8, for example, the fraternity's annual banquet was held at the Queen's Hotel. It began with a fish course – salmon filet with shrimp sauce – and the main course was characteristically Anglo Canadian – roast chicken with dressing, mashed potatoes, and green peas. Although coffee was now the beverage, toasts were still the order of the day. Mike toasted the "sister Phis" – "the fair, the chaste and unexpressive she". On the back of the evening's program was a brief homily from the American theologian Henry Ward Beecher: "It is not work that kills men; it is worry. Work is healthy.... Worry is the rust upon the blade." Mike had already taken the message to heart.[17]

In February 1919 he gathered together his wartime letters and created a "diary", which reflects the way in which he had come to terms with his wartime experience; his compiling it indicates that by then he was enough at peace to confront the war. Like most Anglo Canadians who had served overseas, Mike had become more nationalistic or, more accurately, more Canadian. His future friend and colleague Frank Underhill once said that Canadians went up Vimy Ridge as colonials and came down its bloody slopes as Canadians. While Mike remained a thoroughly British subject and endorsed the purpose of the war as it was defined by Britain's finest statesmen, he came to recognize the distinctiveness of Canada and Canadians. Like Australia's and New Zealand's, English Canada's sense of what it was (and French Canada's of what it was not) became deeply rooted during battle. Thus English Canadians and Antipodeans found it difficult to deny the value of war's purpose, unlike Americans and Europeans, whose sense of nationhood was rooted in an extensive pre-war tradition.

Like all soldiers, however, Mike understood that the Great War, as it was soon dubbed, had drastically altered the way that we would live. His first diary entry talked about how long the journey seemed back to "those halcyon college days before we dreamed of a world [war] as anything but the illusions of militaristic minds". But then came "a quickening of patriotism here, an increase of hatred there, but above all the desire to be in it, the greatest and most glorious cause in history". Now, in 1919, the cause might not seem so glorious – certainly that is the implication of the diary – but it remained stirring. Those days "as a soldier of the King" seemed, in 1919, "the best and the worst, the gladdest and the saddest days" of Mike Pearson's young life. The gladdest had been in "entrancing" London, the "true heart of a world Empire" that "will be forever such", and on the athletic field, which was, in Mike's youthful view, "the single most important factor in keeping up morale". He was shown the moral force of sports again and again: "I have seen regiments come out of the battle gloomy, tired and disgusted with life after weeks of the blood and dirt of trench warfare"; then, twenty-four hours later, at the football game, these battle-weary warriors became "a happy, shouting crowd of boys". There are stories about the flower of British manhood marching into machine-gun fire, carrying their pocket classics. For Mike and his Canadian colleagues, courage in battle came not from Homer so much as from *The Sporting News*.[18]

At the June 5, 1919, graduation ceremony, the fallen and absent far exceeded in number the graduands. Women took most of the medals, and solemnity understandably marked the ceremony. Three hymns were sung, which called upon the Lord, in the final words of the first and last of them, "to make the sacrifice complete" and "make one music as before". Mike finished third in the modern history honours course, behind Florence Smith and Alexander Brady, who later became a distinguished Toronto political scientist. He received a second in all subjects except English, in which he received a first, which his vigorous youthful prose indicates was fully deserved, and economics, in which he earned a third, which also seems quite justified in hindsight, since the subject was and would remain for him a dismal and unfathomable one.

The economy, however, was a major concern for all those graduating that June afternoon. Workers had taken to the streets, first in

Winnipeg and then in other Canadian cities, just a few weeks before graduation day. Civic leaders talked of Bolsheviks plotting to tear down the citadels of established order, and workers, and even Methodist clergymen, responded by calling for a new order where property and capital no longer called the tune. At the graduation ball Mike danced with one of Victoria's most attractive young women, Mary Austin, the daughter of one of the leading parishioners in Ed's church in Chatham; her heart quickened more to the steps of revolution than to Methodist hymns, and in time, she would cheer on Mao's revolution in far-off China as the wife of missionary and Victoria graduate James Endicott. Mike may have shared some goals with those who took to the streets – certainly many at Victoria did – but we find no such evidence.[19] Rather than marching on the legislature, Mike went farther, towards Osgoode Hall, the citadel of the Ontario justice system, and to the law firm of McLaughlin, Johnson, Moorehead, and Sinclair.

Law was a popular choice among Victoria undergraduates. It promised respectability, and, for many, large financial rewards after an extended training period. In Ontario, at that time, lawyers were not required to have a university degree, but rather apprenticed, or "articled" in a law firm and completed some courses directed by Osgoode to fulfil the requirements set by the Law Society of Upper Canada. Like his father, thirty years earlier, Mike did not take to law. He decided, understandably, that Anson's *Law of Contract* was "the dullest book [he] had ever read" and at that moment he quit law[20] and returned to his parents' home on Liverpool Street in Guelph.

A summer of baseball and football beckoned, and Vaughan and he very quickly found sponsors who agreed to pay them wages to play baseball for the Guelph Maple Leafs in the Intercounty League. (The league was "semi-pro" in that it allowed players to accept some money.) Vaughan quickly established his credentials, with a batting average near .400, and Mike soon made his mark as an infielder. In a desultory way, Mike had to put in some hours at the Partridge Tire and Rubber Company, but for the summer of 1919, baseball was his true occupation.

Guelph, fifty miles from Toronto, was a small Ontario city of about 18,000, overwhelmingly British in stock, mainly Protestant in faith, but with a sprinkling of new non-British immigrants. During the war years tensions rose between the British Protestants and others in the city. Guelph gained national attention when, on June 7, 1918, an armed unit of Dominion and Military Police raided a Jesuit novitiate, three miles north of the city, which they alleged was harbouring draft dodgers. Three novices, including the son of Canada's Irish Catholic justice minister, were detained but soon freed. The Guelph Protestant Ministerial Association, of which Ed was a member, protested against the "favouritism" shown towards the Catholics, but, upon closer investigation, their charges proved unfounded. This quarrel reflected old tensions. The new industrial strife that led Winnipeg's workers into the streets in 1919 had a minor impact there, although *The Guelph Daily Mercury* did describe, in one breathless item, how the Mounties beat down the strikers at Winnipeg's famed intersection of Portage and Main. Ed, now chairman of the Guelph Protestant clergymen and chaplain to the cadet battalion in Guelph, held a special service for the cadets the week the Winnipeg strike reached its climax. The assembled congregation sang "Soldiers of Christ Arise" and "Christ in Flanders" and heard Ed preach from the text "Follow Me", a sermon in which he extolled the value of personal loyalty and lauded the soldiers who had exhibited that quality in wartime. The roots of revolution were shallow, indeed, at Norfolk Methodist Church in Guelph.[21]

It was likely that Mike was in church that Sunday, since he did attend every Sunday he was at home and would do so for a long time after, even though he no longer shared the depth of faith of his beloved father. Earlier notions that Mike would become a clergyman seem to have disappeared with his return, or perhaps even earlier. Certainly, Victoria's class president, honours graduate of the University of Toronto and "Justly famous" soldier-athlete of Varsity fame, seemed destined to become more than a semi-pro ballplayer. However, if the ministry beckoned after law lost its charm, Mike did not heed its call. He told a journalist, in one of his rare comments on the subject of religion, that he had given no thought to entering the ministry when he returned from the war. Instead, he and Duke approached Edson White, husband of Ed's devoted sister Lillian and a senior executive with one of Chicago's great businesses, Armour and Company, which had recently been savagely attacked in Upton Sinclair's novel *The Jungle*. According to one story Mike later told, Edson had been caught up in a wave of patriotism after the United States entered the war in April 1917 and had promised to "look after" the Pearson boys if they came out of the war alive. Duke, newly married, needed money; Mike simply wanted a job. Both reminded Uncle Ed of his promise, and he kept it – after a fashion.[22]

Although he had expected to be appointed executive assistant to the president in Chicago, Mike's corporate career was launched on the stuffing line in the sausage department of an Armour subsidiary in Hamilton. Duke was given an equally menial position with the hides and leather division in Chicago. The company's founder, Philip D. Armour, who bestrode the Chicago packing-house world like a colossus until his death in 1901, had believed that all future executives should start at the bottom.

The "bottom" in Chicago was low, indeed. The uproar surrounding the publication of Sinclair's *The Jungle* prompted some improvement in working conditions in the Armour operation and some reform of the city's nasty and brutish ways, but not enough in the eyes of Carl Sandburg and James Farrell, who became, respectively, the poetry and prose chroniclers of wartime and post-war Chicago. Sandburg had written in 1916 of the "strong, husky, brawling / City of big shoulders" that had become "Hog butcher for the world". In 1919 he was a reporter for *The Chicago Daily News* when tensions exploded between Bronzeville, where almost 100,000 poor blacks dwelt, and the rest of the city, which detested them. Sandburg watched in horror in July 1919 as white punks, the model for James Farrell's fictional creation Studs Lonigan, beat up young blacks. In Farrell's fictional city, Studs and three buddies caught a "nigger boy" on Wabash

Avenue, burnt his body with their cigarettes, stripped him, and then urinated on him; the reality for black Chicagoans was very much worse.[23]

Chicago, however, had another side. The city was America's heart, and it was a divided one. The "big shoulders" of its black, Irish, German, Polish, and other workers supported a level of luxury that would have been the envy of Renaissance princes, whose personal lives the Chicago élite often emulated. It was in Chicago that Thorsten Veblen first wrote about the "conspicuous consumption" of the leisure class, a class that craved things not for their utility but for the impression they made upon others. As distasteful as this sort of life might be to Veblen, its results were often beneficial to the city. Like the Medicis, the Chicago merchant princes inspired a remarkable creativity and intellectual ferment in the city. That most civilized Bostonian, Henry Adams, had come to Chicago's Great Columbia Exposition of 1893 and it showed him his people's future lay in its mechanical sequences, its quest for the monumental and the eternal. In Chicago, Americans could see what they would become in the twentieth century. "Chicago," Adams wrote, "was the first expression of American thought as a unity; one must start there."[24]

Over the next thirty years, Chicago was home to many innovations that captured the imagination of America and the world: Jane Addams's Hull House, which influenced generations of settlement homes throughout the world; Louis Sullivan's buildings, the skyscrapers that were forerunners of the international style that would transform urban life throughout the world more than a half century later; Frank Lloyd Wright's prairie style of architecture; Veblen's awkwardly phrased yet extraordinary insights into human nature; and, of course, the best-known Chicagoan of the twenties, Al Capone, whose scar-faced scowl gave evil in the decade its most memorable manifestation, even if it was most often displayed by James Cagney and not by Capone.

The power of these images dissolved national boundaries. Many influential Canadians, including Mackenzie King, Stephen Leacock, O.D. Skelton, and the economist Harold Innis, had gone to

Chicago's great university, and had brought home what they had learned, although the lessons were not always the same.

Mike Pearson no doubt shared the sense of excitement that Chicago stirred in North America, in the late 'teens and early 'twenties. London had enthralled him and his experience of its multitudinous delights had whetted his taste for twentieth-century city life, a taste that Guelph, Hamilton, or even Toronto could not satisfy. Business and other opportunities, too, were meagre in Canada. The economy in Canada was tottering as Britain turned to traditional markets for many of the goods purchased from Canada in wartime. With hundreds of thousands of veterans trying to find their post-war footing, the national mood was cranky. The country had split badly in wartime. The reforms promised the returning heroes had amounted to very little. Disillusionment with what the war had wrought and what the peace would bring set in very quickly among Canadians, as it did elsewhere. In short, Canada offered no vision to animate the young. Whatever fears and animosities America provoked, its excitement and the sense that it represented the future were an irresistible lure to the young and ambitious Mike Pearson and to hundreds of thousands like him in the 1920s.[25]

And so, after a brief apprenticeship with sausages in Hamilton, Mike went to Chicago to make his fortune in the Armour fertilizer section, where he took up a clerk's position in February 1920. Quite apart from Chicago's appeal, Mike was drawn to Edson White's family. Edson, Mike later recalled, was "a rather legendary figure in our world" and Lillian, Mike's aunt, was a woman of style and generosity. Mike had respectability in Toronto, but he noticed the automobiles, gramophones, wardrobes, and other accoutrements of those of his peers whose fathers were captains of Canada's industries. Like many other parson's sons, Mike enjoyed the company of those who consumed conspicuously. (So, for that matter, did Veblen's student Stephen Leacock who satirized them so well.)

The Whites were exemplary consumers. They lived in Chicago's most elegant suburb, Lake Forest, home to that most splendid icon in the post-war decade, Ceylon Court, the Singhalese Pavilion of the

1893 exposition, where paper lanterns lit up the Oriental turrets during debutante dances on midsummer nights. Lake Forest lay along the bluffs of Lake Michigan, and the earnest Presbyterians who had settled there had nestled their mansions in the abundance of arboreal splendour – much as they had done in Montreal. One of the grandest estates was J. Ogden Armour's Mellody Farm, built in 1908, set back two miles from the road; it had "orchards and an orangerie, similar to that of Voltaire at the Potsdam court of Frederick the Great". The main house, more than five hundred feet wide, had a bowling alley in the basement, a music room on the main floor, silk wallpaper, gold doorknobs, and a direct telephone line to the stockyards. Guests arrived at the Armour private railway station to be met by top-hatted English grooms who whisked them off in carriages or cars to the parties that continued through winter and summer. One summer night Ruth St. Denis, the muse of modern dance in America, danced for the guests on a platform specially erected above the reflecting pool. The Edson Whites were probably there.[26]

Mike spent most weekends in Lake Forest with the Whites, but on weekdays he lived in the Hyde Park YMCA on Chicago's South Side, not far from the stockyards. The South Side, which Rudyard Kipling had described as a huge wilderness where blood fell like a heavy tropical rain, was part of Mike's everyday life in Chicago. Its notorious sounds and smells did not trouble Mike, but Chicago's dreadful mayor, "Big Bill" Thompson, who wooed the Irish and German vote by promising to punch King George in the snout if ever he saw him (an unlikely event), was disturbing. Mike arrived in Chicago in one of its most troubled years. Recriminations followed the race riots of 1919, and the anti-alien atmosphere of the time led to blame for the unrest being placed on foreign agitators and Bolsheviks. The next time, Thompson warned, the army would smash the trouble-makers. The Volstead Act, which closed down bars in January 1920, had opened up opportunities for the Chicago underworld. The massive funeral of Big Jim Colisomo, a notorious racketeer and influential Democrat, had the city's politicians marching solemnly beside its leading criminals. Big Jim's death created a void, which Al Capone quickly filled with road-houses, brothels, and bribes. That same year, 1920, saw the White Sox, who had been American League champions in 1919, become the Black Sox, as horrified sports fans – Mike among them – learned that eight star team members had "thrown" the 1919 World Series. The little boy at the courthouse, confronting the White Sox's star outfielder, the near-illiterate "Shoeless Joe" Jackson, with "Say it ain't so, Joe", seemed to crystallize the corruption of the purest heart and the loss of American innocence.

The city surely was, as Mike later said, a "wild and woolly" place, far more so than the Front had been.[27] And yet the Loop, the Lakeshore, the "Gold Coast", and Lake Forest were as much a part of Chicago – and America – as was the South Side. One can imagine Mike, perhaps in the company of one of the prized Lake Forest "princesses", strolling through the Loop, entering the elegantly baroque State-Lake Theater to see (but not yet to hear) the latest Hollywood production, then sharing tea in the lobby of the Palmer House, a hotel every inch as grand as London's Savoy. Studs Lonigan's Chicago would have seemed remote – at least until the next morning, when the predatory world of Armour fertilizers would have overwhelmed fantasies of Lillian Gish and Lake Forest debs. On Sunday mornings, Mike attended St. James's Methodist Church, whose bulletin was printed, in the advertising fashion of the day, with boxes in which one marked an "x" if you "wished to see the Pastor", were sick, wished to join the Church, wished "to make Christian fellowship", or had changed your address. On Easter Sunday, April 11, 1920, Mike was "received" into the church by certificate; as a Methodist minister's son, he was exempted from the usual period of probation.[28]

One year of Chicago was enough, though Mike came to adore his Aunt Lillian and to appreciate even more Chicago's urban sophistication, even though he knew that his mind and heart would not mesh with the hard edges of Chicago life. He went to Aunt Lillian with his worries, especially about his abandoning of business after so short a time being a betrayal of Uncle Edson. With his aunt's assurance secured, he wrote at length to his parents on February 3, 1921, informing them of his decision and, once again, asking for their counsel and assistance. The letter betrays his fears, while expressing his love and his hopes. It reads as though it had been written in haste, but Mike's purpose in writing it was clear, more so than was usual for this already guarded young man.[29]

I will never be satisfied making material success my whole aim[,] not that I don[']t love comfort & all the advantages money can buy, but it doesn't satisfy everything[;] a business career will never make me really contented. It[']s hard, too hard for me to explain in writing but something has been pulling me the other way. It must be the same Providence that always seemed to tell me what to do when I was overseas. I wonder if you can understand me. Don't think I have failed in what I am at now because I know without appearing conceited, I am doing exceptionally well. Now for the positive side. What should I do? Well, father & mother, to me it became as clear as light all at once that I could never be happy excepting as a scholar or a professional man and my mind is freed on taking up where I left off, finish my education by a post-graduate course and if possible getting a lectureship on a university staff, Toronto, of course if possible. So now you know. Ever since I have made this decision a great load seems to have been lifted from my mind and I am set on accomplishing my aim.

Now as to my plans to reach this goal. I am still as ambitious as ever, only it is changed from business to scholastic and literary attainment. If I am going to be a scholar I want to be the best. So, my dear parents, please don't faint when I say I desire to enter Oxford in the fall and take my post-graduate work there. I, if I save every cent, shall have $500 by Sept. The rest I shall simply have to borrow, because, of course, I can't let you give me a cent except as a business proposition on my note. The only people I have told my new plans to are Aunt Lillian, Duke & Connie & Mr. & Mrs. Hunter. I have talked it over at length with all three of them [sic] & asked their advice and they all think it the wisest thing I ever did. Mr. Hunter said he always thought business was not my field and also was insistent to lend me ⅓ of all my financial requirements but of course I want to keep my obligations within the family if possible. Every cent you lend me father will be paid in 5 years & you certainly will not suffer. I am glad I came here because the year is not wasted. If I had never attempted business & gone in far before, I might have often thought that I should have seized the chance to work for Armour & make a fortune. Now I know I will be doing right. I am only 23 now and if I had gone over before would have been too young to get the full value of it. I am just at the right age, in my own mind, to start on my chosen career.

So what do you think? Would you sooner have me rich and prosperous or making $3000 a year and doing what I think I am best fitted for?

Oh, I can't explain myself on paper. I wish I could talk to you about it. I won't be satisfied till you have given me your views. I shall be waiting every hour to hear. Maybe you could send me a night letter to tell me if you approve or not. In my own mind there isn't the shadow of doubt. I am not destined to live here among this environment. I want to live in my own country and doing the work I am called for. Next to preaching teaching must be the finest profession. If you approve, father might see the Chancellor and try and get me some idea of my possibilities of getting on Toronto Univ. after returning. Or maybe he would have some other opening in mind. But we can arrange the details later. Are you coming over soon? We can talk things over then but I must get it settled. Of course I shall work where I am till late summer. Aunt Lillian & Gertrude [Lillian's daughter] are going abroad in Sept. & I would probably go with them.

Let me hear at once and please tell me that you think I am acting wisely. Uncle Ed doesn't know anything as of course he couldn't understand because he is nothing but business. Aunt Lillian thought it best not to tell him till things are definite. He told me last week though to be sure and never hesitate to leave Armour if I wasn't happy.

All my love to you both,
Lester

Mike (he remained Lester to his parents) knew he would have to tell Uncle Ed, but the dreaded moment passed more easily than anyone had expected. Uncle Ed may have been "nothing but business" but he perceptively recognized that Mike would never come to share the particular mentality that business required. As they walked along the shores of Lake Michigan, the "Gold Coast" beside them, its lavish riches the reward that business bestowed upon its favourites, Uncle Ed and Mike came to quick agreement that business would never be the young Canadian's *métier*. Edson White nevertheless assured his nephew that he was certain that Mike would achieve success in a different career, even though Mike's record to that point surely gave no reason for such assurance.[30]

Since 1917, Mike had often stumbled in the pursuit of his goals. He never reached France, whose trenches he had coveted so often on the Macedonian plains. His flying career had ended ignominiously, and his legal career, abruptly. His triumphs had come principally on the playing fields, and he knew that such victories were, in the eyes of God and greater men, ephemeral. And yet his ambition endured, and hindsight revealed that the paths that had been too stony for him actually led to goals he was best not seeking. His experiences had taught him that the past should not encumber but illuminate the future. Oxford in 1917 was a glorious memory; in the winter of 1921 it loomed as an exhilarating opportunity.

CHAPTER FOUR

OXFORD

Oxford University and St. John's in particular, turned out to be all that I had hoped and dreamed. Seldom are expectations so completely fulfilled as were those of my two years at Oxford.
 — Lester Pearson on his years at Oxford[1]

POST-WAR OXFORD endures in the autumnal mists and mannered idiosyncrasies of *Brideshead Revisited* and, in sharp contrast, the earnest athleticism and moral certainties of *Chariots of Fire*. Both images reflect a part of the richness that attracted Mike Pearson to Oxford. The decision to attend having been made, the immediate problem became the cost; post-war Britain was expensive and Mike's funds were limited. Fortunately for young Canadians, the imperial spirit of the times prompted some of Canada's millionaires to assist the best and the brightest in the country to pursue their studies in Britain. None was more generous than Vincent Massey, Mike's former commanding officer, who had left the university to become secretary-treasurer of the Massey-Harris company. A Balliol man, a devout anglophile, and a somewhat less devout Methodist, Massey was impressed "by [Mike's] desire to forsake the fleshpots of Chicago for the educational opportunities of Oxford". Within a few weeks, Massey was able to arrange an American University fellowship worth $1,250 per year for two years to support Mike at Oxford. Mike wired his father the good news on May 23, 1921, and Ed began to gather extra funds to help pay the ship's fare. In the fall, Mike set off for Oxford.[2]

The war haunted Oxford in the early 1920s. Oxford had lost 2,700 of its 3,000 undergraduates. Eight presidents of the Oxford Union were among the fallen, as were many of the most brilliant undergraduates, including such athlete-scholars as Noel Chavesse and the prime minister's brilliant son Raymond Asquith. An air of tragedy lurked over the school and took substance in the plaques struck to honour those who never returned. Jan Morris, in her portrait of Oxford, claims that "the real Oxford" died with those young men, but even in the 1960s she found that it was those pre-war standards which Oxford "half regretfully, half mockingly, still aspires to". That pre-war culture was only then disappearing, "like the smile of the Cheshire Cat – the substance mostly gone, the shadow now dissolving, until soon there will only be a wicker chair in an upstairs room, or 30 feet of names on a college memorial, to remind us what it is."[3] When Mike came down in October 1921 the names on the memorials were freshly cut and ghosts stalked the colleges. Max Beerbohm's wonderful Edwardian fictional creation, Zuleika Dobson, who made all the undergraduates so infatuated with her that they leapt to their deaths in the Isis when she would not return their love, now belonged to another world. The Oxford mood, however, was far from sombre, and the tone was often unbridled, especially among the large number of colonials and Americans who came there in the early 1920s.

Mike had decided to apply to St. John's College, which had been recommended to him by his army friend and fraternity brother J. Bartlet Brebner, later a distinguished historian at Columbia. Like Brebner, Mike chose the honours school in modern history, which the fourth-year man Jasper in *Brideshead Revisited* described as "a perfectly respectable school", unlike English literature, "the very worst", and modern greats, "the second worst". It is likely that Mike received advice from "Bart" Brebner similar to that which was so freely passed on by Jasper, such as "Dress as you do at a country house" and "Don't treat dons like schoolmasters; treat them as you would the vicar at home." Generations of undergraduates had received such advice.

Oxford had changed fundamentally in one respect: women could now take degrees, having gained that right in 1920. University rules rigidly controlled the opportunities for undergraduates of opposite sexes to mingle, although memoirs of the time suggest that the restrictions meant little to the resourceful and liberated Oxonian. John Betjeman, an undergraduate in the 1920s himself, claimed that "when there was little for men to put faith in, sex-talk was a bond". Mike had already gained a reputation for his popularity with women in Toronto, and such talk, albeit in a refined form, came easily to him.[4]

Mike certainly did not talk about such things in his first letter home. It is, alas, the only one that survives from his Oxford days:

Dear Mother and Father –

Well there is lots to write about. I am safely down here at last and more or less settled. I have a nice room overlooking the quad but am not alone. There is another chap with me; a boy named Chapman from Harvard who is going to study classics. He is older than I, seems very nice and is, I surmise, a sober serious student, which is just as well as I won't be tempted to waste my time. We have a sitting room between us, and each a separate bedroom.... My scout, that's Oxford for servant, is out getting the linen towels etc. and it looks as if that will cost me about five pounds while we spent another pound for prints for the walls. We also need some colored curtains and are getting two pair of pale blue for the windows. The rugs and lounge and table covers etc. are dark red so the color scheme will make the room rather pretty. One side has a fireplace, very ancient; our table, where we eat lunch & breakfast, is in the center, a big lounge and two easy chairs are in front of the fire place, a book case on one side, and a writing desk, while the other has two doors leading into our bedrooms. It's going to be fine when we are settled.

Things are naturally expensive the first term as there is so much to buy and all the college dress to pay, athletic clubs to join etc. I must have a second hand bicycle as our campus is about a mile away and everyone wheels to it. That will cost me about $30 as they are away up in price over pre-war days. But I will spend just as little as I can without failing to take my full share of college activities.

St. John[']s itself is lovely beyond description. You don't know how it delights me to be here. The buildings are very old but perfect in their architecture while the college gardens are indeed a thing of wondrous beauty. They are said to be the finest in Europe, and I can well believe it.... We are really living an aristocratic life. Your scout waits on you hand & foot. Breakfast and lunch he brings & serves to you in your own rooms from the college kitchen. Dinner you have in the college hall in cap & gown....

[He describes his week in London before he reached Oxford.] Last Friday I met Mrs. Cabell & Helen [the American family who had befriended the Pearson boys in London in wartime] in town and motored down to the country with them in their Rolls Royce. They have a marvellous place, 350 years old, full of wonderful paintings, pannelling [*sic*] and works of art, while their gardens and lawns are very lovely.

... Helen's French fiancé was over for the week end & I, of course, met him. He seems a decent enough chap, but, of course, as he speaks about as much English as I speak French it was hard to get well acquainted.

The two solitudes of French and English parted, and Mike went on to London from the country to visit relatives of Duke's wife, Connie, and other friends. London restaurants were expensive but tempting, for he arrived in Oxford unable to button his vest. In Oxford of the early 1920s such things mattered.[5]

When the self-proclaimed "aesthete" Harold Acton came to Oxford from Florence in 1922, he felt he had left "one capital of romance for another. The change of venue was the more exciting because here youth reigned instead of age."[6] Acton and his "dandies", with their outrageous dress and habits, remained distant from Mike's experience at Oxford, but the emphasis on the "new" and the "young" was a common thread of Oxford life in those days. Mike's letter to his parents seems youthful for a war veteran of twenty-four; however, by 1921, the seriousness of the war veterans who arrived in 1918 and 1919 had largely disappeared, and a celebration of youth's vitality had begun on the dance floors and playing fields, in political clubs, literary magazines, and common-rooms. Jazz blared from gramophones, cocktails flowed into the early mornings; and new, more strenuous sports appeared. Women were now around, but the ambiance remained male and, in some circles, homo-erotic. In Betjeman's memory, "life was luncheons, luncheons all the way / And evenings dining with the Georgoisie". Louis MacNeice bluntly declared that he had not gone to Oxford to study; "that was what grammar school boys did". For Mike Pearson, as for most others, study was secondary to the friendships struck, impressions made, and experiences savoured.[7]

St. John's was conservative by tradition; its most celebrated patron was Archbishop Laud, whose devotion to High Church principles had cost him his head but not his influence upon St. John's and Oxford. His ghost, St. John's men claimed, walked headless down the Library. A statue of Laud's beloved Charles I and his Queen, Henrietta Maria, looked over the colonnades at the undergraduates. In Mike's time, the college president was the Rev. Herbert Armitage James, seventy-seven years old and a former headmaster of Rugby. A student of the classics, James had published an edition of Cicero's "Oration for Plancius" fifty years earlier but nothing since then. He was not a scholar, but he was a gentleman. It was said, moreover, that his stamp collection was admired by King George. To Mike he was simply the "Bodger", "legendary, unseen", and ancient. A more distinguished scholar, one of the few among St. John's fellows, was the senior tutor John Powell, whom Mike got to know quite unexpectedly his first day at Oxford.

Upon his first arrival at the Porter's lodge, Mike, who had been fully briefed by Bart Brebner on St. John's peculiar ways, addressed the porter "with that mixture of hauteur and kindliness that was apparently appropriate". "Henry," he said, having learned the porter's name from Brebner, "I'm Pearson, from Toronto. I sent a message about my arrival. I would like to go to my rooms and have somebody bring up my bags." The rather shabbily dressed "Henry" responded in an impeccable academic accent: "Oh yes, Pearson ... we were expecting you. I'll show you to your room. However, first let me introduce myself. I'm Powell, the Senior Tutor." It became one of Powell's most cherished common-room stories.[8]

Mike's first tutor was A.L. Poole, who later became a distinguished medievalist, author of the well-known survey *From Domesday Book to Magna Carta*. Poole had served as a lieutenant in the war with the celebrated Gloucester Regiment, but Mike found his manner "cloistered" and sensed that Poole was discomfited by Mike's "rather bustling North American approach to my work". His second tutor, W.C. Costin, was also a war veteran with a distinguished record, but was not at all cloistered. He had received his first in modern history in 1920 and had stayed on at St. John's. A good athlete, splendid company, and public spirited, Costin was an excellent and tolerant tutor who became an enduring friend and, eventually, president of the college. Mike met with Costin weekly and, as they recalled it later, they would "argue a little bit, and then at the end of the argument [Costin] would give [Pearson] another subject." Costin would then say: "Now do better next week and don't spend all the intervening time playing rugger, lacrosse or some other game."[9]

In fact, Mike spent much of his time at games, as did most Oxford students. Lectures were given in the morning, but most thought the hour was too early and, more justifiably, the professors too tedious. Mike went to few lectures in his two years at Oxford. After lunch each weekday he played rugger, hockey, or, his best sport at Oxford, lacrosse, which was surprisingly popular in Britain in the early 1920s. After the evening meal at the college, the studious retreated to their rooms; others lingered in the common-rooms, or, in springtime, in the quads; the riotous went off to Oxford's many pubs and cinemas. Mike was never riotous, and he kept the Methodist abstainer's pledge even in the alcoholic haze of Oxford.[10] Nevertheless he enjoyed the unique mood of the Oxford pub and went along with his imbibing friends frequently. By the early 1920s even devout Methodists – and Mike was no longer so devout – went to the cinema. Mike's fascination with film began early and endured throughout his life. Even in wartime London, he preferred a silent Charlie Chaplin or Buster Keaton film to live theatre. Very rarely did Mike spend a night reading. Reading was for vacations, not for term.

In fact, Mike's reading reflected his changed interests. Although English literature had been his best subject during his undergraduate years, his interests had shifted towards history and what we would now call "international relations". On the ship to England Mike read Willa Cather, but by the time he reached Oxford, novels had given way to works on public affairs and to newspapers, which he followed avidly. Mike chafed at the tendency at Oxford to have history end in 1870, but Oxford in the early 1920s had enough debates and lectures about current affairs to satisfy his interests in the modern world. In the college he and some others formed the Sophists Club in which political, philosophical, and even religious issues were debated long into the night. He also became president of the Colonial Club, which brought speakers to the university. The Ralegh Club, also a speaker's club, of which Vincent Massey was a founder (omitting the "i" in Raleigh was a Massey affectation), naturally admitted Pearson, a Massey scholar and a strong Empire man, and he was even invited to join the exclusive King Charles' Club, a dining club founded by Prince Rupert three centuries before, for which Southern Ontario dinner tables had ill prepared Mike. Good drink and rich food abounded at the dinners, which ended usually with an inebriated toast paying tribute to "King Charles for his bounteous graciousness in sending Prince Rupert to dwell amongst us".[11]

The spirit (and spirits) of the King Charles' Club was much different from that of Canadian Methodism, and Mike did not report its doings to Canadian Methodists. He did, however, report many of his other activities. Prior to his departure, Mike had worked out an arrangement with Dr. W.B. Creighton, editor of *The Christian*

Guardian, whereby he would be the *Guardian's* English correspondent at a rate of $10 per story.* He filed most stories anonymously, under the by-line "A Canadian in England". Of these stories, only one – a description of Oxford that he published under his own name – appears in his papers (including his University of Toronto file). He did not retain the others in his diligently kept scrap-book or include them in his collection *Words and Occasions* or, apparently, make reference to them in writing his memoirs. This omission is significant in understanding Mike's intellectual development, a subject to which we will return after we use these articles to trace Mike's experience at Oxford.[12]

His first report was filed shortly after his arrival and was entitled "At the Heart of the Empire".[13] England had changed: "Khaki has almost disappeared from the streets", as had the "carefree, unselfish spirit of those days". After his American experience, where first names were used and intimate personal details were exchanged freely in conversation, the English seemed personally aloof. They also tended to belittle their own merits and see the world too bleakly. The crowded hotels, "the restaurants thronged with smart looking, expensively dressed people", and the "sold out" theatres and football games made London seem now, even more than in wartime, the Empire's heart, the world's capital. But there was trouble; in those first weeks before term began, Mike journeyed through industrial Lancashire, where factories and mines had closed down and workers kicked around footballs midafternoon. Mike managed to find grounds for optimism in the "cheery contentment" on the faces of these football-playing workers. "The playing fields of England," he claimed, "are just as efficacious in preventing revolutions as in winning Waterloos." Nevertheless, the unemployment situation was serious. In London he had witnessed thousands of ex-servicemen

---

* Dr. Creighton was the father of the distinguished Canadian historian Donald Creighton. I have found no evidence that Creighton was aware of this tie between Mike and his father. Creighton attended Oxford, but his father did not appoint him a correspondent.

marching and shouting, "Our babies are starving", and his sympathies were with the marchers. Still, Lloyd George's government had accepted responsibility for post-war reconstruction and was calling on all parts of the population to help in finding a solution. Most were giving it, "with the rather noteworthy exception of the Labour party who, it is suspected, are playing the game of politics.... They do not advance their cause by such tactics but rather give weight to the opinion of certain sectors in England that Labour in politics can only criticize and cannot carry responsibility." On other issues, too, Mike's sympathies rested with Lloyd George. In the case of Ireland, Mike argued that Lloyd George had been as conciliatory as possible. The radicals in Sinn Fein now had to face the modern world and escape the shackles of the past that had bound Ireland to its misery. He was optimistic about the forthcoming Washington conference of the major powers that was to set limits upon armaments.* American suspicion of British intentions was unwarranted, and Lloyd George's absence from the conference did not reflect British insincerity. Arthur Balfour, the head of the British delegation and a former prime minister, inspired confidence. The suggestions that Winston Churchill would be better suited "by temperament and heredity to work with Americans" was misplaced. Churchill's "past career" made it certain that Balfour was "the safer man". This conference, following upon the "terrible nationalism" that "gripped" the world after the Versailles conference, was of fundamental significance. In twenty-four-year-old Mike's opinion, "High minded and Christian statesmanship might conceivably make it the turning point in world history."

---

* The Washington Conference of 1921-2 dealt with the problems created by the American failure to join the League of Nations and the potential conflicts among the Japanese, British, and Americans arising from their interests in the Pacific region. A five-power naval limitation was agreed upon which did seem to offer hope that a new naval race would not begin. The conference established British-American parity in capital ships and in that respect reflected the shifting balance of international power. Sir Robert Borden served as a member of the British Empire delegation. He reported that the final agreements would be "a very notable step" towards peace in the Pacific. Within a decade, it was clear that it was a step to the side, not ahead.

Considering the serious problems Britain was facing, Mike found the "furore" over the attempt to close pubs at 10:30 p.m. untenable. His disgust was unmistakable: all the "hackneyed arguments of personal liberty are brought out and given an airing", he wrote. For a nation of Britain's grandeur and influence to waste "all its energies in a fight for an extra half hour of drink" was "not only making itself somewhat ridiculous but is also trifling with serious realities." Dr. Creighton was surely proud of his new "correspondent", and Ed and Annie must have beamed with pride in the Methodist parsonage in Guelph.[14]

A couple of weeks later Mike filed another "letter" from "the Heart of the Empire". The rain had fallen continuously for three days and a "damp chilliness" penetrated his room. He found the weather depressing and longed for the sun's rays, although one must question how warmly those rays were being felt in Toronto in November. The English took inclemency well and simply said: "Ah, but this is good old English weather." Mike thought their "cheerfulness" did not come from any "love for rain and wet" but from "the fact that we are now experiencing the usual. According to tradition this is the way the weather man should act. A change, even if for the better, is not appreciated."

The force of tradition remained strong in English life, and a new tradition had taken hold on November 11. Superficially, "the character of Armistice Day" seemed to be "deteriorating"; although dances and special programs at the cinema now marked the occasion, "underneath, the heart of the nation beats true." The following passage, one of the most reflective that Lester Pearson ever wrote, speaks to the way that the war had affected him:

One sees throughout the country, even in the smallest villages, war memorials to the fallen, usually simple, dignified columns of stone; mute testimony to the respect and reverence in which the dead are held. In villages they are usually erected on the green, the centre of the community life of England.... Henceforth those village greens will form a connecting link between that peaceful little community and the sacred soil of Flanders, the sun-kissed sands of Mesopotamia and the fatal fields of Gallipoli. The children of generations yet unborn will play around the bases of these pillars and learn with pride of the deeds of those whose names are inscribed thereon. The memorials are always kept decorated with flowers from the relations and friends of those who fell, but now as November 11 approaches, the grey of the stone is almost hidden by wreaths. Truly they are not dead whose memory is kept so green.

Now, with memories still so green, Lloyd George battled the new forces of darkness, represented, on the one hand, by the "die hard" Unionists who opposed any settlement of the Irish question, which undermined British pre-eminence, and, on the other hand, by Sinn Fein and Eamon de Valera, the Irish leader who was exhibiting an "insane lack of judgment". The darkness also hovered in the battle against the liquor trade, which even Lloyd George, the political expression of English nonconformity since his "magnificent" oratory first electrified Parliament, could not seem to win. Here, Mike reported to the Canadian Methodists, Britain lagged far behind Canada. There "all the old cries of personal liberty, so long discredited in Canada", were "shouted out ... as unanswerable argument". Canada and the United States had gone much beyond Britain's shortened pub hours and had enacted full prohibition. The effects of prohibition on North America were "hideously" distorted by the British liquor interests. This distortion was being assisted by a notable Canadian, Stephen Leacock, who had announced to the British that he was willing to speak without charge against prohibition. "Having crossed the ocean with the aforementioned gentleman," Mike sarcastically declaimed, "I am in doubt as to whether his statement was inspired by love of speaking, the desire to show his contempt for money or by a dislike of prohibition. He exhibited traces of all three characteristics on board." Editors feared libel less in those days. Besides, Leacock would never have read *The Christian Guardian*.

Leacock did not impress Mike. Dr. John Clifford, who had fought valiantly with Lloyd George for non-conformist causes such as prohibition, did. Mike heard the old non-conformist warrior give a message to "the present time". He found its words so stirring that he expressed the wish that Canadians should read the eighty-five-year-old Dr. Clifford's address in its entirety. He especially liked Dr. Clifford's ending, which pointed to the evils besetting humanity and then concluded: "There is no ground for despondency though, and every reason for faith in God and in the immeasurable value of goodness. The fires of God are cleansing the thought and the life of the world.... The teaching of Jesus is as clear as it is authoritative. The longer I live the stronger is my confidence I learnt from my mother as a lad." Mike echoed Dr. Clifford in the conclusion to his "letter": "What an inspiring message from a great and good man. If true for an individual, how much more so is it for a nation, for a world. 'Find out the right and follow it in scorn of consequences.'"[15]

Dr. Creighton's anonymous correspondent slowed his pace and lost some of his fervour in the following months. By mid-November 1921, Mike was deeply into college sports, and he had little time for his studies much less *The Christian Guardian*. For a fee of two pounds, five shillings, he had become a member of the Oxford University Lacrosse Club, which was affiliated with the South of England Lacrosse Association. Mike's physical quickness and skilful play-making soon established him as one of England's finest lacrosse players. He was the highest scorer in the South of England League in 1921-2, and led Oxford to the South of England championship in that season.[16]

Mike's successes were not restricted to the lacrosse field. He did not try out for rowing, Oxford's most celebrated sport, because, as he later said, it required daily practice and meant that there was no time for other sports. However, Mike liked variety and tried out for almost everything else.[17] As a Canadian, he had an advantage in hockey, which, like lacrosse, had an unusual popularity in Britain in the early 1920s. He joined the Oxford University Ice Hockey Club, whose captain was Canadian Kenneth E. Taylor and whose secretary, Frederick Neyland, was a graduate of St. Michael's College at the University of Toronto. In mid-November Mike was asked to try out for the Oxford team, which had been invited to tour the continent during the winter vacation. After a November 30 trial match on one of Britain's few artificial ice surfaces, in Manchester, Mike received an invitation from Taylor to join the tour of Belgium and Switzerland scheduled to leave Oxford on December 13.[18]

The team was made up of Canadians, except for one Harvard graduate. Taylor, the captain, a Rhodes scholar and a graduate of Queen's University in Canada, was the goaltender. E.G. Pitblado, scion of a distinguished Manitoba legal family; Dick Bonnycastle, a future Winnipeg mayor; and F.M. Bacon of Harvard were the forwards. G.R. McCall, formerly of McGill, and Mike were the defencemen. Neylan; J.C. Farthing, son of the Anglican bishop of Montreal; and Roland Michener, a graduate of Alberta's young university, a Rhodes scholar, and a future governor general, were the reserves. By Canadian standards (then, if not later, the highest in the world), the team was passable. On the continent, where ice hockey was as rare as games of the South Sea islands, the Oxford team was "magnificent". The tour was a striking success. It began with a 5-1 triumph over the Belgian national team, followed by a 27-0 defeat of the Cambridge University team at Mürren in the Bernese Oberland of Switzerland. (Cambridge had neither Rhodes nor Massey scholars and thus few Canadians.) Mike's stick-handling was so spectacular that the Swiss crowd dubbed him "Herr Zigzag". Oxford's *Isis* sneered that the referee had needed an adding machine and that Cambridge had forever been vanquished. Roland Michener later recalled that the Cambridge team had an English goaltender: "I remember he couldn't skate, and when he got far out of goal we always had to stop the game and get him back in again."[19] By the end of the tour, the Oxford team had won all six games and had scored eighty-seven goals; only two goals had passed Taylor's pads.

The social life on the tour was equally memorable. Christmas Day was spent at the Palais des Alpes at Mürren, and the repasts were so splendid that Mike saved the menus. One suspects that Annie's Anglo-Canadian cooking evoked no fond memories as Mike dined with his teammates on "Fruite de Rivière argentée", "Asperges de

Saxon avec Sauce Divine", and "Dinde de Noel trufée avec Marrons". A few days later the team gave what the *Isis* described as a "hilarious welcome" to the New Year, but the hilarity ended in time to trounce the Swiss national team on the soft ice at Château d'Oex, II-I.[20]

Mike reported on selected aspects of the trip to the *Guardian* (omitting the hilarious welcome to the New Year). After complaining about Switzerland's high costs, Mike admitted that he and his fellow Canadians enjoyed "hobnobbing" with the aristocratic and moneyed crowd that savoured Mürren's winter charms. "We are becoming quite adept," Mike reported, "in carrying our noses two degrees higher than our eyes, and in receiving the scrapings and bowings of uniformed flunkeys with the proper sang froid and haughtiness." The Swiss scenery brought forth effusive praise. Although Mike did not describe his Christmas feast or the cosmopolitan ambiance of the Palais des Alpes, he did report how snow fell on Christmas eve upon the evergreens, "which clung everywhere to the hillsides". "The sun shone brilliantly, the air was crisp and cold, below us in the valley we could see clouds drifting along." The sensation was of a world apart. Christmas Day service was memorable. There, "in a small chapel of rough hewn timber ... the old familiar hymns were sung" and the Christmas story was once again retold. "Glory to God in the Highest" had a new meaning that morning, "high among the Alps". Only a gentle breeze that "curled the loose snow into tiny swirling eddies" disturbed the morning's calm. "The spirit of goodwill must surely have been in everyone's heart that morning" and, Mike might have added, in everyone's stomach as well. It was indeed a grand tour.[21]

Mike had barely returned to Britain's damp climes when he received a note from H.O. Hopkins, an Australian who captained Oxford's lacrosse team. "Dear Pearson," Hopkins wrote in venerable Oxbridge style, "you have been selected to tour the U.S. universities with the Oxford and Cambridge lacrosse team." The team would leave on March 17 and return on May 7. A definite reply was requested by return mail. Mike did not hesitate, for a trip to North

America was deeply desired. Costin was an understanding tutor and, on St. Patrick's Day, Mike and the Oxford lacrosse team embarked for America.[22]

In the early 1920s American universities and their students were entranced with the traditions and style of Oxbridge. In 1922, a team of Oxford Union debaters toured America for the first time. In Martin Green's words, they "dazzled" American collegians with their "much more spontaneous, impudent, paradoxical, ingenious, and charming" style. America became, for the Union men, "that audience of bigger, stronger, slower cousins before whom Englishmen paraded and peacocked."[23] For the debating team, quickness and impudence were sufficient to carry the day; however, for the lacrosse team, the American cousins' size and strength presented problems. In fact, the visit was slightly absurd, as was often the tone of collegian life in the 1920s. The "Oxford-Cambridge" team was made up mostly of Canadians. While better teams could be found everywhere in North America, the Oxbridge patina was enough to ensure that the stadiums would fill. As always, appeals to American pride brought in profits to the promoters. "Old John Bull Gets Whacked", *The Baltimore Sun* reported as the Oxbridge team fell 11-2 to Johns Hopkins. The mayor tossed out the ball before a crowd of five thousand, and the Hopkins band played "God Save the King" as the British fell. Lloyd George, they said, wept. The agent, who guaranteed team expenses in exchange for all the profits, certainly didn't. Nor did the players, even though they lost more often than they won, and the larger, rougher Americans left their bruises, including quite a few on Mike.

The team participated whole-heartedly in the absurdity. The sole American on the team, Frank Morley, affected an impeccable Oxford accent acquired in less than two years on the banks of the Isis. The team whetted the American taste for title by granting V.C. Wansbrough, a London commoner, a baronetcy. The sports pages were filled with photographs of "Lord Wansbrough" playing lacrosse and granting interviews explaining how he had learned the game at his country home. The agent distributed a photograph of Mike, lacrosse stick aloft, charging forward, threatening all things human with a hard rubber ball. Mike's military record became a heroic four years as a lieutenant in the Royal Flying Corps. No mention was ever made of sausage-stuffing or fertilizer. Interviews became ever more outrageous. When team captain Hopkins was asked what he noticed first in America, he said "the lack of highballs" and "the very high skirts". The former, the Australian impudently stated, "must prove terrifically annoying." "But the high skirts," he added with a blush, "rather take one's mind off the highballs, what?" When asked how "Duke" Wansbrough (he had been elevated in the peerage) should be addressed, Hopkins replied: "Just go up and say, 'Your Dukes' it's a fine day or something like that." He did say, most truthfully, that the team was "having the time of [their] lives".[24]

For many of the players, those lives had not always been easy. Many had been in the war. Neylan, the manager, had been wounded and gassed in France and Belgium. Sherwood Lett, who played goal exceptionally well, had served with distinction in Flanders trenches. The players' sense of fun, and Mike's, came from an understanding of what they had escaped. The banter and bonhomie that became so much a part of Mike Pearson's style was picked up on the playing fields and in the dining-halls of those days. Being in North America, Mike wanted to see his family, and Ed joined the tour for its last games. "Lord" Wansbrough recalls that Ed's clerical collar was overlooked as his sporting enthusiasms and geniality made him good company. Mike was thrilled to see his father once again.[25]

Mike returned to Oxford in early May. He promised Costin that he would pay more attention to his studies, but did insist upon being permitted to return to Switzerland on winter vacation. The team from the previous year reassembled, with the exception of Neylan, who was replaced by E.A. Nanton from Winnipeg, and Mike starred in the games played on outdoor rinks before the untitled aristocracy of the Swiss Alps. According to numerous witnesses, his exploits in that winter of 1922-3 were as memorable off the ice as on. At Davos's Grand Hotel et Belvedere, Mike danced with Gladys Cooper, one of the great actresses and beauties of the age, who had quickened the pulse of kings and princes for a generation, and persuaded her and her friend to accompany him and Edward Nanton at dinner. There, over samples of the fine cuisine he had developed a taste for, Mike tried to charm Miss Cooper. His heart surely stopped when she accepted his proposal that he take her back down to the chalet. As the luge sped down, Mike told her how he had gazed at her picture every night in the trenches in France. The luge stopped; Miss Cooper rose; Mike waited. "Mr. Pearson," she said, "every soldier did." And she walked into the night. Mike saved the menu and the ticket to the dance.[26]

When Dick Bonnycastle returned to Oxford, he told fellow Manitoban King Gordon about Mike's exploits. Mike's athletic skills, easy ways, growing sense of frivolity, and popularity with both sexes won him respect and friendship. His classmates' image of him was not much different from that of his first tutor, although they did not disapprove, as Poole had, of the "bustling North American" who voraciously consumed the experiences of Oxford.[27] Studies mattered, but they formed only a part of what the university could offer. In the summer of 1922, after one year at Oxford, Mike assessed the experience for *The Christian Guardian* in an article entitled "Oxford – Ancient, Yet Modern". The perspective is romantic; industrial Oxford's smoke-stacks and the monotony of the row housing of the new suburbs are ignored. Instead, Mike's eye focused on "the sleepy college town, its ivied college walls, its towers and turrets, its spires and minarets, revealed against a forest background". He pointedly overlooked what he much later and truthfully described as its medieval heating and plumbing, and guided his readers to the exquisite gardens and splendid porticos of the colleges.

Mike mocked the American tourists out on the 10:45 train from Paddington station who doubted that such venerable dignity could produce "results" that matched those of the American technical university. Beneath the crests of tradition, Mike countered, Oxford's "classic halls ... send forth [men] well equipped to govern the Empire – aye, the World". There was much truth in Stephen Leacock's jest that the essence of an Oxford education was to visit your tutor once or twice and be smoked at, but that jest wrongly narrowed the Oxford experience. Oxford, unlike "American" educational institutions, did not emphasize the material world, did not "aim to make a man a good business man, a good journalist, a good teacher rather than an educated scholar". While Oxford probably did not place enough emphasis on the practical and the quotidian, "in a world that had largely forsaken the finer and more intangible things of life, it is well to have places where the training of the mind, the developing of the power to think rightly and clearly, is still the chief aim of instruction". Against the claims of modern science and materialism (Mike appears to have thought them equivalent), Oxford held dearly the traditions of the classics, philosophy, history, and politics. The tolerance of Oxford, where the Union elected a Labour man and an American as president in successive years, maintained standards for a modern age. In the "rapid, swirling stream of modern life" Oxford, like her oarsmen, kept pace with the modern world and kept faith with the past. Such was her charm, and all who knew her well succumbed to it.[28]

Just after completing this article Mike spent two months at another great European university, Heidelberg. Roly Michener, Dick Bonnycastle, and Mike decided to spend their two months of summer vacation taking advantage of the low prices in Germany and learning the language. The gaiety depicted in *The Student Prince* had vanished from Heidelberg's halls as relentless post-war inflation destroyed homes and hopes and the Occupation continued. A full meal with a bottle of *Sekt* cost less than a shilling. Mike did not take to the country or its people, although he did manage to survive on only ten pounds sterling for the entire German stay. In his report to *The Christian Guardian* Mike told how one "fat burgher" mistook him for a German and unfavourably compared the British changing of the guard with the German spectacle of the goose-step. The British were tolerated; the French were hated. Germany's schoolchildren were taught that hatred, while old men, such as Ludendorff and Hindenberg, dreamed of "the time when they will be able to send forth other millions of young Germans to a glorious war of revenge". Mike despaired: "Why is it impossible to tear out the spirit of international hate from the minds of millions of human beings who boast of their modern civilization, and who glory in being followers of Him who said 'Peace on earth, good will toward men'?"

As he wrote these lines, Mike heard a "great tumult" in the street below. "Down the road come eight or ten youngsters in strict military formation complete with wooden swords and paper hats. They goosestepped with Prussian precision to a relentless drum." Mike prepared to confront these young warriors with a massive quantity of chocolates he had bought for a pfennig. The gesture was, he wrote, "the cheapest as well as the most efficacious method of preventing international complications". It worked against toy swords; he knew it would fail against tanks and aeroplanes.[29]

Vacations were for study at Oxford, and Mike had much of it to do. In his second year, he remained active in intercollege sports and even joined the Archery Club, which represented the finest expression of St. John's elegant athleticism. Each Thursday of the summer term, the élite Archery Club members donned white flannels, green blazers "adorned with a crest of crossed arrows", and straw hats, and "after a recherché luncheon, of which the most prominent item was a strong sweet punch", they would repair to the garden, officially known as "The Groves", and loose their arrows at the targets. As V.C. Wansbrough recalls those languid hours, the archers "may not have been as proficient as the bowmen at the Battle of Agincourt, but we hit the mark surprisingly often, given the circumstances." Mike also played rugby for the Oxford Rugby Club, a rare accomplishment for a Canadian. At St. John's "The Sophists" gathered for weekly debates on such subjects as "That the principle of nationalisation is out of date, that religion is purely sentimental, and that this House would welcome the introduction of birth control". Once they debated the need for capital punishment in Mike's rooms. We do not know what point of view Mike took on these issues, but we do know that the club was restricted to only one-tenth of St. John's students (thirty) and that admission was subject to "blackball". Mike, clearly, was of the élite of St. John's. One of the Sophists was Robert Graves's brother John, who had rooms opposite Mike's. One day Robert arrived and was reintroduced to his former cadet. The next Sunday Mike and John cycled out to Robert's home at Islip where they had "an excellent lunch", which they "washed down with good cider".[30]

Mike's interests, unlike those of the Graveses, tended more and more in the direction of politics, as his friendships off the playing field indicate. Mike had probably seen Harold Acton, his grey bowler, side-whiskers, and long black coat, prancing along High Street or shouting out poetry from Christ Church's tower. He also likely read Evelyn Waugh's delicious comments on Oxford Union debates in the *Isis* ("Mr. S.F. Villiers-Smith made the sort of speech which one associates with aged colonels"; "Mr. Nobbs actually used the expression 'made the Empire what it is'"; and "I detest all that Mr. A. Gordon Bagnall says always"). Bagnall was a Sophist, and Mike shared the wound. The Waughs and Actons established a tone that affected all undergraduates, but their circle was small. Freud attracted Waugh's "set"; Lloyd George captivated Mike's. They danced to jazz; Mike's dance cards list the waltz, the fox trot, and the one-step.

At the Ralegh Club, where Waugh would not have been caught dead, Mike heard the imperialist Lionel Curtis speak on Ireland, Sir Benjamin Robertson on the Russian famine, Dr. Wilfred Grenfell on Labrador, and other imperial worthies on worthy imperial subjects. The Colonial Club was more social. In 1923, Mike presided over the club's seventy-ninth meeting, held at the Cadena Café. The program called upon Mike as president to welcome the guests in no more than five thousand words. One hopes he used fewer. H.L. Brose of Christ Church gave a "clever representation" of a pianist. Mr. Coates of Queen's "and three other cotton merchants" used their vocal cords "to some effect". Those who survived were then "able to amuse the ladies by themselves". The meeting ended with "truite à la Norwegienne", followed by "Caneton Rôti". The appetizer – "Coupe Baldwin" – perhaps reflected the politics of most club members. Stanley Baldwin had become Conservative leader in 1923 and the party began to establish the hegemony over British politics that it maintained until 1945.[31] Baldwin's Britain was not Lloyd George's Britain, nor was it Mike Pearson's.

In his biography of the American author and journalist Walter Lippmann, Ronald Steel describes how Lippmann heard Teddy Roosevelt, freshly returned from the Battle of San Juan Hill, and immediately developed an enduring admiration for the asthmatic, astigmatic hero-genius. Roosevelt became, Lippmann later wrote, "the image of a great leader and the prototype of Presidents". Roosevelt's effect on Lippmann led him to be "less than just to his successors because they were not like him". It was not Roosevelt's daring alone that intrigued Lippmann but rather his ability to "express the inarticulate needs of [his] people" and "help them subdue unnameable fears and paralyzing doubts."[32] Mike's reaction to Lloyd George was very much the same. Never again did Mike respond to politicians as he did to Lloyd George, not even to Churchill in the years of the blitz, certainly not to Mackenzie King. In his *Christian Guardian* articles, Mike portrayed Lloyd George as a giant among pygmies. His oratory was "characteristically brilliant"; criticisms of him were "harassment". In the many troubles of 1922, he was "the only man capable of dealing with these problems." The "little Welshman's position" (Roosevelt was small too) was "as sound as ever and his long ascendancy in the most difficult period, in many respects, of British history, remains a source of wondering admiration to his friends and admirers, and of chagrin to his enemies." Whatever the Welsh wizard's wand touched seemed destined to succeed. In one of the falsest prophecies ever, Mike predicted that, after the Irish settlement of 1922, Michael Collins, the former Sinn Fein leader, would become "the *Conservative* head of a united Ireland and the staunch supporter of a British community of nations".[33] An assassin murdered Collins eight months later; the despised De Valera became president ten years later. Mike still could not imagine the sun setting on any of the Empire's outposts.

The Christian Guardian articles, perhaps because they offered anonymity, more likely because of Mike's youth and distance from home, allow us to penetrate the reserve that grew to obscure his thoughts and feelings in later days. They bear out Mike's later statements that he matured intellectually at Oxford and that he went up to Oxford in 1921 with a "wide enough range of experience, to savour to the full the incomparable charm and stimulus of life at Oxford".[34] He "savoured" Oxford and England, and his tastes became more defined there. Lloyd George is but one example of his growing confidence in his own opinions about politics and life, and the well-spring of Mike's admiration for this brilliant politician with such abundant human frailties can be identified.

Lloyd George was a reminder of the war and, in particular, the victory. Entering the prime minister's office in the darkest hour, throwing off the feckless gentility of Asquith, Lloyd George restored the flagging spirits of the Tommies and summoned up the greatness of the British people. He established mastery over drift, to use a Lippmann phrase of the time, by skilled management and personal brilliance. Mike never doubted the validity of the British cause in wartime, and his respect for Lloyd George in 1921-2 indicates his rejection of Keynes's attack on the Allied peace-makers and of the "revisionism" that sought to distribute "blame" for the First World War. Indeed, he explicitly rejected Keynes's arguments in one *Guardian* article. Mike did agree with Keynes that Lloyd George was the "extraordinary figure of our time", a siren, a "goat footed bard", and a "half human visitor to our age", but, unlike Keynes, Mike found Lloyd George rooted in something and a leader of substance.*

Those roots and that content derived from Mike's own. Mike's response to Germany reflects his continuing belief, as expressed in his article on Heidelberg, that the war had been fought between British liberty and democracy, on the one hand, and German militarism and

---

* In his memorably vitriolic sketch of Lloyd George in his *Essays in Biography,* which was written in 1919 but published in 1933, Keynes wrote: "Lloyd George is rooted in nothing; he is void and without content; he lives and feeds on his immediate surroundings; he is an instrument and a player at the same time which plays on the company and is played on by them too; he is a prism ... which collects light and distorts it and is most brilliant if the light comes from many quarters at once; a vampire and a medium in one".

authoritarian tendencies, on the other. The former impressed him more deeply each passing month at Oxford. It expressed itself in the British people's refusal to be defeated or become flustered. It impressed Mike that "Drake bowled while the Armada approached".[35] This equanimity was characteristic of the lineage that passed from Agincourt through the Armada and Waterloo to the triumphant hundred days of 1918 when Lloyd George's Britain triumphed so decisively. Those were Mike's roots. He had felt them in Chicago; they were nurtured at Oxford.

Mike, then, naturally shared Lloyd George's affection and respect for the Empire. In 1917, Lloyd George had summoned the dominion prime ministers to Britain to strike down the overreaching generals and to bring the voice of the full Empire into the councils that managed the war. Mike admired Lloyd George because his imperialism bore little of the overweening arrogance of the British Tories whom he identified with the "brass" of the First World War who, thoughtlessly and even heartlessly, had run the war until Lloyd George put them in their proper place. Mike's imperialism derived from a liberal belief in the beneficence and generosity of British rule. The horrors of Amritsar in 1919 were not part of this tradition nor were the Black and Tans who brutally beat up Irishmen in 1920. They were Tory remnants in an increasingly democratic Empire. In predicting that the rebel Michael Collins would have a conservative future, Mike was expressing the liberal belief that "responsibility" for the Empire's fractious parts would come with time and education and would strengthen its bonds. Mike's imperialism flowed from the tradition of Gladstone where rule meant responsibility, care for the downtrodden, and, when necessary, moral outrage. It was the imperialism of David Livingstone, not of Cecil Rhodes; of the Methodist chapel, not of St. Paul's Cathedral; of Lloyd George, not of Colonel Blimp. Mike contrasted Lloyd George's willingness to use the newly created "international assemblies" to settle disputes with the Tories, who feared any interference with British sovereignty, and with the French, who, in Mike's view, looked fondly back "to the old days of secret diplomacy, of military alliances and of the German menace".

As Lloyd George bluntly told the Tories: "Better a thousand experts around a conference table now than a million experts in the trenches a year from now."[36] Mike in 1922 was already a strong League of Nations supporter and the seeds of his internationalist vision germinated in the rich soil of liberal imperialism.

Mike's liberal imperialism and his anglophilia spring from his Southern Ontario Methodist past and flow directly to his later internationalist vision. The Christian faith expressed in his articles, however, was near exhaustion. Sometime in the early 1920s, most likely at Oxford, perhaps on his return to Canada, Mike Pearson moved away from his Methodist and Christian commitment. How strong and how intimately bound with his patriotism it had earlier seemed. Writing home from Salonika in September 1916, he told of the service he attended at an American agricultural mission run by Dr. and Mrs. House, who had served in that rough countryside for forty-four years. He left with a heart "full of admiration for men and women like these who will spend half a century in a district like this purely for the sake of helping their fellows to obtain that greatest of all gifts, the knowledge and love of God, and its results, viz happiness enlightenment and prosperity." "Such heroes" as Dr. House and his helpers "do more than a thousand soldiers for the good of a country." This letter, the most explicitly Christian of his wartime letters, was not returned in his papers.[37] The war weakened his and many others' conviction that Christian belief invariably produced happiness and prosperity. It did not, however, dissolve his Christian faith.

The Christian Guardian articles that have a strong religious tone are not to be found in his papers. The religious content of these articles is striking because it is so absent in his later writings. The last article with strongly religious content appeared in late February 1922. In it Mike complained about an Anglican controversy concerning the nature of belief: "the whole of the controversy seems ... to have degenerated into hair-splitting. It brings to mind the wise saying of ... Marcus Aurelius: 'Our anger and impatience often prove more mischievous than the things we are angry and impatient over.'"[38] Mike, one suspects, had become weary too of the controversy that marked Canadian Methodism in the early 1920s as it moved towards church union. He deeply welcomed union because his own spirit was ecumenist, but by now the secular world was overshadowing the spiritual one for him.

And he had become secular. The dinner with Gladys Cooper at Davos; the rollicking nights at the King Charles' Club; the modern music and thought that penetrated even casual chats at the "Mitre"; and, not least, the doubts about what peace had achieved all tested the foundation of faith for Mike and many like him. One of the most serious students of faith in the 1920s, the American Allyn Foster, concluded at the end of the decade that "To be modern in thought and religious in spirit is a rare combination."[39] At Oxford Mike certainly became "modern", a direction he had been heading since his college days.

Mike did not reject God, as did his close friend and colleague Norman Robertson, who, it is said, desperately tried to convince the census-taker to list him as an atheist. Mike simply stopped going to church. In 1923 he was twenty-six, and his faith had become his own. He had left his father's home spiritually, but traces of his upbringing endured in his actions and, surely, his thoughts. When asked to speak about religious matters he was oblique or took refuge in humour. When he wrote his memoirs he treated his parents' faith less fully and seriously than its influence upon his life merited. He did not stride away from the church; he quietly closed the door, for John Wesley's stirring call to commit "all thy griefs and ways" to Christ no longer evoked a response in him. Perhaps two lines of Wallace Stevens's 1923 poem "Sunday Morning" caught Mike's mood in that year much better than the words in the Methodist hymns: "Complacencies of the peignoir, and late / Coffee and oranges in a sunny chair." The ghosts of Sundays past must have been there for Mike, as they are for all who leave their father's faith, but after 1923, coffee, oranges, and *The Sunday Times* were his normal Sunday concerns.[40]

CHAPTER FIVE

MARYON

The boys arrived Saturday after a rough and unpressured flight from Ottawa – just as well you didn't take it – even though it would be so much nicer if you were with me. It would – really – you know. Heaps of love dearest.

– Mike (Paris 1956)[1]

Someone should design a poster depicting Maryon Pearson as an early hero of the feminist resistance, an *agent provocateur* wearing a single strand of pearls, determined to undermine and expose the hypocrisy of Canadian public life.

– Susan Riley[2]

MIKE PEARSON'S rich social and athletic life had slowed his Oxford studies, making a third year (three years was the normal length of an Oxford B.A.) seem the most sensible course. His two-year fellowship was not a problem; the ever-generous Massey Foundation would surely extend it. Besides, Costin, Mike's tutor, had warned him that he was unlikely to receive a "first" if he took his "schools" (Oxford, for final examinations) at the end of his second year. However, Mike had been approached by Professor G.M. Wrong, the head of the history department at the University of Toronto, with the offer of a position for him at Toronto in September 1923 if he got a "first". Since his ultimate goal in studying at Oxford was an academic posting at the University of Toronto, and since he owed a substantial debt, financial and otherwise, to Ed and Annie, Mike could not refuse Wrong's offer.[3]

The "schools" loomed all the more menacingly, in light of Wrong's required "first". The written examinations, conducted "morning and afternoon, day after day", were followed by an oral examination. In Mike's view, one shared by most others, the "schools" were "not a valid test of educational progress and achievement". Like most other students, Mike "crammed", but there was too much to cover and too little time in which to do so. The treasured "first" eluded him, as it did virtually all Canadian students in those days at Oxford. His examiners were a distinguished group, including A.L. Poole, his erstwhile tutor, and Mike did well to get a high second, which Wrong decided was no disgrace. Mike quickly accepted Wrong's renewed offer.

It is not surprising that Mike had attracted George Wrong's attention. Wrong was a close friend of Vincent Massey, Mike's financial mentor. Moreover, Wrong's ideas and attitudes, as described by Massey's biographer Claude Bissell, mirrored Mike's own: "the scholarly generalist who wanted to play a part in the events of his time; the Canadian proud of his native inheritance, yet glorying in the Empire and at home in the imperial centre; the Christian moralist who was not bound by puritan legalities".[4] Any reader of *The Christian Guardian* would have attributed those views to its anonymous English correspondent. At Oxford, Mike's presidency of the Colonial Club, vice-presidency of the King Charles' Club, and two half-blues for lacrosse and hockey indicated that the young Oxonian possessed those values and skills that made for a splendid colleague, a citizen, and, as Professor Wrong said, with male condescension, a gentleman. Oxford, after all, bred gentlemen, and Professor Wrong's department preferred them to the cloistered researchers allegedly required in the American universities. Mike's article on Oxford had extolled that venerable institution's refusal to take on "the purely material standpoint of learning something in order to be more prosperous in life than your fellow." For Mike, the university represented tradition and the "finer and more intangible things in life". The professor, in Wrong's and Pearson's view, spoke for the highest values in a society, and his influence upon individuals within it endured while material influences evanesced.[5]

By the time George Wrong and Mike met in Oxford at the Ralegh Club annual dinner on June 2, 1923, Wrong had probably read Mike's article on Oxford. (In his University of Toronto personnel file, it is the sole representative of his pre-1924 writings.) Only fifty-eight persons had attended that dinner, but a glance at their names is suggestive of what Oxford meant to Mike, then and later. As a result of efforts of such Canadians as Massey and Wrong, Oxford in the 'teens and early 'twenties was a training ground for a future English-Canadian élite. Lionel Curtis and Vincent Massey, the co-founders of the Ralegh Club, had a vision of an imperial commonwealth whose statesmen paraded the mantle of humanitarian service and British liberty throughout the far-flung Empire. In the post-war period, this vision was less striking, blurred by colonial nationalists and British economic decline, but the table guests that June evening who toasted "The King", "The Empire of the Bretaignes", "The Dependencies", "India", and "The Club" could not have dreamed what the future held for their beloved Empire. Mike sat beside Sir Henry Lambert, commissioner of the Crown colonies, and Lionel Hichens, a prominent British public servant, one of Lord Milner's fabled "Kindergarten" for future imperial administrators. Across from him was Sir George Guggisberg, the governor of the Gold Coast. The head table included Major-General Lord Loch; Sir James Allen, New Zealand's high commissioner in London; and the Rt. Hon. Leo Amery, the first lord of the admiralty. Also among the fifty-eight were several men whose illustrious careers would intersect with Mike's over the next five decades: Graham Spry, a life-long friend and a leader in the creation of the Canadian Broadcasting Corporation and the Co-operative Commonwealth Federation; Sir John Shuckburgh, whose son Evelyn, a British diplomat, worked closely with Mike when Mike was Canada's secretary of state for External Affairs in the 1950s; Gladwyn Jebb, one of Britain's greatest diplomatists in the post-Second World War period, who lobbied, from his own august position, to have Mike made secretary general of the new United Nations in the mid-1940s; and Harold Macmillan, who, as

Britain's prime minister in the late 1950s and early 1960s, responded to those "winds of change" that were sweeping away the remnants of the dream that brought those British subjects together in the late spring of 1923.

There were, naturally, Australians and New Zealanders who later became prominent in their homelands. The cosmopolitan character of the Oxford student body was the university's most attractive quality. Students within each college not only came from many continents but also reflected a wide variety of interests. Glancing through the St. John's biographical register, which follows each class member through his career, one can see how diverse and stimulating Mike's classmates were. One became a tea merchant, another a senior UNESCO civil servant, another a major in Australian Army intelligence; one taught English in Barcelona, another became an Indian politician, another became Archbishop of Wales, and yet another would be a supreme-court judge in Nigeria. There were numerous future barristers, headmasters, and clerics, and they often wandered through Malaya, Rhodesia, or Barbados during their long careers. In tracing the decline of British power in the twentieth century, political scientist David Calleo has suggested that one of the causes may have been the educated classes' strong tendency to look beyond Britain's borders and to think "internationally". That these classes did so is indisputable and that doing so weakened Britain's domestic fibre is perhaps true. Mike, however, found the British "international mind" akin to his own, and its character, one of the most attractive qualities of Britain, its schools, and its people.[6]

Leaving Britain in the summer of 1923, Mike surely must have thought about the contrast between Oxford and the University of Toronto. His Canadian roots remained strong; the history department at Toronto was familiar and comfortable, and its ties with Oxford were close. Collegiate sports retained great allure for Mike, and his reputation as a team captain marked him as a potentially good coach. Moreover, Toronto paid him a salary of $2,000 a year, roughly $800 more than the average Canadian worker's wage in 1923. He also received a "free and comfortable" apartment at Middle

House in Burwash Hall as a reward for his duties as a don at Victoria. The department of history in those days emphasized teaching rather than research, and, as Wrong's tenure as department head ended and Chester Martin's began, Wrong's legacy remained in the continued reluctance to embrace the so-called scientific history that was becoming increasingly fashionable among American historians. Martin, like Wrong, was deeply committed to the British tie, but in the early 1920s both were a part of an active debate about how Canada should set about to claim an equal place in the post-war empire. Defining a nation was an exciting task, and the Toronto historians were to play a major part in refining that definition. Mike returned to Toronto bearing opinions that were a curious blend of Canadian nationalism, traditional British imperialism, and nascent internationalism. The Toronto debate would add spice to that blend, remove some of its impurities, and make it more palatable to the Canadian taste.[7]

Mike returned to Canada with the Oxford-Cambridge lacrosse team, scheduled to play a series of games against Canadian teams. An injury pre-empted Mike's triumphant return to Varsity Stadium, but it did not prevent him from joining the revelries that followed the games. In the game at Oshawa, Prime Minister Mackenzie King "threw out" the ball, which Mike retrieved. At Orillia, Stephen Leacock hosted a dance for the team at his Brewery Bay home, which ended with a mad boat ride across the lake with an inebriated Leacock as captain. When the tour ended, Mike travelled to Walkerville, near Windsor, where his father had accepted a call from the Lincoln Road Methodist Church. He no longer needed a summer job and devoted himself to sports that summer. He played in a late-summer tennis tournament, which he won, and formal confirmation of his appointment arrived in September just before his teaching duties were to commence. He had already begun practising with the Varsity "Old Boys" for a football game against the current Varsity team. On September 26, at 10:00 a.m., he gave his first lecture, to a class in English constitutional history since 1603, in Room 4 of Baldwin House.[8]

One of Mike's tutorial students for that course was a youthful, vivacious Winnipegger named Maryon Moody who had come to Victoria College in 1920. Her father was Dr. Arthur William Moody, the chief medical officer of the Manitoba division of the Canadian Pacific Railway. Dr. Moody, who was born in Britain but raised in Hamilton, Ontario, journeyed to Western Canada in 1882, an eighteen-year-old school teacher. He served two rural school districts before deciding to study medicine, which he did with distinction at the Manitoba Medical College. Soon after, he became superintendent of the Winnipeg General Hospital and married Elizabeth Jane Holland, the nursing superintendent, in 1899 in Cornwall, England, where she had grown up. They had two daughters, Grace, then Maryon, and a son, Herbert. The family was prosperous, Methodist, and devoutly Conservative.

The home was strict, and Mrs. Moody was the dominant presence. Maryon was closer to her brother than to her older sister, Grace, who was "the ringleader in ... childhood scrapes". Herbert recalls that Maryon "always had lots of friends as well as a few not-friends". At an early age she developed a reputation for strong opinions. In Herbert Moody's view, Maryon "was more self-centred than Grace and demanded her own way when she could possibly get it, – (which under our parental care she did NOT always get.)" She seemed to be the favourite of her father "whom she knew how to wheedle when necessary". However, her mother was not so pliable, and it was she who sent Maryon east for university.[9]

Maryon, twenty-two in 1923, was in her last year at university when she enrolled in Mike's history course; Mike, twenty-six, was in his first year of teaching. Maryon, who knew Vaughan Pearson, had heard of Mike before classes began from musician Hugh Ross, who, like Mike, had just returned from Oxford. Nevertheless, she first met him – "Leslie" Pearson, as she reported to a friend – in the history tutorial. She (also inaccurately) reported to another of her numerous male admirers that Mike had just returned from spending three years at Oxford on a Rhodes scholarship.

Maryon Moody entered university just after the triumph of female suffrage, but in the early 1920s, for women students, it seemed that the new day had not progressed much beyond dawn. There were, in Canadian historian Veronica Strong-Boag's words, "an intrepid few" who ventured into the traditionally male professions, but "never more than a meagre, if resourceful, handful". At university, men and women worked and played more closely together than elsewhere as barriers of chaperonage, political restrictions, and traditional formality broke down in the aftermath of war. Heterosexual friendships flourished as never before on campus, and equality in the classroom and egalitarian marriages were much talked about. So, too, was sex. Two of Maryon's Victoria College acquaintances and friends of the Pearson family, Jim Endicott and Mary Austin, aspired to an egalitarian marriage based upon economic and political interdependence. They also sought out and, more importantly, found advice on sex practices and problems. If "sex talk" was a bond among men at Oxford in the 1920s, it was at Toronto, too. The coeducational atmosphere of Toronto may have given that talk a different flavour, but the fascination with sex in the Freudian dawn was equally great. Modern "advice" mingled with and undermined traditional attitudes. Maryon's thoughts in her last years of university focused upon the tension arising, on the one hand, from the excitement created by intellectual and social activities and, on the other, from the knowledge that marriage would be and, in most eyes, should be the lot of the female undergraduate. As the (male) president of the notable women's college Smith said, the "outstanding problem confronting women [in the 1920s] is how to reconcile a normal life of marriage and motherhood with intellectual activity such as her college education had fitted her."[10] The same problem confronted Toronto's women graduates.

Maryon chronicled her feelings and hopes in her letters to an idealistic and romantic male friend who had left Toronto to teach in a Christian school in Smyrna, Turkey. The friend, Kenneth Kirkwood, had met her through the Student Christian Movement (SCM) that had flourished at Victoria, and the relationship ripened on a trip to England in the summer of 1922 for an SCM conference. The SCM was liberal, even radical, in its theology and its political activism, and both Maryon and "Ken" gave it many hours and formed many opinions in SCM debates. Maryon also acted as de-facto treasurer for the SCM publication *Canadian Student*; did some volunteer work for *Canadian Forum,* Canada's major journal of the intellectual left;* and organized campaigns for European relief, then the major "cause" on campus.

But if their activities were on the cutting edge of 1920s liberal modernism, their letters – especially Maryon's – were more Henry James than James Joyce, more Daisy Miller than Molly Bloom. In 1922-3 Maryon wrote regularly and fondly to Ken, and the first extant letter she sent captures the flavour of their relationship well: "Letters *are* the nicest thing in the world aren't they? – except maybe *fires* and *talking* – because *letters* mean *friends* – and there you are – I always feel sort of inspired – after getting one of your letters – much more so than when I read the Bible – sort of eager to go and do something decent and worthwhile to make me worthy of a friend like you or – your opinion of me – because I'm *not* – you know, Ken – not a bit but please keep on thinking I am because maybe I will be someday – *maybe.*" Her "ideal of friendship" had been "nearly destroyed" by "Art", a friend of Ken's whom she had dated, but Ken had restored her faith in that "cherished" ideal.

She missed Ken and had fallen behind in every subject as she went to an endless round of "meetings, or groups, or forums, or dances, or teas etc. etc." College days should bring more, the "chance to learn ... to assimilate knowledge of the world – of life". She knew she was failing in matters of faith: "To know Christ means to study his life – to study means *time* – much time – and that is where I feel hopeless. That's what being a Christian involves doesn't it Ken? – studying & *knowing* Christ – believing in him above everything else – making for his Kingdom – and loving other people – really caring about them

---

* A group of faculty and undergraduates founded the *Forum* in 1920. It was an offshoot of another Toronto periodical, *The Rebel*. Its "credo" was "rebellion against convention, not against society". Barker Fairley, a scholar of German literature, was literary editor and C.B. Sissons of Victoria was political editor. The Group of Seven appeared regularly in its early pages as did the labour MP J.S. Woodsworth.

enough to want to know them?" For Maryon and many other Methodists then, faith meant a life in imitation of Jesus, a faith of this world to be worked out in everyday life. Such a faith may be the foundation of a later secularism, as Ramsay Cook has so cogently argued, but that argument does not deny the strength of this "everyday" faith in Maryon's mind in 1922.[11]

At Varsity, Ken had been Maryon's mentor as well as the admirer of the striking, hazel-eyed westerner. She voraciously read works he recommended, especially the classics, and reported to him her reactions. Her opinions on books and cultural affairs were sharp. Paderewski was "a wizard on the keys but strangely lacking in soul." In a perceptive comment on the "stomping and howling" of the Toronto crowd at a Paderewski concert, Maryon suggested that their boisterous pleasure derived from their "amazed admiration of his miraculous skill". Skill without soul, however, brought only limited pleasure to the young Toronto coed.

After classes had ended in June 1923, Maryon wrote to Ken from Winnipeg to tell him of a dream she had had about him the previous night. He still seemed to be with her throughout the next day. She asked: "Isn't that funny – I have never done it before and yesterday I wasn't thinking about you very much ... but last night you came and we talked and had a picnic somewhere – and it was summer ... because you had on white flannels and a jersey! Can you explain this strange phenomena [sic] or shall we go to Mr. Froide [sic]...." "Art" had telegraphed that she had received a "B" average, which, in light of her social and other activities, was a decent standing and what she deserved. More important to her was Ken's impending return in August. In the meantime she hoped to get a summer job at a Winnipeg bank "to do something practical and earn a little of the filthy lucre so sought after in this material old world just for the sake of accomplishing it and feeling a wee wee bit of the joy of independence".

Maryon did not get a job or independence; she spent the summer with her parents, reading (mostly novels, some in French), playing tennis and bridge, and writing to and receiving letters from Ken. "How much more real in worth and vitality are friends than blood relations – for they are kinships of the *soul,* not of the body!" But Ken did not come home that August; instead, he took up his post in Smyrna. "It's perfectly splendid," she wrote to Ken, "your new appointment and I am really awfully glad for you." He must accept the position even if his absence brought her sadness: "All you might accomplish and *will* accomplish for Smyrna and education among the heathen Turk and Eastern Christians is a goal not easily disregarded or lightly thrown aside – and such experiences – sights of history and nature and foreign sounds of men are to be thankfully and exultantly welcomed and seized upon by youth so fortunate as to be offered them." How much more stimulating than Toronto then awash in materialism and "the hunt for personal gain". Ken really had no choice, and despite her sadness, her heart was not broken because of her pride in him and his work. As a young woman her role was to encourage capable young men to realize their potential. "As I have said ... before," Maryon continued, "women can't accomplish these things themselves but they can help in a humble way and be just as eager and ambitious about them." Having expressed that peculiar humility, Maryon resisted it: "It's no use pretending I *like* being a woman – and admire her sweet humble helpfulness! I *don't* – I have always thought my great misfortune on being born on the 13th was being born a girl – but – oh well, one *does* resign oneself, since one must." And so she ended her letter assuring him that her thoughts and hopes would accompany him to Smyrna, but she herself returned that fall to Annesley Hall in Toronto.

Soon Maryon was caught up in a frenzied campaign to sell manicures, shampoos, and even makeups and shoeshines in Annesley Hall, all in support of European Student Relief. Hugh Ross, whom she had met in the summer, was calling on her regularly. With "Art" she was trying to maintain "friendship" but nothing more. In the previous year, Art had "fallen in love" with her, but now she wanted a purely "Platonic" relationship. He did not. Before going to Toronto, Maryon had attended an SCM conference at Muskoka's Elgin House. The conference affected her: she resolved "honestly to try this year (for the first time) to study and pray and live as far as possible – Jesus –." She was even moved to take a Bible-study class. Before each class she spent some time with Dr. H.B. Sharman, one of the SCM's mentors, who kept her a week or so ahead of the students. Sharman's method, the Canadian historian Richard Allen writes, "was simplicity itself.... He assembled, in more accessible form, the records of the life of Jesus and asked only who is this man? And what is he saying? The conclusions he left to his students." To the students, this "non-directive" leadership was exhilarating. Maryon's bi-weekly Bible-study class was led by S.H. Hooke, professor of Old Testament studies, who fell victim that year to an inquiry into the character of his beliefs by the Methodist Church. She rallied to support "Hookie" who, besides being a theologian, was a fine athlete and delightful company. "Poor old Hookie," she lamented to Ken the following year, "he has been asked to leave Victoria" because of his beliefs. "It seems a shame that a man of such brilliant intellect should leave a University on account of old fashioned Methodists."[12]

Bible study soon took second place to socializing in those first months of 1923. "Mr. Ross" took her to a debate, which, in Maryon's view, was a "dreadful contrast" between a brilliant Oxford Union team and a Toronto team, which "could merely drive home facts". Ross invited his Oxford colleague Pearson along, no doubt in an attempt to impress his date. Soon, however, Ross returned to Winnipeg, and Maryon began to attend her tutorials with Mike. She continued seeing "Art" and went out to tea, as was the custom then, with Bill Franks. He was intelligent, she thought, but was "so egotistical – and I have too strong a mind myself". Maryon liked both Art and Bill but could not be in love with either. The friendships, thus, were flawed. That, she told Ken, "is the beauty of you – and why I feel I can depend on you so much – because we are unalloyed friends." Lacking a serious male friend, Maryon spent most of her days on worthy causes and good conversation with her best female friends, Marion Hilliard, a serious and intelligent medical student, and Mary Rowell, a delightful and witty daughter of the earnest lawyer-politician Newton Rowell.

The fall term passed quickly, and Art reluctantly accepted the

"Platonic" relationship and took Maryon "everywhere imaginable". In a letter to Ken on February 4, 1924, Maryon confided that she wished that she could love Art for he was a "dear". For two weeks, she refused to see him, but Art pleaded with her to meet him once more. In those two weeks, she "went to Bill's frat. dance ... and to a party with Lester Pearson (in the History dept. – the one from Oxford – awfully nice)." Whether Mike gave her any advice about the constitutional-history examination that was scheduled for February 5 and "about which [she knew] very little" we do not know.[13] Somehow one doubts it.

While Maryon learned little about constitutional history over the next few weeks, she certainly learned a lot about its instructor, Mike Pearson. On March 13, five weeks after her casual reference to the party she attended with Mike, Maryon informed Ken "the most wonderful thing on earth has happened to me at last – and I can't really believe it *is* me yet – but it must be because I feel his very heavy signet ring on my finger – Can you keep a secret Ken? I think you are safe enough being so far away – but don't tell a soul because we aren't telling the public till after term. I am engaged!"

The reaction of the doting admirer in far-off Smyrna can easily be imagined. Maryon, finally, was in love. "I am engaged," she continued portentously, "to Lester Bowles Pearson – but I call him Mike (unromantic name isn't it?)" She had "known him really at all well [for] a little over a month", but already they loved "each other more than anything else in the world".

They certainly could not tell the world because Maryon was Mike's student and their engagement would be controversial. In a later, more cynical age, it would be grounds for Mike's dismissal, but in the world of Toronto Methodism, in the early 1920s, the splendid spiritual qualities of the young lovers gave assurance to the relevant authorities, notably their parents.

Young lovers they certainly were in that feverish late winter of 1924. The world beyond them vanished as the smallest details of their relationship became endlessly fascinating. What was Mike to

Maryon? "... heaps of brains and oh just generally wonderful." He played "everything ... even the piano." "Oh," she exclaimed "I can't go on recounting his many deeds of prowess." They were simply too many. She herself was just learning them, for she and Mike had "reversed the order of things and fell rather precipitantly in love before [they] had been *friends* very long." Telling Art was especially painful, but he was "awfully manly" about it. For her part, Maryon felt like a *worm*. She vowed not to hurt anyone else as she had Ken and Art and others. "Mike says I am safe now and in the interest of the rest of the world he thinks he ought to remove me from any more chance of damage...."

They would marry the next summer (1925), the soonest date her mother would countenance. Mike needed time to save some money, and even then they wouldn't have much. "Professors never do – do they?" an obviously well-informed Maryon asked Ken. But in love's fresh bloom she was sure "they would have *such* fun together planning every cent." Between the spring of 1924 and the wedding, Maryon would live in Winnipeg where she would "learn to cook & sew." Her plans had changed so abruptly: "Oh, I just *can't* believe that I am actually going to be married – *I* who always thought myself immune – and meant to have a career." The career was not to be; her immunity was gone; she was to be a wife.[14]

First, she had to complete her courses. The teacher and student now in love met furtively in the library stacks. In the evenings, Maryon would sneak out of Annesley Hall, wearing a splendid cape for her rendezvous with Mike. Her knowledge of the British constitution, *inter alia,* increased greatly. The secret, as usual, was poorly kept, although Mike's colleagues apparently did not know. Not even Methodist self-righteousness could have excused Mike's serious dalliance with one of his students in the eyes of George Wrong.[15] Fortunately, they were able to avoid his stern gaze. Mike marked her history paper and she got 80 per cent, a first. She also received a first in English, seconds in French and zoology, and a third in ethics, a course that she had detested. The examinations finished, departure to

Winnipeg loomed. The last days together became, in Mike's words, "a prenuptial honeymoon".* It was, in Maryon's words, "just a general orgy of self-indulgence and extravagance": "We play tennis all morning, lunch, go to a movie, go out to dinner – and to a theatre or to dance or out to the Old Mill [a romantic retreat]. I haven't been in Annesly [*sic*] any longer than to change my clothes...." Mike asked her to go to England with him for the summer, "but of course we can't". "Mother" was soon arriving for graduation and to see Grace off to Oxford, where she would be spending the summer. After graduation, Maryon and Mike would visit the Pearsons in Walkerville.[16]

Ken finally replied to Maryon's "effusions", as she termed them, and he, like Art, was awfully manly. Her response to his letter suggests that scattered among his congratulations were some questions about her future course:

> You know what I have always thought about marriage – as one sees it commonly on all sides – That it seems to be a "settling down" of two young people both perhaps with good minds, and full of intelligence, into a sort of humdrum rut of meals – economy – and eventually family! Well – it has never appealed to me – as such – and I have always dreaded the idea. But Mike seems to feel the same way – we don't want to settle and stay set – as it were – with the whole wide world to see and so many things to do. I want to do something myself – besides keeping house for him. It will be wonderful to be together and to do and think together but I do want to do some mental work myself.

She thought of writing, editing, or newspaper work, but that was for the future. In the meantime, she had to learn to sew and cook, and she would continue to write to Ken, who she knew loved her "as a

---

* No letters from Mike to Maryon written during this period survive. This comment is the only view of the engagement from Mike's perspective. In his memoirs he is circumspect: "... one group of fourth-year girls in my European history course seemed even more attractive than the others. In that particular group, one pretty dark-haired girl with a clear and enquiring mind (which, as a professor, was what I was supposed to be solely concerned with) was by far the most attractive of the eight.... She has remained so ever since."

friend as I love you – and we shall always mean that much – which is a very great deal – to one another."[17]

The year in Winnipeg passed slowly, except for Mike's visit from mid-August to mid-September. She had passed on one of Ken's letters to Mike who claimed that he enjoyed it and looked forward to meeting him. Mike told Maryon that Ken must be an unusual person – and a great friend. She hoped Mike and Ken would become friends and perhaps all of them could holiday together: "Isn't it rather nice to think of some far off but possible green Ionian island where we could gather together a few chosen wonderful friends and live together for a summer." But already one dream, that of writing for the newspaper, had been shattered. Other disappointments followed. She did learn to sew, embroidering six towels, but she "hated" it. She did some work in the reference section of the Winnipeg Public Library, and worked to make herself "more worthily equipped to be Mike's wife". As expected, Mike impressed her parents and Winnipeg friends, except for his nickname, which her father claimed undermined his professional dignity. It was, Mike said, a view that his own parents shared. But Mike was "so lighthearted and full of fun and youth" that it was "hard to consider him a Professor & many ladies gasped in amazement when they saw him because they had imagined him grave, austere & professor like!" "Lots of times" Maryon felt that Mike was younger than she "because he acts like a small naughty child". Maryon's formidable mother was charmed, and treated him "like one of the family". Maryon's father charmed Mike, who found him "the personification of all that is fine and generous and unselfish in the family doctor."[18]

Winnipeg and home became boring after Mike left. Ken's travels around Turkey intrigued her; Grace's plans to go to the Gold Coast with her future husband, Norman Young, provoked some jealousy. Maryon's mother insisted that Grace and she have a double wedding ceremony. It meant waiting and also sharing the most important day of her life. With no hopes of employment, Maryon went to Business College to learn typing but loathed it and soon quit. She returned to monogramming pillowslips and towels and making "nighties and things".[19] Her future maid of honour, Marion Hilliard, continued in medical studies in Toronto, and, for Maryon, the contrast between the feckless existence in Winnipeg and the challenges of the classroom in Toronto grew. In January she decided she had to visit Toronto. She told Ken that she would be staying with Marion and Mary Rowell, whose father had, in some undisclosed way, discouraged Ken from ever returning to Canada. Maryon tried to cheer him up by telling him that he would have a more adventurous and interesting life abroad. What a fascinating old man he would be. "I hope I shall still be privileged to know you then and revel with the others in your scholarship and renown. Because you know Ken, I thoroly [sic] believe in you and I know that you are going to have no ordinary life – but a great life...."[20]

The "great life" eluded Maryon on her return to Winnipeg as tonsilitis struck and embroidery piled up. The streets became "springtime sloppy" and her mood worsened. She had learned how to sew and cook but she was determined, as her wedding approached, that she would not let such domestic tasks be her "chief job in life". "I refuse," Maryon declared, "to have recipes occupy more space in my mind than literature and the Great Things of Life." Sometimes she wished she were "more domestic – and cared more about fine cooking". But she would not be, "and Mike will manage to live I'm sure". She refused to become disillusioned with marriage's prospects, for Mike and she were "friends" above all else and their "Ideals" remained strong. She had learned that she could appreciate the beauty of great art but not create it, and in that respect her future had darkened. Her mind was in "mental chaos" as the great day approached. Mike – Maryon now called him "my Michael" – came west briefly in May, before he returned to teach two summer courses for teachers, "Renaissance and Reformation" and "England under the Tudors and Stuarts". Norman Young returned from England for the double ceremony on August 22. The excitement mounted as the final preparations were made.

Maryon confessed to Ken that she loved "her wedding gown & train & veil etc. Never did I think I would be raving this extravagantly about the 'Greatest Moment in a Girl's Life' – but so it is!"[21] And so it seemed on August 22, 1925, when Maryon walked down the aisle to meet Mike, Norman, and her prospective father-in-law who carried out the ceremony in Broadway United Church. She wore a "quaint robe de style of ivory crepe Romaine flounced with rich Chantilly lace arranged in Van Dyke points and outlined in silver threads". The reporter's adjectives tumbled over each other:

> A tiny scalloped yoke of the lace formed a pretty adornment at the neck. Her full length train was fashioned of georgette in a succession of tiny pleats bordered at the base and along one side with the lace, a spray of orange blossoms forming an artistic finish at one corner. Her veil of tulle, with which was also worn the short chapel veil, was arranged in a Juliette cap and secured with a French medaillon wreath of forget-me-nots, orange blossoms and tiny buds. Her bouquet was Colonial in design and was composed of sweetheart rose buds centred with forget-me-nots and lily of the valley and collared with lace.

She was strikingly beautiful on that August afternoon as she took her place between Marion Hilliard and Mike. The journalist did not describe Mike who, despite a top hat, white gloves, and tails, looked remarkably youthful. And on that day she believed more than ever that love was "the greatest thing in the whole world ... a wonderful and beautiful gift". There were a few problems. Herbert, their best man, "hissed" at Mike during the ceremony: "Mike, I couldn't find your going-away pants to pack". For an already nervous Mike, the comment "conjured up a frightening vision of a deplorable beginning to ... married life". Norman Young's speech was "eloquent and witty"; Mike spoke second and his was "little more than 'Me too'". Maryon told him it was "the worst ever made by a bridegroom". It surely wasn't, and everything else went as planned. The day after the ceremony, Grace and Norman left on the eastbound train bound, ultimately, for the Gold Coast. Maryon and Mike left in his automobile, bound, most courageously, for Quebec and then for their new Toronto apartment.[22]

Ken did not come to the wedding but sent a striking piece of

Turkish embroidery along with his best wishes. In a letter written ten days before the wedding, Maryon thanked him for his gift but even more for his friendship: "It has always meant a light for me – and never need you fear to love that corner of my heart and thought that is dedicated to our friendship. It is one of the greatest things in my life – because somehow we have always kept it pure & unsullied and so true."[23] That fall Ken did return to Canada to teach at Appleby College in nearby Oakville, but his health was poor. Maryon and Mike settled into the spacious third floor of 12 Admiral Road, built by Charles Gibson in 1896-7, and described as "an eclectic mélange of Queen Anne / Romanesque / Classic Revival forms". Maryon's mother arrived a few months later, and on January 13, 1926, Maryon, her mother, and Mrs. Pearson "received" for the first time since her marriage. In a letter to Ken, she said the reception went off "without mishap" and about eighty-five ladies "called". They had not seen each other "for a long time" (obviously Mike and Ken had met) but, yes, they would go to *The Student Prince* with him that weekend. Would he stay over? He could make "any other appointments he might want".[24]

This rather formal letter was the last of Maryon's correspondence with Ken. The friendship did not endure and, although Mike and Ken both became diplomats, they were not close.* Nearly all of

---

* Kirkwood entered the Canadian foreign service in 1928. The Pearsons and Kirkwood were together briefly in Ottawa before he was sent off to Canada's new embassy in Tokyo in 1929. He stayed there for a decade, and his career probably suffered from his absence from Canada. His "friendship" with Maryon had died; his relationship with Mike was always cool. Mike and Ken's colleagues were vaguely aware that there was "something" between the two of them. They heard about a poem, "Three Loves", he wrote in Tokyo about Maryon and him.

Oh Amy the fickle and shallow of heart
Who in rapturous kisses vowed never to part
From the happy young lover of Locksley Hall
Who offered his life, his love and his thrall,
Broke her sweet pledge, and married a fool
Who had only the "brains" to make her his tool.

Maryon's later letters were destroyed; those that remain are uninteresting. Maryon spoke more clearly in her letters to Ken than in any other documents we have, and in a voice that is markedly different from the one that is remembered by Mike's future colleagues or even her own acquaintances.

They most often recall a sardonic and tart woman. Senator Keith Davey found her caustic and jealously protective of her own and Mike's rights. Tom Kent, Mike's personal assistant in the early 1960s, could not abide her and described her as a nag in his memoir of the period. A biographer of Canada's political wives called her "one of the most trenchant and interesting of Canada's political wives", and a forerunner of modern feminism. Still, even she emphasizes Maryon's sharpness, describing her as "a splash of astringent right in the eye".[25] Others speak of her aloofness, biting wit, and aversion to public life. What "happened" to the young woman described above?

In his memoirs Mike wrote that in August 1925 Maryon "married, as she thought, a professor, to live the tranquil life on a university campus which most appealed to her." Her best-known remark, repeated on the same page in Mike's memoirs, is "Behind every successful man there is a surprised woman." Yet we know that she did not want tranquillity and that she was certain that Mike would be a "success". She had confided to Ken in May 1924 as Mike and she planned their future together that they did not want "to stay set". She wanted to live in "foreign climes". "I should love him to get into the diplomatic service some day – and be Ambassador somewhere – After all why not dream? We are young and foolish – and can have Ideals for a while longer at least." But the "Ideals" became less than

---

And the love of the other one, happy at first
Now became bitter as he felt his life cursed.
Yea, the landlord of Locksley had cause to be sad
When he saw that his Amy had married a cad.

The poem appeared in Kirkwood's privately printed *Song in My Heart,* published in Tokyo in 1932. In the 1950s as Kirkwood had some career problems, the Pearsons did not obviously help him.

such. Success came for Mike, but the surprise was that the success was so much his and not hers. Her career hopes withered, and her Christian faith waned quickly after marriage – perhaps because of marriage. Her desire for independence, so strongly asserted as a student, remained in the vigour with which she expressed her opinions, which, alas, were not always taken as seriously as she had hoped.[26]

Maryon and Mike's marriage, then, was not made in heaven, but neither was it a hell, as some have suggested. Charles Ritchie, who listened to people so well, perhaps understood Maryon's dilemma best. She was, he says, an intelligent woman who very early became accustomed, because of her beauty and her education, to having an independent voice. In the restrictive world of university and diplomacy, that voice lost its audience; she raised it in order that she might be heard. Mike grew in wisdom and stature, the audience clustered around him, and Maryon was crowded out. She resented it and retreated to the private world of literature and to a cynical pose in public life. Perhaps it did not become her, but today we can understand better why she chose that pose.[27]

CHAPTER SIX

ACADEMIC
INTERLUDE

There are no sporting papers here. It is also against the law to sell
Candy in the drug stores on Sunday.
... We are the only nice people in Canada.... I would like to hit all Can-
ada a coup bas [low blow].
— Ernest Hemingway in Toronto 1923[1]

TORONTO IN THE 1920s can be pulled apart like stripping leaves
off an artichoke. For Maryon and Mike, however, the core
beneath the stiff coverings of Protestant rectitude was richly satisfying because of the memories and friends that surrounded them. They
settled down easily in their third-floor flat in an unusually tall late-
Victorian house. The neighbourhood's first residents, Toronto's
merchants and professionals, were moving on to grander homes in
Forest Hill and Rosedale, leaving the "Annex", an attractive area
with an eclectic blend of architecture and people, within a five-
minute walk of the university and scarcely farther away from many of
Toronto's charms – the Royal Ontario Museum, Kensington Market, and the Public Library. Marion Hilliard and Mary Rowell regularly visited 12 Admiral Road, and Maryon, in turn, was received by
Mary at the much grander quarters of her prosperous father, Newton
Wesley Rowell.[2]

Toronto in the 1920s was an Anglo-Canadian city of just over half a
million people, more than four-fifths of them of British origin and

more than one-quarter actually born in Britain. Shops were crammed with British woollens, tea, china, and books, but the influence of the United States was increasingly evident at the cinemas, on the magazine racks, and in the ballpark. The Toronto Maple Leafs baseball team won the so-called Little World Series in 1926, and Mike cheered them on. The next year Mike's friend Conn Smythe, who had started out with the Varsity team, bought the St. Patrick's hockey team, in the spirit of 1920s nationalism renaming them the Maple Leafs. Equally in the spirit of that nationalism, the team's promise was not equal to its performance. Sports, school, and family took Mike's friendships far beyond the boundaries of the University of Toronto. Roly Michener had come back from Oxford to practise law. He and Mike shared not only a love of tennis but also a commitment to the League of Nations, and they often talked about international affairs. V.C. Wansbrough, his peerage now abandoned, had emigrated to Canada largely because of Mike and was a sometime weekend visitor from Montreal. His army chum Billy Dafoe was becoming increasingly well known in medical circles, and in sporting circles where he and Mike were both recognized as good coaches. Vaughan, also, was in Toronto, along with numerous Bowleses and Pearsons.[3]

Signs of prosperity and achievement abounded in mid-1920s Toronto. Near the Pearsons, the Park Plaza Hotel was being built over Taddle Creek, and other Chicago-style skyscrapers began to jut above the Victorian city. Union Station's Classical Revival style pointed to the past when it opened in 1927, but its massive Front Street frontage seemed to forecast the emergence of a major metropolis. The university boasted about the Nobel Prize that Frederick Banting and J.J.R. Macleod won in 1923 for the discovery of insulin, although there was some unseemly controversy over who actually deserved to win it. Toronto's financial community, bolstered by the riches of the Canadian Shield, was asserting national pre-eminence. The provincial government, headed by G. Howard Ferguson, was gradually loosening the restraints on alcohol, to the horror of churchmen; but cocktail lounges and pubs were still a couple of generations away. Parkland, picnic areas, and amusement parks reflected the greater leisure time of Torontonians. Sunnyside was Toronto's Coney Island with its Ferris wheel, roller-coaster, and boardwalk, although the Sunnyside bathing pavilion, which opened in 1922, rigidly enforced regulations against even *males* bathing with their chests exposed. Toronto's conservatism was also reflected in federal and provincial elections where Conservatives won virtually every Toronto seat throughout the 1920s, and in municipal elections where the "Orange" slate presented by *The Telegram* usually won most aldermanic posts.[4]

The bombast of the flamboyantly imperialist mayor, Tommy Church, the blatant anti-Semitism and nativism of many newspapers and public officials, and the hilarious attempts to censor "modern" literature embarrassed most people in Maryon and Mike's circle. *Saturday Night* magazine attacked "the scum of Europe" arriving in Toronto and mocked Jewish names. The police in 1928 banned public meetings in foreign languages lest the Bolshevik virus spread. The *Globe* and *Telegram* applauded this action. *The Telegram* was virulently anti-Semitic. In 1924 it called for a poll tax to keep out Jews: "They engage in the wars of no country, but flit from one to another under passports changed with chameleon swiftness, following up the wind the smell of lucre." Not surprisingly, in a Hart House debate in the late 1920s, the proposition that "Toronto is deserving of her reputation for intolerance" won overwhelming support from the undergraduates. Many of the brightest and most creative people were leaving Toronto for the United States in the 1920s, in part drawn by money and opportunity but equally repelled by the traditionalism and conservatism of Toronto. For example, R.M. MacIver, perhaps the most distinguished social scientist at the university and the head of the political science department in the mid-1920s, left for Columbia in 1927. The University of Toronto, like Oxford, did not permit the teaching of sociology, MacIver's field; unlike New York, which would be at "the center of the great movements of the times", Toronto, in MacIver's view, would remain on the periphery. One of

MacIver's strongest memories of Toronto was how reactionary Anglo-Canadian patriots had prevented Jane Addams from speaking at the university. It fell to MacIver to write the abject letter of apology to the great Chicago social worker.[5]

Looking back at their years in Toronto, when they were newly wed, young, and short of money, Maryon and Mike always spoke of how "contented" they were. Certainly the pressures of diplomacy and politics, which they faced later, were more intense. Since there were no children for the first two years of marriage, the mornings could be shorter and the evenings longer. They both enjoyed the theatre – Shaw was a particular favourite of Maryon's – and Mike's writings indicate that he and Maryon often went to the cinema, which, of course, began to talk in 1927. Still, even in the first year of marriage, Mike's schedule must have left him very little free time, for he taught not only a large number of courses during the academic year but also extension in the evening and very often summer courses. Moreover, his commitment to Varsity sports was extraordinary. He "loved" coaching, which he claimed "took up *only* [my italics] two or three hours a day". In the winter he coached and travelled with the Varsity hockey and football teams; in the spring he was the playing coach of the lacrosse team on its American tours.[6] Maryon was attracted by and attractive to athletes ("Art" had been a Varsity football star), but Mike confessed "she was never interested" in sports. He tried to get her interested in his favourite spectator sport, baseball, especially when they were posted in Washington whose bad American League team played the great Tigers, Yankees, and Red Sox teams in the mid-1940s. He finally persuaded her to go out to a Washington-Detroit game on a beautiful midsummer night. The score was "nothing-nothing" in the eighth; his hopes billowed: "We both had score cards and I saw she was writing something in hers. I thought 'She's getting interested, she's looking at her score card and even keeping score.' But then I looked a little closer and she had written 'we owe cocktails to'." Mike wisely gave up trying to make Maryon a fan.[7]

Maryon probably attended few of the athletic events in the Toronto years, but the responsibilities of faculty wives were considerable in entertaining colleagues and students. Mike suggested in his memoirs that the department of history was a "most congenial" group and, in the mid-1920s, it was also a youthful group. When he arrived in Toronto Mike was reunited with his former army buddy "Bart" Brebner. "Bart" had known Maryon too, and she, like Mike, was disappointed when he left Toronto for Columbia in 1925 (in her view because the university officials thought the department was "too young"). She and Mike both grew to like George Glazebrook, who came to Toronto from Oxford in 1925, and soon became a regular visitor to 12 Admiral Road, as did the law and political science professor N.A.M. MacKenzie. George Brown and Frank Underhill, who joined the department in 1925 and 1927, respectively, quickly took to Mike and vice versa. Underhill had a gift for friendship and his penchant for the politically outrageous amused Mike for whom Underhill's good nature excused nearly every fault. Donald Creighton, whose father, W.B. Creighton had hired Mike as *The Christian Guardian*'s English correspondent, and who shared so much of Mike's background, did not become a friend after he joined the department in 1927. Maryon may have remembered Creighton's caustic attacks on the SCM from her student days.[8] Whatever the reason, the Creightons and the Pearsons were not friendly.

The reason was certainly not Creighton's sharp pen and tongue, for they were no match for George Wrong's son Hume, who, despite objections from the university president, joined the department in 1921 as one of the university's first lecturers. Hume himself had warned his father that he knew little history, but his Oxford B.Litt., penetrating intelligence, and family lineage soon made him one of the department's outstanding figures.[9] The distinguished historian Charles Stacey recalls Wrong's lectures as "elegant performances, meticulously staged". But his snobbery and cruelty also repelled students: "On one occasion [Stacey recalls] an unfortunate young woman wandered into one of his lectures very late. Wrong suspended his discourse and with an angry and dramatic gesture, his voice rising to something like a scream, ordered her out; she fled, overwhelmed." By common admission, he had a clear sense of who his inferiors were. And they were many. Paul Martin, another student from that time, recalled his astonishment when, at a meeting of the élite Historical Club, Hume "tartly" corrected a historical argument presented by his esteemed father.[10] Wrong left the department in 1927 when his father's close friend Vincent Massey, newly appointed as Canada's first minister in Washington, invited Hume to join him as first secretary at a lavish salary of $5,000.

Despite the differences in style and personality, Mike and Wrong were friendly, and Maryon admired the strong personality of Hume's wife, Joyce. Moreover, there is evidence that Mike and Wrong shared some viewpoints. Wrong quickly formed a low opinion of Toronto's students and of North American democracy upon his return from Oxford. What was the view of his new colleague Mike Pearson upon his arrival at Toronto? Anonymously and with the humour that characteristically blunted the sharp edges of his opinions, Mike summarized his view of students at Toronto and North American democracy in early 1924. The article, written for the university audience, was entitled "Robots and Robotism":

There may be some of you who have never read the play of [Karel] Capek. I forget that the undergraduate of today is more interested in rugby than Robots, and that he will tell you more about Carol Dempster (is she a "movie queen" or the wife of a pugilist?) than about Karel Capek. What I mean by Robotism, then, is this. It is the crushing curse of sameness, the destruction of individuality, the dead level of mechanical mediocrity. Robotism is the vice of standardization, the cult of the plain man. I have heard it called democracy. You will remember the story of Periander? No, you won't for it seems that education to-day (so-called education) is only concerned with plumbing, printing and plain cooking. Periander was a very wise Greek who, when asked by Thrasybulus as to the best method of preserving a tyrannical government, said nothing but took his tyrant friend out

into a field of corn and silently lopped off the tallest ears. That is pre-
cisely the effect of our twentieth century Robotism. We are lopping
off the tallest ears and not silently.

The "culprit" was, of course, the United States. "They have spent a
century or more over there perfecting the standardization of inani-
mate things and now, forsooth, they would standardize personality."
Then, Mike attacked the American way: "For the deep crimson of
genius, the deep blue of wisdom, the deep green of sin, they would
substitute the deep grey of nothing at all. A hundred million robots!"
Mike, of course, is posturing here, but one can well imagine that
Wrong, who denounced the United States and Americans as "barba-
rous" and unintellectual, was one who appreciated that particular
posture. He also would have applauded his junior colleague's fear of
creeping Americanization and "Robotism" among his students.
Mike claimed that most students regarded the university simply as a
"social nursery" where they came to be "spoon-fed" with "the food of
material advantage". At Victoria, Mike could find only "half a dozen
individualities"; the rest were sheep and the shepherd was "public
opinion". "Among you," he told the students, "to be subtle, brilliant
and clever is to be peculiar and, hence, to be unpopular. That is the
reason that I, myself, in writing these inspired words, have to take
refuge under the cold shadow of anonymity. It is a safe enough refuge, for no-one suspects that I am not a Robot like the rest of you."[11]

Hume Wrong probably did see that there was more to Pearson
than met the eye. Both shared an intense dislike of pomposity and
pretence, although Wrong expressed his dislike sarcastically. To most
at the University of Toronto in those years, however, Mike did seem
very much like "the rest of them". Charles Stacey, one of Mike's students, recalled Mike as having "a cheerful sort of adolescent charm".
But even as a second-year student, Stacey thought that Mike "was no
massive scholar. He had other interests – notably coaching both the
hockey and football teams – and it was sometimes evident that he had
not done his homework with much care." Stacey recalls one morning
when Mike arrived in class without his lecture notes on the English

Civil War but with a copy of John Drinkwater's play *Oliver Cromwell*. He then simply read it to the undergraduates, who enjoyed it even if the lecture was, to say the least, remote from the latest scholarship. Similarly, Paul Martin recalls that Mike in those years was "an amiable and outgoing fellow", well known on the campus for his coaching but not highly regarded as a lecturer. Donald Fleming, a future political foe, is rather kinder. He was in Mike's first lecture on English constitutional history and recalled Mike as an "entertaining" lecturer who became "popular" with the class but who looked, "apart from his gown, more like a student than a professor".[12]

As usual Mike's easy ways concealed seriousness of purpose. Some of his lecture notes have endured, and they reflect careful preparation (he probably had forgotten them that morning recalled by Charles Stacey); indeed, Mike wrote out his lectures in full, even placing the jokes in the text. His lecturing load was light since Toronto followed the Oxonian model, emphasizing tutorials rather than lectures. In the tutorials, Mike's charm and quick wit soon became apparent and, with them, his popularity with the students. Like most junior lecturers, Mike had little choice in what he taught, but his courses were on subjects familiar to him: British history and British constitutional history. The tutorials ranged more broadly and included not only British history but the history of the Reformation and medieval Europe. His reading lists, which survive in department files, contain the major and most recent works on the subject. In 1927 and 1928, Mike, again following Oxford ways, taught a "special subject" on "international relations" in which he considered some of the so-called revisionist works on the origins of the First World War. Old teachers forget, and Mike may be excused for believing that he was overworked as a lecturer (about three hours per week) and for saying that Canadian history and recent history were ignored at the University of Toronto. In fact, Canadian history was reserved for the department's most distinguished members: George Wrong, the department's founder, and W.P.M. Kennedy, its best scholar but an erratic colleague. Kennedy, who had taught Mike, lectured on Canadian and British constitutional history, but his difficult personality

combined with his present-mindedness took him out of the department of history, initially into a one-person department of constitutional history, then to political economy, and finally into the new
department of law.[13]

Mike himself taught courses that touched upon the present.
Besides his special subject, "international relations", Mike and Kennedy shared a course on institutions of the modern British Empire.
Some indication of his lecturing style, his broadened viewpoint, as
well as his continuing faith in British pragmatism is evident in the
notes for his final lecture in that course in 1927. After describing
Macaulay's famous attack on Indian civilization and his defence of
the superiority of Western culture and institutions, Mike claimed
that "the modern point of view is much more tolerant of native differences and native institutions. The white man is perforce broaden-
ing his vision":

> No British statesman today would accept the views or use the words
> of Macaulay.
>
> We know now that India has a right to her own civilization, her
> own forms of religious worship, however repugnant some of this may
> be to British eyes. Indeed the British no longer feel they have a mission
> to make the world drink beer, play cricket and learn how to vote and
> they are even willing to admit that often the process of Europeaniza-
> tion has done more harm than good – has often introduced not Chris-
> tian ethics and regular government, so much as European diseases,
> European vices, European firearms and European race slavery.

In reference to Southern Rhodesia, Mike prophetically suggested
that "no problem in the British Empire" was more difficult than the
black-white antagonism in Rhodesia. Mike, however, was not so
prescient in his final remarks to the class: "Therefore it is with
confidence that I look a hundred years ahead to a classroom of earnest, eager young faces, their pens moving with lightning rapidity, to
catch the fleeting word, that flows from the lips of an ambitious
young lecturer, who is giving a course on 'The successful solution of
Britain's Imperial problems in the 20th century.'"[14]

There was, of course, no successful solution to Britain's imperial problems, but in the 1920s the end of the British Empire could not be imagined, especially in Toronto's history department, where British history remained central to the undergraduate program and where the current and future state of the Empire was continuously the subject of faculty debate. In 1920, the Toronto historian W.S. Wallace had written that "the real significance of Canadian history lies in the fact that, in the evolution of that new and unprecedented phenomenon, the British Commonwealth of Nations, Canada has played a leading part." Canada had won responsible government first and had shown how colonial nationalism could become a force creating a new, stronger, and democratic Empire. In his history of English-Canadian historical writing, Carl Berger has described the historical literature emanating from the "Toronto school" as one that "treated the Canadian experience as the enlargement of freedom". It was, he further argues, a historical literature that saw the present as the "desirable consummation" of the past and that presented Canada as a leader in the British Empire and a model for peaceful change in a world striving to assure such change.[15]

From this imperialist base, which celebrated Canada's constitutional leadership, George Wrong and his successor, Chester Martin, at the university and Mary Rowell's father, Newton, in the public arena, pointed out how the new Commonwealth, with its multinational character, could serve as a model for broader international co-operation in the League of Nations. Kennedy, who taught the constitutional-history course with Mike and whose knowledge of constitutional precedents and practice overwhelmed Mike, was a vigorous exponent of the view that nationalism was a retrogressive force, one that led to pettiness and conflict and denied "the universal principles of justice and humanity on which the ideal state should be founded".[16]

These words and this view recur often in Mike's later writings. Indeed, his First World War diary already reflected his deep distrust of nationalist feeling, as did his columns for *The Christian Guardian* where, for example, he deplored the German children's toy swords and ritual chants. In the 1920s, Canadian imperialism provided fertile soil for the growth of the so-called internationalist mind, and Canadians of Mike's background and interests prided themselves on their rejection of parochialism, whether Canadian, British, or American. So many of the underpinnings of the Anglo-Canadian sense of nationhood had eroded during the war and its aftermath. To frame a new vision for Canada that was consistent with its British past was the task that befell Toronto's scholars in the 'twenties. Their attempts to define that vision seem as distant today as the medieval arguments about angels on the head of the pin, but in their time those many musty volumes by Wrong, Martin, Kennedy, and others appeared to occupy the centre of the currents flowing through Canadian political and social life.[17]

Mike, however, made less of a contribution to this debate than his interests and ability would suggest. In his memoirs, he says that the department never indicated that he had to "get a Ph.D. quickly or depart". It was expected that he and the other young professors "would in time publish learned articles and a book or two about them". This recollection is misleading for Maryon's letters of 1924-5 report that George Wrong had recruited Mike to help him with a school text on British history and that he was encouraging Mike to undertake a major research project. The department published *The Canadian Historical Review,* the major organ for historical scholarship in Canada, and junior departmental members, including Hume Wrong and "Bart" Brebner, had produced serious academic monographs. The competition among the younger scholars as well as George Wrong's urgings prompted Mike to go to Ottawa rather than England during the summer of 1926 to begin research for a thesis and a subsequent book on the United Empire Loyalists. When he arrived, the archives were abuzz with scholarly activity as young academics from across Canada began projects that would establish the foundations of modern Canadian historical scholarship.[18]

Mike arrived in Ottawa, which he correctly described as "a rather ragged national capital", just as the Canadian Parliament was debating Lord Byng's refusal to grant Mackenzie King a dissolution of

Parliament.* King thereupon angrily resigned, and Lord Byng called upon the Conservative leader, Arthur Meighen, to form a government. While Maryon stayed in Toronto in June, Mike watched the dramatic events from the parliamentary Visitors' Gallery. The Alberta historian A.L. Burt, whom Mike had met through Roly Michener, was a friend of the Conservative member for Edmonton East, A.U.G. Bury, and Burt used their friendship to pass through the throngs that crowded the Commons' corridors to see Canada's greatest constitutional drama unfold. Together Burt and Pearson watched in awe as the Commons debated the report on the customs scandal that would bring down the King government on June 28. In the early evening of June 24, Pearson and Burt sat through a dramatic, raucous all-night debate on the customs report during which four cliff-hanging votes took place; the Conservatives broke out in song as the division bells rang while others amused themselves by throwing their order papers at each other. In a letter to his wife written the next morning, Burt assured her that what he and Pearson saw was "certain to be long remembered in Canadian history". Pearson and he returned on June 29 to see the Tories take over. In another long letter to his wife in Edmonton, Burt made excuses for his absence from the Archives: "But it is one of the crises in our political history and we may never see the like again."[19]

Mike's letters to Maryon have not survived, but later evidence suggests that he shared Burt's disgust with King's manoeuvres, doubts about Meighen's wisdom, and support for Lord Byng's actions, on the grounds that they were constitutionally correct. In a later

---

* The October 1925 general election had returned 116 Conservatives, 99 Liberals, 24 Progressives, and 2 independents. The Liberal prime minister, Mackenzie King, stayed on with Progressive support until a customs scandal undermined the government's position. Byng, a popular governor general since his appointment in 1921, thought that King should not have the right to a dissolution of Parliament in these minority circumstances. King thought he had such a right as a dominion prime minister. King made the public issue one of nationalism versus imperialism; privately in his diary he wrote on Aug. 25, 1926, that he believed God had chosen him to fight: "I go forward in the strength of God and His Might and Right to battle as my forefathers battled for the rights of the people and God's will on earth."

interview, Mike recalled that he was not impressed by King as a political leader and that his sympathies were entirely with Lord Byng on this issue. He added, however, that Byng would have been wiser to have granted King a dissolution and to have allowed the Canadian people to decide. Mike had earlier been scornful about King's understanding of constitutional questions and his pernickety legalism in the conduct of the imperial relationship.[20] King's stock had reached its nadir in that late spring of 1926, and few expected to see it rise again. Burt, a Westerner, looked to the Progressives for leadership through the mire of the customs scandal; in bringing down King, the Progressive party, Burt claimed, performed "the great function for which it was inaugurated – the purification of our politics". Mike was not so vehement but he held a view of Canada's Conservative and Liberal parties shared by academic critics from Goldwin Smith through George Wrong, to the young scholars gathered at the Archives in the summer of 1926: the old parties fell short because of their narrowness of vision and their "parish pump" view of the political process. They pandered to local interests and ignored the great questions facing the nation.[21]

When the King government fell, Mike was in the Diplomatic Gallery with Paul Martin, a Franco-Ontarian who had a much more optimistic view of politics and politicians. Moreover, Paul Martin, a classmate of Maryon's, did not share Mike's Conservative inclinations and his low estimation of King. Sitting in the Diplomatic Gallery, the future prime minister and his future foreign secretary saw King abruptly resign, and afterwards they repaired to the office of J.S. Woodsworth (whom Mike knew through his father) to share a meal of brown bread, cheese, and tea with the former Methodist minister, now a socialist parliamentarian. The "kindly" Woodsworth lamented the compromises he himself had made in politics and the impossible position in which Lord Byng found himself.[22] The experiences of June and July 1926 remained deeply etched upon all who were in the Commons in those early weeks of summer. The so-called King-Byng affair and the general election that followed threw the world of constitutional scholarship into the cauldron of political controversy. Although King was not popular with the scholars around Mike that summer, his nationalism, as it was expressed in the 1926 campaign, reflected the spirit of those young academics. With Mike, as with Hume Wrong and many others in the mid-1920s, imperialist sympathies were giving way to a Canadian nationalism as it became clear, on the one hand, that Britain would not share the reins of the Empire however valiantly the colonials had served its cause and, on the other, that Canadians had developed a sense of their own distinctiveness and achievement.

As a teacher of British history, a self-styled "British-Canadian Conservative", an anglophile whose most joyous moments were spent at the Empire's heart, Mike must have regarded events with melancholy and ambivalence. The élite Historical Club reflected that ambivalence in a 1924 debate about the rumoured appointment of a Canadian ambassador to Washington. The alternative, the creation of an imperial diplomatic corps in which Canadians would serve and presumably achieve its highest offices, was favoured 14 to 10. Without the British Empire, Canada's horizons were limited and the bulwark against Americanization would fall. In the following year, when Mike served as faculty adviser to the club, the students debated whether the "anomalies" of British foreign policy, such as the commitment to protect European boundaries, created "a grave menace" to the British Commonwealth of Nations, as the Empire was now increasingly called. Speaking for the affirmative, the future distinguished barrister J.J. Robinette argued that Britain's insistence on running its own foreign policy without consultation meant that Canada should not be bound by such decisions, especially when they might lead to war. His opponent E.G. Davies simply argued that Canada as much as Cornwall had to "stick by" the flag in time of danger. Robinette and his cause lost 10 to 12. In an indication of past and future problems, the negative also won 13 to 15 on the question, "Resolved that Canada is fortunate to include the Province of Quebec."[23]

Confusion is perhaps the most accurate term to describe the thoughts of the best and the brightest *male* history students at

Toronto in the mid-1920s (there were no females in the Historical Club). Mike appears to have shared that confusion, and sometimes he lapsed into an uncharacteristic gloom. When A.L. Burt met him in Toronto in the winter of 1925-6, he found him "dejected". The cause of this dejection was more likely doubts about his career than concern over the future of the Empire. Mike's hopes for a return to England – that honeymoon he had promised Maryon but had not delivered – were abandoned as he began to work on his book on the Loyalists. His first two years on the Toronto staff came as a "sessional" appointment, and his "dejection" in 1925 probably arose from his concern about his promotion to assistant professor, which, after some delay, came through in June 1927 as did a salary of $3,000. A grateful athletics department also bestowed some furniture upon him at the end of rugby season and in 1927-8 he received a "modest" honorarium.[24] He and Maryon had an increasingly crowded apartment, many friends, a position with some prestige, but, in looking around them, they could see that many of the old beacons shone less brightly and there was some sense of disappointment with their lot. In the boom of the 1920s, Mike and Maryon no doubt envied the prosperity of their contemporaries, such as Roly Michener whose legal career brought better cars, larger apartments, and more luxurious surroundings. Disappointment, however, never brought despair.

Mike revelled in the success of the teams he coached. In the *Varsity* of those years, "Professor Pearson" is rarely mentioned but "Coach" Pearson appears regularly. Mike's coaching tricks, such as having his line jump in unison to throw the opponent offside, and his inspirational leadership in the clubhouse, so valued in the decade of Knute Rockne, garnered attention and approval throughout the campus, if not at 12 Admiral Road. By 1927, he was honorary head coach of the hockey team as well as the "Orphans" rugby team, and it was rumoured that he was to become Varsity's first athletics director. In fact, however devoted he was to the football field and the hockey rink, Mike had doubts about the direction in which North American sport was heading. Fresh back from Oxford where athletes bought their own uniforms and where the values of amateurism ranked high, Mike satirically lamented the trend towards making "the gate" and not "the game the thing": "No longer is a game possible without a 'gate' and that cannot be secured without publicity. The result is that before any important sporting event today there is as much ballyhooing as was used in the Middle Ages to commence a crusade. The Americans excel in this. They have become the greatest ballyhooers in history. To them the game has almost completely vanished in the frantic excitement of the spectacle, and the spectacle has become a matter of vital national importance through the feverish exertions of the press." In American colleges, football had become "a highly specialized, highly developed form of big business". This "amazing" situation had not yet developed in Canada, but some dangerous signs were appearing. For Mike, the lesson was obvious: "Unless we draw our ideals from the universities of the old land our game will soon enough be Americanized. Unless we succeed in avoiding the two great evils that threaten to destroy the athletic life of American universities, the evils of too much organization and too much money, the football tail will soon start wagging the academic dog."

Mike wrote these sentences in 1924; four years later his own football and hockey "tail" had become a burden upon his academic pursuits as he set aside his plans for a doctorate and a book on the Loyalists. He had to decide soon whether his future interests would be at the lectern or behind the hockey bench and at the football sidelines. Earlier, he had warned that it would be difficult "to persuade the [coach] who has a chance to earn [a large salary] by winning games that the playing of the game is greater than the winning of it". Now he might be in the unfortunate position of testing that proposition himself.[25]

Mike knew, however, that coaches age as poorly as athletes. But while Maryon had little interest in sports, and his parents surely regarded sports as insufficiently serious for their talented son, Mike must have found his alternatives less than attractive. For Mike, as for George Wrong, history was a moral teacher, and therefore had to have access to the broadest of audiences and to focus on the concerns

Lester – now known as "Mike" – during his "Chicago days" in 1920 – showing off a pike caught in Wisconsin, and all set for the tennis court. Though he was a mere clerk in his uncle's firm, he rubbed shoulders with the wealthy on the weekends – and his speed and agility as a sportsman no doubt helped open doors.

A fellowship to Oxford let him expand his horizons further, socially as well as intellectually. He spent Christmas 1921 hobnobbing with the moneyed crowd at Mürren, Switzerland, and returned in 1922 as part of Oxford's (completely North American) hockey team. The Swiss called Mike (below, front right) "Herr Zigzag". (Above, NAC PA-110822; below, NAC PA-119892)

ABOVE: The Moody girls' double wedding, August 22, 1925. Grace Moody and Norman Young towards the left; Mike and Maryon right of centre; Marion Hilliard and Herbert Moody to the right of Maryon. (NAC PA-68799) BELOW LEFT: Maryon and Mike on the Moodys' lawn in Winnipeg, the year after their wedding. (NAC PA-117608) BELOW RIGHT: Mike with their first child, Geoffrey, in 1928.

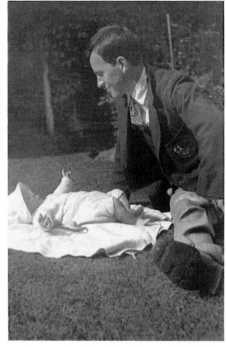

Mike and O.D. Skelton on board the *Berengaria* in 1923, on their way to the League of Nations. Skelton created Canada's modern Department of External Affairs. (NAC PA-110825)

of public life. In the 1920s, however, this view of the role of history and the historian lost strength among younger academics who began to talk about the professionalization of the discipline and the need for specialization and archival research in scholarship. Although the constitutional debate of the 1920s forged a continuing link between historical research and contemporary politics, those younger scholars at the Archives had a different view of history's future. They snickered about George Wrong's lack of knowledge of the "sources"; attended a seminar on documenting research; pored over old orders-in-council, land titles, and yellowing letters; and planned conferences where they could share their research. An enthusiastic A.L. Burt recounted that, at the Archives in 1921, he was the only visitor "digging in the mine of the manuscript room". By 1926, there were about a dozen professors and several graduate students besides. "Certainly," he told his wife in midsummer 1926, "all the professional historians in Canada are turning their eyes on the Archives during the summer and a revolution is bound to come about as a result."[26] The revolution came, but Mike was not on the barricades.

Although Burt reported that Mike was "quite intoxicated by his study of the Loyalist settlement in Upper Canada" and was "a daily joy" that summer, in sharp contrast to "the dejected fellow" he had met the previous winter, Mike's intoxication with historical documents did not endure.[27] He left the Archives at the end of July, after about a month of mining the rich Loyalist records, and he never returned to tap the lode. Mike never wrote a scholarly article during his five years in Toronto's history department. He did write a delightful piece for *Acta Victoriana* that mocked the pretensions of scholarship and historians. Entitled "The New History", the article pretended to advise students on how to get an "A" in their essays. Beginning with an admission that it was indeed "most humiliating [for a student] to receive a D- for your contribution on 'Henry VIII's Attitude to Companionate Marriage' when you have slaved for all of two hours on the subject and have thoroughly digested all the pertinent material in the *Public School History for Beginners*," Mike recommended that students turn to one of the four forms of the "new history". The first was the "picturesque" wherein "effect must be heaped on effect, metaphor on metaphor, until the reader is ready to fall into an ecstatic swoon". The second was revisionism, in which "one need only prove that all the villains of the past have been heroes, and all the heroes, villains". Mike then constructed a sample introduction to a revisionist essay that would surely receive an A "from the liberal-minded, truth-seeking" members of the history staff. The subject was Nero: "A much misjudged and misinterpreted man, Nero. It is my privilege to show in this essay that Nero was really a hero. Recent documents brought to light from the ruins of Casa Loma show that Nero did not fiddle in fiendish glee as Rome burned. Rather, that Nero had collected thousands of poor, homeless, refugees in the palace gardens, and there, his eyes brimming over with tears of compassion, he tried to take their minds off their awful plight by playing softly and tenderly, 'Just a Song at Twilight.' And so, I repeat Nero, a hero." George Wrong, his senior colleague, and Donald Creighton, his junior colleague, were likely not amused.

Mike gave further illustrations from the "hidden cause" school through which he established that Catherine of Braganza "killed" Pitt in 1806, because the great British leader died of gout, which was the product of port, which was imported to England after Charles II married Catherine of Braganza in 1662 (Mike incorrectly cited the date of marriage as 1660). His final examples came from the "psychological" school, through which he claimed it was possible to prove that the Kaiser's withered arm caused the First World War, that the wart on Cromwell's nose incited the outbreak of the English civil war, and that Napoleon's "behaviouristic emotional super-complex for war" arose from the march past his Corsican homestead by a regimental band when Napoleon was eleven months old. If any of the four forms of the new history were followed, success for the student was assured, for all knew that the history department was "partial to new ideas".[28]

Beneath the humour and the sarcasm lay some serious doubts about the direction the writing of history was taking. At a time when his colleagues were beginning to produce footnote-laden tomes, written for their colleagues rather than for a broader public, and when younger scholars, such as Harold Innis, were arguing that the true scholar must indeed reside in an "ivory tower", far from the madding political crowd, Mike began to regard their disputes as trivial and this stance as hypocritical and even cynical. Just as Ed believed that God's message belonged to the masses, not to narrow-minded theologians in a seminary, Mike believed that history could never be a truth proclaimed from the academy and understood only by its members.[29] Theory and abstraction were, for him, the enemies of common sense, the value the Pearsons cherished.

In his five years on the Toronto faculty, Mike published only one article on a historical subject. In 1927, the diamond jubilee of Confederation, he wrote an article, "Some Fathers of Confederation", for *The New Outlook,* the United Church's successor journal to *The Christian Guardian*. The article celebrated the fathers of Confederation, Confederation itself, and the British Empire, which had bestowed so many blessings upon Canada. The tone, style, and argument were most unlike what one found in *The Canadian Historical Review,* controlled by the University of Toronto history department, in which Mike never published. In its historical method, "Some Fathers of Confederation" belonged to a time when history served as a moral and patriotic tutor. In its celebration of "men who were leaders, not followers of opinion; directors, not slaves of destiny", the article repudiated most of the historiographical fashions of the day, choosing to wear Victorian crinolines rather than the flappers' clinging skirts. While "Some Fathers of Confederation" falls short of scholarly standards, then and now, it reveals a great deal about the state of Mike Pearson's mind in 1927. First, his high praise for Macdonald and Cartier suggests that his inherited Conservative viewpoint remained strong. Secondly, his belief in the Empire also endured to the point where he could still talk about the "westward march of the British Empire" and claim that the preservation of that Empire "must stir the sense that looks behind, that reverences the past, and sees in it hope for the future". Pearson was certainly a "nascent Canadian nationalist" for after his tribute to the Empire and its architect, Disraeli, Mike added, "But the construction of an infant state, Macdonald's task, and the task of all those who worked with him, rouses the spirit that gazes into the future, and would build on nature itself a new nationality." And finally, Mike's definition of that new nationality underlines the liberality of his outlook and foreshadows his own political achievement. Canadian nationality, Mike wrote, must imply "a frank and real recognition of the essential unity of all Canadians, irrespective of creed or race; not uniformity, the badge of inertia, but a deeper unity based on the recognition of differences."[30]

The article appeared the same month he received his promotion and raise and a few days before the joyous nationalist rituals that were enacted across Canada on July 1, 1927. Whatever his doubts about his profession and future, Mike shared the general good cheer of the time. In April, Victoria College awarded Mike's father an honorary doctorate. In the ceremony, Victoria's dean described Ed as "always well informed, with a well balanced mind, with sanity of judgment, and with a warmth of heart", which made him the "ideal Christian minister". Mike no doubt beamed at these words although he might have been embarrassed when Dean McLaughlin described Mike as a scholar of unusual merit.[31] More good fortune followed later in the spring, when Maryon told Mike she was pregnant. After this news, everything else became of secondary importance that year.

The pregnancy was difficult for Maryon and for Mike, who had come to rely upon her not only to cook, sew, clean, and entertain but also to manage their financial affairs, a task she handled with a skill that always impressed him, and who now had to take on some of these duties himself. "Billy" Dafoe, fortunately, was the reassuring obstetrician, and, when Geoffrey Arthur Holland Pearson entered the world at 11:58 p.m. on December 24, Dafoe obligingly agreed to mark the birth certificate 12:02 a.m., December 25. This deception accomplished, Billy prodded a reluctant Mike to go into the delivery room to see Maryon and Geoffrey. Finding Maryon asleep, Billy and Mike went to a corner to discuss the university hockey team's forthcoming Ivy League tour while Mike ate a ham sandwich. Mike tells the story well: "My wife awakened and instead of a proud and loving husband leaning over to thank her for the gift of a son and heir, she saw him turned away from her, munching a sandwich, and eagerly discussing hockey with the doctor! I have never been allowed to forget this mismanagement of the arrival of Geoffrey Arthur Holland Pearson."

The incident, in fact, was symbolic.[32] Years later, when Geoffrey was engaged to be married, Mike confessed that "when I look back I am acutely conscious of my own failures as a father". His career took him away so often; the children went off to boarding-schools and spent too much time with nannies. They never had the seventeen years with him that he had spent with his own father in "a secure and anchored home base". But, Mike continued, "of one thing I am sure, my mother – who is a saintly person if there ever was one – could never have centred her deepest hopes and love on me as your mother has on you and [their daughter] Patsy. There is really no dross of any kind in that gold, though you have to go deep, often, to find the vein."[33] Such honesty and self-deprecation endeared Mike to his two children. They cherished his presence and love then; today they revere his memory and the moments they shared playing baseball, scrambling around the floor, dancing with him at embassy balls (this in Patsy's case, of course), and welcoming home their always ebullient father. Maryon was at home, and she often seemed stern to the children, but Mike more than anyone knew how deeply she cared for her children even if that caring was sometimes encased beneath a hard shell.

Maryon's pregnancy in 1927 prevented Mike's return to the Archives that summer. Just before he left Ottawa in July 1926, Mike had attended a dinner at the Ottawa Country Club given by Sir George Perley in honour of Arthur Doughty, the dominion archivist. He sat beside O.D. Skelton, who had become undersecretary of state for External Affairs in 1925 and who planned to develop the department into a genuine foreign office. Skelton, the former dean of arts at Queen's and a distinguished scholar, told Mike that the department was searching for bright and ambitious university people to stuff the new Canadian foreign service.[34] Mike claims that he was interested but that he returned to Toronto with "no thought of changing either my occupation or my residence". His colleague W.P.M. Kennedy had other ideas however, and on January 30, 1927, wrote to Skelton, whom he knew well, and asked whether there was a position for Mike, who he thought would be an excellent applicant. Kennedy added that lack of promotion opportunities at Toronto might be an incentive for Pearson to apply. On February 28, Mike himself wrote Skelton, asking about what positions were available and how he might apply. Kennedy wrote again on April 6, 1927, suggesting another candidate because Pearson's situation at the University of Toronto had improved. In Skelton's reply, however, he indicated a continuing interest in Pearson.[35]

This detail is important because it contradicts the account in Pearson's memoirs as well as the popular lore that External Affairs just happened along Pearson's path. In his memoirs he claims that he heard in the winter of 1927 that examinations were being held for first and third secretary. In fact, there were no examinations scheduled for these positions and he contacted Skelton himself. What appears to have occurred reflects strategy on Mike's part more than serendipity. According to the sole survivor of the 1926-7 history department, George Glazebrook, Kennedy liked Pearson, as all did, but thought that scholarship was not his métier and scholarship was ever more important at the university. Mike was competing against several able young colleagues, including Glazebrook, Underhill, Wrong, George Brown, Ralph Flenley, George Smith, and Donald Creighton. Not surprisingly, Kennedy encouraged Mike to think of External. The improved situation Kennedy described to Skelton in his letter of April 6, 1927, probably arose because Hume Wrong had decided in February to go to Washington with Vincent Massey to open Canada's first embassy. Mike's letter to Skelton asking about a position seems perfectly understandable in this light. Mike managed to make his career seem a matter of good luck, of being in the right place at the right time. There was more design and more direction than he admitted; his Methodist heritage and his genuine humility made him minimize his ambition and abilities. In fact, he had an abundance of both.[36]

A year later, the first-secretary position came open, and Kennedy and Newton Rowell encouraged Mike to take the examination. Kennedy wrote Skelton, telling him that Mike would be in Ottawa to do some work at the Archives and asking whether he would like to see Pearson. Skelton replied affirmatively, and Mike presumably met him in Ottawa. Mike knew that the Canadian foreign service, which Skelton was constructing in his own image, was to be based on competition rather than on patronage, as was the case in the United States, and was to be the élite of the Canadian public service. Skelton and External thus promised a career in "a new and attractive branch of the public service" in which Mike could look forward to that ambassadorial post that he and Maryon had dreamed about during their courtship. He applied in late May, giving Kennedy, Rowell, and Sir Robert Falconer, the university president, as his references. Kennedy's Irish enthusiasm for Mike's cause led to pardonable exaggeration when he wrote in his reference that "Professor Pearson had a distinguished war record, both in camp and on the field of battle...." When Mike was queried about these peculiar and inaccurate comments in his interview, he replied that his distinction lay in picking up stray papers on St. Martin's Plain and hitting a crucial home run for the 4th Reserve Battalion team. The answer, apparently, was satisfactory.[37]

Mike's performance on the civil-service examinations went much beyond satisfactory. He wrote them for four days in late June and attained an average of 85.6 per cent, the highest score of any candidate. His marks were as follows: Essay 88 per cent; International Affairs 86 per cent; Précis 80 per cent; International Law 79 per cent; Modern History 80 per cent; and Education and Experience 90 per cent. Kirkwood was second at 84.3. Norman Robertson scored 77.4.[38] In his memoirs, he modestly conceals the fact that he stood above the more obviously intellectual and better-educated Hugh Keenleyside, Norman Robertson, and Kenneth Kirkwood. Mike's education was certainly uneven, it is true, but it was his manner and personality that led others to underestimate his considerable intellectual abilities. There was an elusiveness about Pearson that derived from his emotional reserve, and his jaunty amiability and sporting tastes seemed to belie that reserve. He fitted into no clear categories. After the examinations in which Mike obtained his outstanding record, Skelton wrote Massey, indicating that Pearson was the likely choice for first secretary. Massey expressed interest and added that his only criticism was that there was "something curiously loose-jointed and sloppy about his mental makeup which, as a matter of fact, is reflected in some measure in his physical bearing." A few days later Skelton replied, after interviewing Mike: "You have hit the nail on the head. There is something curiously loose jointed in his physical bearing and perhaps to a lesser extent in his mental makeup." Nevertheless Skelton recognized that Mike had a "very distinct capacity and attractive personal qualifications". It would be "a close run" between him and Kirkwood for the prized first-secretary position. Once again, as with Maryon, Mike won out.[39]

On August 10, the telegram from Skelton arrived just as Mike had returned from an eye examination. With the world and the telegram still blurred, he sought out an astounded librarian who read the telegram's brief message. Skelton told Mike he had finished first and asked him to report on the following Monday, since he was leaving for Europe on Thursday.[40] On August 22, *The Toronto Daily Star* reported that "University Coach Glad of Appointment". The university tried to convince him to stay, offering him a promotion to full professor and a raise that would bring him above the $3,450 the government offered if he would become director of athletics and head football coach. Mike and Maryon, who was pregnant once again, decided quickly that coaching could never be Mike's career. It was an easy decision; and it was definitely the correct one.[41] And so, to Ottawa they went, the last year before depression struck, and their world was lastingly changed.

CHAPTER SEVEN

THE OTTAWA MAN

We can end war in this generation if we as Christians are in real earnest about it. First we now live in a new order. New conditions prevail. If it be true that man has always fought for his family, his food supplies and the security of his prosperity, the same instincts of self-preservation now urge him to make peace secure.... Secondly, the sentiment of the world has changed. Think how recent is the development of the sentiment of horror regarding war.... This new sentiment is granted us at an hour when the swords of men are so scientifically destructive that, of necessity, they must be beaten into ploughshares, or earth will become a hell of desolation and civilization perish among men. Thirdly, the institutions of our time are new. At last we have in the League of Nations an instrument through which the goodwill of all people may make itself heard and felt.

– Rev. E.A. Pearson (1927)[1]

REVEREND EDWIN PEARSON'S Remembrance Day sermon in 1927 contrasts sharply with the call to arms that gentle Christian minister had issued from his pulpit a decade before as the Empire's armies and his youngest son staggered through the bloodied muck of Passchendaele. We do not know whether Mike was in London, Ontario, that weekend to hear his father's words, but in 1927, when glimmerings of hope for an enduring peace seemed to relieve the dark fears of another war, Mike surely shared most of his father's sentiments. He was not so much an idealist and certainly not as much a Christian, but this sermon had special meaning for it is the only one Mike saved. One passage in particular must have affected Mike, the one in which his father spoke about war meaning "surgeons and physicians and nurses patching up broken units of mankind who might have been standing erect for God in an endeavour to make the world better and happier." Instead, "they came home with limbs gone, with sight gone, with reason gone and their dependents robbed of complete human fellowship."[2] Mike had helped to mend whatever human units he could in Macedonia and he never forgot.*

In August 1928, Mike had to rush to Ottawa because Skelton and Prime Minister Mackenzie King were sailing to Europe where the prime minister would sign the Kellogg-Briand pact, under which the contracting parties not only condemned war as a solution to international controversies but also renounced it as an instrument of national policy. In his magisterial history of Canadian external relations, Charles Stacey, who was in Paris that summer, remarks that the pact recalled the comment in *1066 and All That* about King Edward VII's activities: "King Edward's new policy of peace was very successful and culminated in the Great War to End War." And it is true that American secretary of state Frank Kellogg insisted that wars of self-defence were excluded and that this exclusion could cover most wars of the previous century. Commentators at the time ridiculed the pact as a diplomat's New Year's Resolution or a letter to Santa Claus. Historians have been equally harsh in their judgment, with the British diplomatic historian Christopher Thorne dismissing the pact as the end of the field-day for moral platitudes.[3] In Ottawa, whose soil is especially fertile for such platitudes, politicians uttered many of

---

* In the 1960s Mike saw *Oh, What a Lovely War* with diplomat-scholar John Holmes. After the play, Mike and Holmes walked London's streets as he "poured forth accounts ... of his experiences in Salonika, bitter not about personal sufferings but about the brutality and the bungling, the callous neglect of the common soldier." His niece Pamela asked Mike during the Second World War to assist her in going overseas. He refused, saying that although he fully supported the war he would not send anyone over.

them when the Kellogg-Briand pact was debated in the House of Commons. Nevertheless, the role of Kellogg was especially welcome in Canadian eyes since it suggested that the United States was overcoming its distrust of internationalism and all things foreign, a hopeful belief, which the 1928 election of Herbert Hoover, who had the most outstanding international record of any living American, seemed to confirm.

Looking back over the rubble of the Second World War, it seems that the dreams of the later 1920s for a lasting peace were futile and perhaps even damaging in their naiveté. And yet the movement was strong, as Ed Pearson's sermon, the newspapers of the 1920s, and the deep-seated convictions of the internationalists of the 1920s and 1930s, such as the great Spanish league delegate Salvador de Madriaga, the British aristocrat Lord Robert Cecil, and Canadians J.W. Dafoe and Paul Martin, attest. Although the events of the 1930s, including the rise of the dictators, cast dark shadows upon the movement for peace through internationalism and disarmament, in the 1920s the movement's supporters could rationally believe that history, human progress, and common sense were on their side. Indeed, sixty years later, we can affirm they were. More recent studies emphasizing social and economic rather than diplomatic perspectives have pointed out that while the later 1920s did not re-establish the *belle époque* in Europe, certainly a prosperity and an optimism almost unimaginable in the bleak days of 1919-20, when Europe seemed to be a doomed civilization – in Ezra Pound's bitter condemnation, "an old bitch gone in the teeth" – were achieved. "A Western Economy linchpinned upon American participation was functioning again. Savings were reconstituted.... For those who wrote or performed, a new republic of letters seemed at hand. Harry Kessler chatted at cafes about Proust and Valéry, flitting among the celebrities of a culture that embraced Berlin and Paris."[4] Public opinion in the democracies, scarred by the memories of 1914-18, was fired by this stability to become more strongly committed to the idea of a league that would prevent war. In 1928, Gilbert Murray, a strong British league supporter, said proudly, and accurately: "All parties are pledged to the League ... all Prime Ministers and ex-Prime Ministers support it ... no candidate for Parliament dares to oppose it openly."[5] Even in Canada, which was widely regarded as one of the most reluctant participants of the league, the late 1920s saw more commitment; Prime Minister Mackenzie King, later one of the league's strongest antagonists, was heard at the time to boast that his nation "was united" in the effort "to further the work of the League of Nations" because "it holds strongly to the cause of peace and desires to see peace furthered not only within its own borders but amongst the nations of the world."[6] In 1927, on the encouragement of Ernest Lapointe, the leading parliamentarian from traditionally isolationist Quebec, King agreed that Canada should accept a seat on the council of the League of Nations.[7] While Canada had stepped hesitantly into the international arena in 1919 and 1920, it now seemed to be finding its stride.

This background suggests some of the attractions that External Affairs held for thirty-one-year-old Mike Pearson in 1928. Like so many of his generation, Mike respected the ideal of service that his father, and his profession, represented even though Mike's lack of faith was an insuperable barrier to his following his father's path. In the cause of international peace, Mike and his father's purposes converged, and his father approved of his decision to leave teaching. (When Ed accidentally opened the transcript of Mike's marks for the civil-service examinations, he forwarded them with the inscription "wonderful news".) Ed surely knew that Mike had not been satisfied with his career, his coaching successes notwithstanding. Now, a new opportunity appeared, and Mike, with the full encouragement of his family, grasped it firmly.

Mike left for Ottawa abruptly and did not try for the "leave" Skelton had mentioned in his telegram. Maryon reluctantly stayed behind to pack and Mike sublet the apartment of Jean Désy, a foreign-service officer who had been posted to Paris. In the press stories reporting Mike's appointment, it was mentioned that he would be taking up the post of first secretary in Tokyo when that embassy opened in 1929. The story in the newspaper likely came from Mike himself, and it suggests that the exotic intrigued Mike as much in 1928 as it had in 1916 when he sailed out to the Middle East. In any event, the Tokyo post went to Hugh Keenleyside, who entered External the same month as Mike and who has left a detailed sketch of Mike's first months in the department.

Keenleyside came upon Mike his first day in Ottawa when Skelton ushered him through the East Block of Parliament, to the third floor, to a narrow stairwell that led to a musty, cramped room whose starkness contrasted sharply with the prime minister's splendid Victorian office two floors below. There, "huddled" under the eaves, Mike sat at a desk on the right of the East Block attic's one narrow window. Only September's cool nights made human habitation possible in this garret and surely Mike and Keenleyside wondered about External's reputation as the élite of the civil service.* Mike and Keenleyside, who had met earlier in Toronto, shared these cramped quarters with an elderly secretary who did their typing, badly, on a crank-handled machine whose mechanical mysteries eluded all in the public service but her and a sister. Luckily, Mike and Keenleyside had similar backgrounds. Both came from devout Methodist families, and, as Keenleyside puts it well, "language and manners were subject to conventions we both accepted". Both liked sports, and had studied and taught history, although Keenleyside was a more active scholar than Mike. "I believe," Keenleyside wrote in his fascinating memoirs, "that our philosophies, personal interests, and behaviour patterns were much alike." At a time when only a small fraction of Canadians had university educations and a minuscule percentage had advanced degrees, Keenleyside and Pearson knew that they were becoming part of a Canadian élite. Good-looking in the casual collegiate ways of the 1920s, and possessing an admired athletic leanness, the two attic dwellers of 1928-9 sensed that their educational achievements, polished manners, and good looks were precious tools for shaping the nation they now served – and for escaping the attic.[8]

One difference, trivial now but significant then, existed between

---

* I certainly wondered when as a summer student I was consigned to this same garret, by that time assigned to the department's Historical Division.

Mike and Keenleyside. Keenleyside turned down a drink when Skelton invited him to his first lunch at the Rideau Club. Mike, however, now imbibed. In a medical examiner's report in September 1928, it is noted that Mike had become a "very temperate" drinker, consuming on average "a bottle of beer a week". The most he had consumed in one night was four ounces of spirits. When one considers Mike's righteous denunciation of Britain's failure to maintain prohibition in 1922, and the tremendous importance the Canadian Methodists placed upon abstinence, one can see that Mike had moved far emotionally from those beliefs he even recently held. Although Roly Michener recalls champagne flowing in celebrations with Mike at Oxford, other evidence, most importantly the testimony of "Wanny" Wansbrough and his college bills, which indicate no liquor charges, suggests that Mike, like Ontario itself, turned to liquor in the mid-1920s, not in a grand passion but with caution and a bit of guilt, which those who lacked the latter still noticed in Mike in his seventies.[9]

If some of the old Methodist rigidities had slipped away, the move to Ottawa made Mike's resolve firmer and his ambitions more focused. Keenleyside found Mike in his early thirties "in good physical shape, vigorous and alert". He was a wonderful office mate for ten months in 1928-9: "cheerful, amusing, keenly interested in his work, ambitious for the service and for himself". He "looked and was youthful and happy." The relationship ended with Keenleyside's posting to Tokyo, and Keenleyside wrote Mike a letter, "thanking him for his companionship, expressing [his] regard and admiration, and adding that when he found himself moving rapidly toward the top of the public service, as [Keenleyside] was sure he would," Mike would have no more "zealous supporter" than his early companion. The difference between this recollection and that of his former students (see page 124, above) is striking. The comments reflect the difference between the uncertain scholar and the determined diplomat. Hume Wrong, who knew Mike in Toronto and Ottawa, suggests as much in a comment he probably wrote in 1931: Mike, he claimed, was "quick, intelligent, and full of initiative, and fitted to do good work either in Ottawa or at a post abroad. His output is large; he *used to be rather slipshod and careless* [my italics], but I think he has improved a bit in these respects." In fact, Wrong's remarks are grudging; in his early years at External, Mike was extraordinarily hard-working and remarkably focused. The "curiously disjointed fellow" described by Massey and Skelton gave way, in Skelton's own view, to an exceptionally able foreign-service officer. Mike had discovered his *métier*.[10]

Mike's genius for companionship flourished in small groups. George Glazebrook recalls how Mike once tried to incorporate dramatic gestures and adopt various personae in lecturing to a large class, as Hume Wrong and, for that matter, Vincent Massey did so effectively and easily. The class erupted in laughter, for Mike was no actor and his personality remained obstinately his own, not Cromwell's or Henry VIII's.[11] In smaller gatherings, however, Mike's gift for anecdote, his willingness to listen to others, his quick wit, and, most of all, his ability to poke fun at himself and his flaws, made him splendid company. In the late 1920s and throughout the 1930s, the small and homogeneous External department was a setting where Mike's qualities and skills were displayed and admired. Housed in the East Block, nestled within the capacious bosom of the prime minister's own office, the department was small enough for its men to be intimately known, and those in it had privileges denied to other public servants. There were only fourteen "External men" (there were no women officers for over a generation) when Mike joined in August 1928, and twenty-one men two years later (nine in Ottawa and twelve distributed among Canada's five postings: London, Paris, Tokyo, Washington, and Geneva).

The posts were the great cosmopolitan capitals. Skelton sought out Canadians who would be neither rustic nor colonial, who should know that one sipped cognac but downed aquavit; that one used "one" in certain company; that Gladys Cooper and Diana Cooper were not sisters, though both were actresses and exquisite women; and that, according to Lord Curzon's definitive ruling, gentlemen never took soup at luncheon. Proper, to be sure, but stuffy never, for Skelton's strongly democratic instincts meant that the department rejected the formal trappings that traditionally accompanied diplomacy.* To be sure, Vincent Massey had wanted uniforms and wore one himself, which made him appear curiously picturesque, and Mackenzie King owned a Windsor uniform, which made him seem more than usually well-stuffed. Pearson, Keenleyside, and the others bought uniforms second hand, wore them rarely, and discarded them as the depression years made such ostentation more offensive. Even in the 1920s, the younger officers made fun of Massey's pretence. When Mike went to Washington in the summer of 1929, he received an invitation to a reception from the British embassy asking that he wear "decorations". He told Keenleyside that he prepared himself by "furbishing up his Garter, washing out his Ruth, and fastening on his Varsity Hockey T."[12] Their tastes were modern, and their politics fashionably liberal, but vulgarity was always the cardinal offence. The External men were quite unrepresentative of the country they served, but their influence derived from their uniqueness and excellence.

When Mike arrived, the department still bore traces of its clerical past when the under-secretary Sir Joseph Pope, who long ago had served John A. Macdonald as private secretary, thought that an active foreign office was incompatible with the spirit of Empire. Suitably inactive, Sir Joseph's daily routine in the early 1920s saw him arrive at the East Block midmorning, stroll around Parliament Hill after lunch, and then depart in top hat with cane in hand at a decent hour in the afternoon. No competitive examinations existed until 1928, and hiring was at the whim of the minister. Borden, for example, placed his troubled (and troubling) brother in the department. Pope had left in 1925 leaving only W.M. Walker, who had been assistant under-secretary since the department's creation in 1909 and whose perspective was that of an earlier age. In August 1928, Mike's depart-

---

* In Skelton's fifteen years as under-secretary, thirty-one of his forty officers had postgraduate degrees from universities outside Canada. Twenty-two had studied in Britain, fourteen at Oxford. Twenty had studied at two or more foreign universities. I am indebted to John Hilliker of the Department of External Affairs for this information.

mental *confrères* included Merchant Mahoney, a relic of the Canadian War Mission in Washington who had stayed on as a "Canadian agent" after the war until Massey set up the legation in 1927 and inherited him. Another officer, Laurent Beaudry, had returned from Washington where he could not get on with Wrong. Philippe Roy, who had served in Paris as a *commissaire général,* did better and was appointed the first Canadian minister to Paris in 1928. Désy, Mike's first Ottawa landlord, went to Paris as Roy's first secretary (Roy needed much assistance; Pierre Dupuy, a young lawyer, was second secretary). In London, Lucien Pacaud served under the high commissioner and leading Liberal-party contributor, the "Salada tea king", P.C. Larkin. The first minister to Tokyo was another wealthy Liberal, Herbert Marler, whom younger officers dubbed "Marblehead". In Geneva, at the league, Dr. W.A. Riddell, a Methodist minister who fully reflected the strong League of Nations support among Canadian Protestant churchmen, represented Canada. The younger officers obviously brought a new non-partisan, secular, and intellectual air to the department. The examinations and requirements that Skelton set for his recruits brought forth the kind of men he wanted. They naturally tended ever more to be men like Skelton himself, and one unfortunate result was a reduction of the percentage of French Canadians in External Affairs. When Mike took the examinations, not a word was raised about the French language, and in External in those days scarcely a word of French was spoken, except by francophones among themselves. What is most astonishing is that Mike and most of his colleagues did not then regard this situation as unusual or deplorable. British diplomats warned as early as 1929 that the situation was unhealthy for the young foreign service. French was not only the traditional language of diplomacy but also of about 30 per cent of Canadians. Canada's greatest diplomat never learned it, and that deficiency was to become one of his lasting regrets.[13]

The early group – Mike, Wrong, Keenleyside, Kirkwood, "Tommy" Stone, Norman Robertson (he joined in 1929), John Read (the departmental legal adviser), Scott Macdonald, D'Arcy McGreer, Alfred Rive, H.F. "Temp" Feaver – were well connected to the Anglo-Canadian university and legal worlds. Their ties with the business community were weak, and the atmosphere at External, in 1929-30 and thereafter, was that of a lively and youthful senior common-room, certainly not a Rotary meeting or a country club. Robertson admired French novels, Tommy Stone French wines, Kirkwood wrote poetry, Keenleyside read it; and Wrong bitched about their lot brilliantly. Although the younger officers respected Skelton's intellect and integrity, they lamented the administrative chaos that too often reigned in the department. Two women, Agnes McCloskey and Marjorie McKenzie, successfully scrutinized accounts and managed files, but a broader sense of direction was lacking. When, for example, Mike rushed off to Ottawa to join External as Skelton requested, he arrived to find nothing to do. The experience was similar to many that followed.[14]

When he did begin work, Mike's first task was to put together a brief for a league conference on the nomenclature of causes of death. It has not survived. Neither does a record exist of his second task, that of compiling a list of imperial treaties affecting Canada. Far more significant were the new friendships made and old friendships renewed in the winter of 1928-9. Maryon's pregnancy limited their social life, but the excitement created by their first house and first car (a second-hand Ford) was surpassed immeasurably by the birth of their daughter, Patricia, on March 9, 1929. This time the doting parents abandoned the child-rearing techniques they had applied to Geoffrey, which required that "However long and violently" Geoffrey cried, "no soothing care" should be given lest he be ruined for life. With Patricia, feeding was flexible, and affection came "on any or no occasion". The parents survived much better.[15]

In the summer of 1929, Mike received his first diplomatic posting to Washington. Washington's torrid heat drove the senior diplomats to their vacation residences at Bar Harbor, Maine, or some other appropriate summer retreat. Someone had to reply to dispatches and read the cables, and Mike filled in. He made good use of the time and quickly struck up friendships with other officers from other embassies and with junior State Department officers who could not escape

Washington. Canadian-American relations in the late 1920s were frayed by American prohibition, which Canadian liquor manufacturers were conscientiously undermining, and by rising American tariffs, which rightly frightened Canadians. A month after Mike's return to Ottawa in the fall, the great stock-market crash complicated Canadian-American relationships even more and increasingly harried those whose task was to deal with them.

Mike was fortunate that no permanent posting came. Keenleyside and Kirkwood soon left Ottawa for Japan to watch in horror as Japanese militarists gained ever greater control of imperial policy and as the Canadian minister Herbert Marler seemed ready, in Keenleyside's words, to "sink the League of Nations to sell a million bushels of Canadian wheat". A half-century later Keenleyside lamented that posting, regarding it as a brake upon the progress of his career.[16] His belief is probably valid. Mike certainly benefited (as Keenleyside claims) from the extensive contacts he developed while performing an eclectic range of tasks his first seven years in External. Mike remained in the capital, travelling abroad occasionally to attend conferences, league sessions, and special gatherings. Being a "floater", as modern office argot would label Mike's position, surely lacked glamour: one can imagine Hume Wrong's wrath had he been assigned a similar role. Mike did complain, but always privately, and he never gave even the dreariest assignment second-class attention. Mike's seven years in and around Ottawa provided him an extraordinary range of international experience, a broad acquaintance with Canadian public life and politicians, and a valuable reputation for "versatility."[17]

By the time Mike returned from Washington, he knew how to mix a cocktail and survive diplomatic receptions. The training was useful for his first major international assignment, the London Naval Conference, which began in January 1930. The conference followed upon an earlier agreement reached among the United States, Great Britain, Japan, France, and Italy to limit their navies. Cruisers, however, were exempted as were some other naval vessels, and by the late 1920s various signatories were taking advantage of this loophole. Canada's invitation to the 1930 conference may have come because the other powers suspected Britain of using the Empire to avoid the limitations. Australia, for example, might build battleships to serve the British in wartime that would not count against the limits. The presence of the dominions, autonomous in their own minds but blindly loyal in the view of others, was therefore necessary for the conference. "So there we were," Mike later recalled, "five dominions sitting around the council table in perfect, if somewhat perplexing, sovereign equality with the Big Powers." Without navies or with navies so small that a 50 per cent reduction would have left half a ship in some cases, the dominions at the conference reflected the constitutional confusion of the time. The subtleties frustrated Mike, but at this conference he came to realize that "behind what might seem to be stubborn and unrealistic insistence on the recognition of equal status there was a very real principle – the right not to be bound by, or appear to be bound by, a British decision which often had to be made because of considerations that were imperial far more than they were Canadian, Irish, or South African." This principle, so zealously guarded by Skelton and King, applied to Canada in a way that it did not to South Africa and Ireland. Whereas the strength of anti-British feeling in Ireland and South Africa was sufficient to assure that those dominions would not commit themselves to British wars, the strength of British and imperial feeling remained sufficiently strong in Canada to ensure a commitment to come to Britain's aid if the motherland was truly endangered. Here lay the paradox that bedevilled Canada's foreign policy in the 1930s as the world lurched towards war: how could and why should Canada maintain an independence of decision when it seemed clear to other countries that her citizens would rally to aid a threatened Britain? Skelton obdurately denied that Canadians would respond as in 1914; in his heart King knew his countrymen better and so did Mike.[18]

For a young Canadian diplomat, the constitutional complexities of the 1930s presented splendid opportunities to observe the panorama of high diplomacy. The wise dominion diplomat only watched and did not speak out, for his views were known to be of little, if any, significance in the final decisions made by the Foreign Office. The dominions, in fact, dealt with the Dominions Office, which in theory informed the dominions and advised the Foreign Office and the cabinet of dominion opinion. The system was inadequate; the Dominions Office was a poor relation to the august Foreign Office. In the British cabinet, the Dominions Office minister always ranked below the foreign secretary. When, for example, J.H. Thomas's performance in the new Labour government in 1930 was considered substandard, he was "shunted off" to the Dominions Office where he could do less harm.[19] In fact, he did much harm, for the sententious Labour parliamentarian lacked the sophistication and experience dominion statesmen and diplomats expected from the British. Much of the British influence upon colonials came from tradition and bearing: Thomas lacked both. Increasingly, so did British governments.

For most Canadians in 1930, however, the awe of British statesmanship endured. "Minister's Son Honoured," the United Church's *New Outlook* proclaimed when Mike was appointed a delegate to the Naval Conference. Ed had probably sent in the story. *The Varsity* was similarly impressed, and in a headline that tells a great deal about Canadian diplomacy (and Canadian universities) in 1930, it reported: "Popular Football Coach Goes as Secretary to Canadian Delegation."[20] On January 10, Mike and Maryon left from Halifax for their long-delayed British trip, thrilled by the dignitaries and ceremonies that awaited them and comforted by a remarkably generous expense account. Both brought diaries to record each day of the conference, and these diaries reveal how enthralled with the city and each other the young couple were. Diplomats in London, such as Roger Makins and Gladwyn Jebb, who saw them frequently at the numerous social events, recall how brisk and businesslike Mike was and how uncomfortable Maryon seemed to be. Her diary suggests, however, that the apparent discomfort was more likely a combination of shyness and a "colonial's" terror of using the wrong fork, saying the wrong thing, or curtsying to the wrong person. They stayed at the Mayfair, dined at the Trocadero, and entered London's private chambers as privileged guests. Maryon revelled in the conference events and renewed the infatuation with London, which had begun with her first English experience nine years before.[21]

The conference began on January 19 at Buckingham Palace. "The King," Mike began his diary, "had the pleasure of meeting me this afternoon." Constitutional controversies immediately ensued:

> We all congregated in an immense room, hung with priceless pictures, and after kicking our heels for half an hour, filed into the throne room, where the chief of each delegation introduced his advisers to the King. A constitutional issue of infinite magnitude arose! Should [British Prime Minister Ramsay] MacDonald introduce all the delegates of the Commonwealth or only the U.K. ones, leaving each [Dominion] chief to introduce his own advisers. The Br. wanted the former. Col. [J.L.] Ralston fought for the latter. He won. Our national autonomy was saved.

Mike also reported that "His Majesty ... stood the shock of meeting me as well as might be expected."[22]

The Canadian delegation was excellent. Led by the admirable Nova Scotian J.L. Ralston, the delegation had three other members: Georges Vanier, Mike, and Commodore Walter Hose. The Pearsons and the Vaniers quickly formed an enduring friendship. Mrs. Ralston left less of an impression than the effervescent Pauline Vanier, who entertained everyone she encountered. On a rare night when there were no official duties, the Ralstons took the delegation to a play in the West End and then to the "KitCat Night Club", where they had supper and danced. "It was great fun," Maryon wrote, "wonderful band & floor & not very crowded.... We three women were worked to death as there were 5 men – Commodore Hose & Col. Ralston are both keen on dancing and we had hardly a still moment. We left about 1:30 – It was a very good evg." Many good evenings followed with the Jebbs, Lord and Lady Harding (she was a

Huxley), Capt. Bellairs (a Conservative MP), Ishbel MacDonald, and many other "notables", as Maryon quickly dubbed them. One weekend in Oxford, Maryon met Mike's tutor Costin and was pleased how "very keen" he was on Mike. He was, however, "a rather surprising type of bachelor – shy and yet anatomically outspoken." He spoke few words but apparently swore often. In Maryon's view Costin seemed "to crave a wife but wouldn't know what to do with one".[23] One weekend taught Maryon little about Oxford's particular ways.

Neither the stock-market crash three months earlier nor the Labour government whose members hosted the conference cast a pall upon the splendour with which Britons overwhelmed their guests. The conference opened with a banquet at the elegant Savoy where the Pearsons dined on "Caviare d'Astrakan, Bisque d'Ecrevisse, Délice de Sole Walaweska, Supreme de Volaille Monselet", and sipped Amontillado sherry followed by an extraordinary Château Lafitte 1865, Château d'Yquem 1921, and Taylor's 1904 port. Talleyrand's advice that a splendid table and spirits were the best accompaniment to successful diplomacy was rigorously taken to heart by Britain's socialist government. The French foreign minister, Aristide Briand, the victim of a long lifetime of Paris's sumptuous tables, could no longer take wine or rich food. Britain's proletarian leaders did so but appeared nervous as they chewed upon their "Caviare d'Astrakan" and other culinary delights. The dominion delegates, *The Evening Standard* reported, showed no such restraint as they greeted each new course and glass with gusto.[24]

If the culinary standards of the conference exceeded expectations, the working sessions were disappointing. Mike came with some optimism about the negotiations, but as the meetings "dragged on", he soon realized how fixed positions were and how different were the conceptions of security, even within the British Commonwealth. In a long-established pattern, which continued through the 1930s, the dominion delegations met to discuss what policy the "Empire" should follow. The Canadians, the Irish, and the South Africans bristled whenever it was suggested that there should be a common Empire policy or that a British position was necessarily theirs. The Australians and New Zealanders were generally more acquiescent. In these sessions Mike honed his gifts for compromise.* His reputation for common sense and the ability to find the middle path grew considerably through the 1930s. That middle path, however, became overgrown with thickets as the decade progressed, and few others had the capability or will to cut them down.

In his memoirs Mike sums up the Naval Conference well: "I seem to have written at length about this conference without mentioning its purpose, its work, or its results. This is no doubt because its purpose was obvious, its work unfinished, its results negligible." In his diary at the time, Mike gave a good analysis of the conference's failure as it prorogued without much agreement in late April. Some observers claimed that the conference had failed because of lack of preparation. Not at all, Mike wrote: "No conference ever received more thorough preparation, preparation by experts who knew their subjects thoroughly. The failure was not due to this. It was due to the fact that the subjects could not be discussed merely as legal problems. They were political ones, and this made any attempt at a solution at this time bound to fail." The Naval Conference revealed to Mike the limitations of "experts", of the governments they served, of "goodwill", and of institutions such as the league, which could subvert the very purpose of peace-making that it was created to serve.[25] In the academic language of the day, Mike's first experiences in international diplomacy made him more a "realist", one who accepted what is, rather than defining and planning what might be. Still, his Christian heritage and his own nature made him trust, as did Tennyson, that somehow good would be the final goal of ill even as the darkest

---

* As the Naval Conference ended in April, the British Commonwealth delegates faced a seemingly intractable roadblock when South Africa and Ireland objected to the use of the term "British Commonwealth of Nations" on certain tables and schedules in the final agreement. With Ralston gone, Mike was able to work out a compromise whereby the term "High Contracting Party" was used. As he noted in his diary, Ireland's days in the Commonwealth were clearly numbered.

clouds gathered. This faith saved him from the despondency that afflicted so many in the dreadful decade of the 1930s when assumptions about "civilization" and its progress were shattered.

Midway through the Naval Conference, Mike left for The Hague for a league-sponsored conference on the codification of international law. There Mike saw the brick-by-brick approach to international order that seemed so tedious to politicians but so essential if a lasting structure was to take form. The social life was considerably slower, and Mike took responsibility for territorial waters in the conference negotiations. In his first comments at an international meeting Mike spoke out in support of a stronger legal regime governing territorial waters. As Canada's prime minister more than three decades later he provided impetus for Canada's leading role in the historic law-of-the-sea negotiations, which established a stronger regime.[26] In the intervening years many bricks were toppled before the structure gained final shape. And so it would be in so much that Mike did. A letter he sent to Skelton in March while he was on the way to The Hague suggests why Mike became so highly regarded in the foreign service and elsewhere. Mike had talked with the British delegation and had heard the seasoned if not cynical British diplomats cast doubt upon the success of the conference. He told Skelton that the British "may be correct in this and of course it is dangerous to expect too much from any international conference but, on the other hand, I think it will be most unfortunate if the various delegations went to The Hague with the idea that nothing much was likely to happen. I went as far as telling the British this."

As usual, Ottawa had not sent definite instructions and Mike had to divide up duties with his two colleagues at the conference. Meanwhile in London he made himself busy helping Commodore Hose draw up rules for submarine warfare, preparing a memorandum for a proposed amendment to the League Covenant, and writing a radio speech for Ralston on "The Scot in Canada" and a Canada Club address, which, he immodestly told Skelton, "received a great deal of praise on all sides". He also assured Skelton (who shared Mike's Irish background) that all the superlatives he bestowed upon the Scots were accompanied with "what the Italian Delegation here would refer to as, a 'general reservation,' in favour of the Irish". Mike further added that "The result of all this has been that when the Conference itself was marking time I had quite enough to keep me from wasting my time."[27]

The Naval Conference taught Mike that conferences with pious aims were all too often a waste of time. He realized after London that disarmament had a distinct aura of unreality. At London, he noticed that France "nearly always managed to manoeuvre herself into a position of being a minority of one."[28] Throughout the 1920s France's insistence upon security before disarmament and its corollary, a system of collective security that had teeth, had bedevilled disarmament discussions. In seeking the heavens, the French, in the view of many North Americans, assured that all efforts fell short. In the 1930s, the ambitions of the Japanese, the economic rivalries exaggerated by the world-wide depression, and the stirring of German nationalism complicated the disarmer's task enormously.

As these new menaces to peaceful settlement loomed, the League Council finally set the date of February 1932 for the general disarmament conference that had been promised long before in the League Charter. Mike had begun to work on disarmament questions in 1929 and his Naval Conference experience marked him as the departmental official best qualified to prepare the Canadian position. In spring 1931 the government set up an interdepartmental committee on disarmament and a technical subcommittee, which Mike chaired. The final report of the committee was signed by Skelton, Pearson, and Rive for External and, for the Defence department, General A.G.L. McNaughton, chief of the general staff; the navy's Commodore Walter Hose; W.B. Myres; G.V. Walsh; and H.D.G. Crerar, who seems to have been the most active Defence person on the committee and who worked very well with Mike. Mike's contribution to this final document was large; indeed, its style and substance suggest he wrote all except the technical sections. His writing impressed his superiors; his views perhaps affronted them.[29]

Mike had tested his other opinions on official and unofficial

Ottawa. In those days before the web of security legislation was cast upon Canadian public servants, Mike (and others) talked about significant public issues with friends, small groups, and various interested Canadians.* Ottawa was small; opinions were tested among friends. As Mike worked on the interdepartmental committee, he spoke on disarmament to the Ottawa branches of the League of Nations Society and the Canadian Institute of International Affairs. He even published a portion of a memorandum on disarmament in *The Canadian Defence Quarterly,* using the curious pseudonym "Scrutator". As he polished his opinions in the last months of 1931, the Japanese began their brutal assault on China that would last fourteen years. The attack shook the foundations of the league system, but Mike's faith in that system had already eroded in the aftermath of the London Naval Conference. He continued to believe that the Great War, "that monstrous aberration of policy", had proven "the futility of war as an instrument of national policy". Its lesson was clear: "If armaments could ever have prevented war they should have in 1914." Instead, they encouraged it, and proved that no nation could rely on armaments to assure security. From this perspective, the victors drafted a league covenant that committed its members to work towards general disarmament. They had done so fitfully, concentrating on the many "technical problems". "But what of the preparatory political work?" Mike asked. The fate of the disarmament conference depended "almost entirely" on "the world political situation". There the preparations remained incomplete.

In Mike's view, the disarmament problem was "primarily" a European one. That old troubled continent was once again "an armed camp" with more men under arms in 1931 than in 1914. To the east, "the Russian bear is sharpening her claws and occasionally permits herself the luxury of a militant growl." Germany, disarmed by

---

* Even the Liberal J.L. Ralston, Pearson's political superior at the Naval Conference, continued to receive Pearson's disarmament memoranda after the Conservative Bennett government came to power. Other recipients of Pearson memoranda included Sir Robert Borden and Newton Rowell.

Versailles, chafed at the restrictions as her eastern and western neighbours bristled with arms. Now when one looked across the Rhine, one saw Nazis more fearsome than Prussian guards, and pocket battleships more potent than pre-war dreadnoughts, and politicians more extreme than the Kaiser's Reich had ever imagined. Germany's recent ugly face was deplorable, but it was perhaps understandable because her traditional enemy, France, had behaved so badly since the peace conference. To Mike, France was the greatest obstacle to disarmament. She maintained the largest army on the continent, built new fortifications, kept a navy much larger than the naval agreements allowed, and whined endlessly about "security". France argued to all who listened that there could be no disarmament without security. France's demand for a guarantee of security was most often expressed as insistence that the League of Nations possess the force to guarantee security. To other nations, such as Canada and the United States, that request was unreasonable. To "producers of security", France was solely a consumer and an especially greedy one. France's view that the League of Nations should enforce peace through sanctions had in fact weakened the institution France professed to value so highly. The young Canadian diplomat reflected his government's (but not all Canadians') opinion in stating that application of sanctions would be "completely futile" and "would really weaken League action in cases of emergency".[30]

It is supposed that sanctions would be applied by unanimous vote of the Council of the League. To me it is almost inconceivable that any occasion would arise in which unanimous action of that kind, or even action by two-thirds majority, would be possible. It is virtually impossible at any time ... to agree on an aggressor. It would be quite impossible to do so if such an agreement meant that all the members of the determining body, the League Council, including apparently members interested in the dispute, would be called upon themselves for military and naval action....

Sanctions, then, would only mean two things:–

a) Hesitation and probably inaction on the part of the Council
b) An encouragement to unscrupulous states to start trouble.

The League, with only moral force behind it, is far more likely to use that moral force to the full extent of its powers, than it ever would be to invoke any machinery by which an aggressor would automatically be determined and military sanctions automatically applied. And it is easy to argue that the most effective sanction the League can apply is "moral force", the sudden focussing of world opinion on a meeting of the Council specially convoked to deal with a disturber or disturbers of the peace.

These opinions are conventional, sewn together from bits and pieces of Canadian opinion in the early depression. Reflecting the spirit of those times and of his superiors, Mike's solutions are modest: a French recognition that it must reduce armaments; "equality of rights with respect to armaments" (which Germany wanted); and a permanent disarmament commission. Mike's prose was as crisp as his ideas were stale, but his conclusion contrasted sharply with the preceding passages. Its tone bore little of the "pragmatic realism"; he called for movement "Forward – towards a new world where each nation is part of an organic whole, respecting the rights and sharing the duties of others. Backwards – to the old world of self-centred sovereign 'states....'"[31] Despite these lofty sentiments, Mike admitted to Colonel Ralston that he "found it difficult to summon up much optimism" about the conference. In January 1932 he left for Geneva, his spirits still low.[32]

Accompanying Mike on the S.S. *Europa* were secretary of state Sir George Perley, solicitor general Maurice Dupré, Harry Crerar, General McNaughton, and Winnifred Kydd, dean of women at Queen's University and president of the National Council of Women (NCW). Prime Minister Bennett, characteristically impulsive, decided to appoint the NCW president without knowing who she was, expecting someone suitably mature and severe, and getting Miss Kydd – svelte, quick, and in her twenties. The first night in Geneva,

Miss Kydd was, in the opinion of Dr. W.A. Riddell, the reserved Canadian advisory officer to the league, the delight of the evening.[33] However, on the whole, it was not a happy group. McNaughton, the chief of the general staff, had seen expenditure on his cherished air service cut from $5,232,000 in 1931 to $1,750,000 in 1932 despite the deteriorating international situation, and he was most embarrassed while in Geneva when many of the released airmen announced they were setting off to save China. Disarmament conference or not, Canada was disarming; indeed its defences could not have withstood a determined attack by the Boy Scouts of America. Sir George Perley was an exquisite period-piece: seventy-five; sporting an Edwardian goatee and Victorian opinions; and suspicious of levity, modern contraptions, and most of all, modern people; Dupré was able but not well informed; and the delegation as a whole had not decided what it would do now that it was in Geneva. One thing Crerar and Mike did was repair to the "Bavaria" tavern in the evenings where Lake Geneva's charms and the wines of Burgundy and Alsace cleared away the darkening clouds that were gathering over the conference's work.[34]

Less than three weeks after his arrival, General McNaughton claimed that he was serving no useful purpose at the conference and announced that he should return home. He was gone in early March, convinced the conference would fail and indeed would make war more likely. Mike's mood was no better: he told McNaughton that the delegation missed the general and his wife – "far more so, I am sure, than you miss us and Geneva...." Initially, Mike was to stay in Geneva for three years, but its attractions were meagre, especially without his family, and the Disarmament Conference promised few career rewards. He requested that McNaughton ask Skelton to bring him home or make arrangements to send his family over.[35] His grumbling began with his first letter to Skelton just after his arrival. Playing upon the well-known Skelton suspicion of British motives, Mike claimed that the dominions secretary, L.H. Thomas, had met with the dominion delegations and had indicated that Canada was expected to support the British and "keep the old flag flying". "It was," he continued, "an amazing performance.... General McNaughton and I could hardly believe our ears; I personally, and he also ... were incensed at what we could only consider an intrigue." In normal moods, they would have seen it as the foolishness it simply was. Mike brusquely noted that "the conference opened yesterday ... without significance."[36] Later, through the prism of war, he recalled that day differently, a reflection of lost hopes and sanguine memories.* In late March, the conference prorogued and he left for Britain where he learned that the British had few illusions about the conference, expecting it "to completely fail". Sir Harry Batterbee of the Dominion Office told Mike that the British, if pushed by the French to take a stand on "the French idea of strengthening the sanctions and guarantee provisions of the League Covenant", would "prefer to consider an entirely new League of Nations", without any provision for sanctions. The British did not want the league as a "super state" but would much prefer it to be "a channel for the expression of international opinion". Recent events in Manchuria had convinced the British government that sanctions, "far from assisting the League in settling the dispute, had really proved a hindrance in the work of mediation".[37]

The conference, the offspring of a malformed league, would surely bear no fruit itself. Mike wanted to return to Ottawa "as soon as possible" to help with the Imperial Economic Conference where, he argued, he could be much more helpful.[38]

Skelton agreed to Mike's request and freed him from the frustrations of Geneva, but he also gently rebuked the fledgling Canadian diplomat. He too was pessimistic about the Disarmament Conference, and he agreed that the gap between the French and British view

---

* In his memoirs, Mike recalls the opening morning, which was "given over to the presentation of petitions for disarmament and peace from the plain and humble people of the world.... The bearer of each country's message was a wounded veteran, a war widow, a 'silver cross' mother or an orphaned child. It was an intensely moving occasion. The emotional atmosphere created was reflected in the opening speeches of the delegates.... Our spirits were lifted in a way that for me was not to be repeated until the opening days of the San Francisco Conference."

of the league had widened. He none the less implicitly chided Mike for taking seriously and approvingly Batterbee's notion of a new league. The league, he wrote, "has great possibilities of flexible compromise, and I think it would be able to hold within its ranks both French and British. After all national policies change as interests and governments vary, and it is hardly worth while considering a new League of Nations until the present one has been given a little more trial."[39]

National policies change; so do individuals. Skelton defending the league; Pearson ready to inter it. In his memoirs Mike writes: "The failure of the Disarmament Conference and the successful defiance by Japan of the League's efforts to halt her aggression in China made it a depressing time for those who, like myself, had hoped that progress might be made toward peace and security by collective action through the League." Mike, as we have seen, did not believe in "peace and security by collective action" in 1932; neither did Skelton, although even he was willing to travel a small way along the road.[40] Like his superior, he feared "collective action" and sanctions and saw the league as too often simply an instrument of France's selfish policies. In a discussion of league reform in December 1933 based upon a memorandum by External officer Scott Macdonald that recommended that Canada should "take a stronger stand at Geneva on the principle of collective responsibility for the preservation" of peace and should support automatic economic and even military sanctions against aggressors, Mike spoke out against strengthening the league and Canada's obligations. The league was "breaking up because Germany and Japan thought it was interfering too much with their national right already." The league, in Mike's view in 1932-3, could be merely a forum for world opinion, which could act to compel an aggressor to desist.[41]

Mike later did not remember how close his stand on the league was to that of Mackenzie King, which he later censured so strongly as naive at best, an evasion of responsibility at worst. Certainly his views in 1932 were not those of the British peace activist Philip Noel-Baker whom he later admired so much.[42] Mike's views reflect inexperience but also disillusionment and confusion, for the events of the early 1930s shattered many foundations for the beliefs he had held and the hopes he had cherished. We must also admit that Mike tailored his views to match the fashion in the department, and here the appropriate cut was defined by Skelton. Still, the setting is the most important factor. The anglophile of the 1920s discovered in London and Geneva that Canada's interests came second to British interests when the two conflicted. Moreover, the young League of Nations supporter heard and read too much empty rhetoric from its podium and saw too much intrigue in the corridors of the Palais des Nations. The London Naval Conference and the World Disarmament Conference were education by the current event, and the lessons Mike derived suggested caution rather than commitment. As late as fall 1931 Mike believed that the last war still made war unthinkable. In his paper on disarmament, he explicitly assumed that no nation would start an "offensive" war and that the economic distress of the 1930s would lead to a reduction of spending on armaments. As Edwin Pearson had said in 1927, there seemed to be a new sentiment regarding war, created by the knowledge that another war would bring a "hell of desolation". Then, in September 1931 the Japanese moved into Manchuria; in January 1932, they attacked Shanghai. The new world looked very much like the old, only crueller, with even less rationality and civility. The result was so unexpected – and so sad.

Ed Pearson died unexpectedly of appendicitis at sixty-three on September 6, 1931, just before the Japanese made their move and Mike left for Geneva. It was a case of bad medicine, in which a doctor badly misdiagnosed Ed's ailment. The obituaries were generous and invariably referred to Ed's good nature. The death shocked the family and left Annie with a meagre pension of about $700. Vaughan, now a stockbroker who had lost his father's savings in the market crash, lived with Annie for the rest of her life. Mike and his father were not close in the sense that they shared their private feelings, but there could be no doubt about their personal devotion and love. To Ed's final days, Mike always remained to him what he proclaimed him to be in the war years: as fine a son as any father could ever have.[43]

Mike was grumpy after his father's death. Perhaps his pessimism in Geneva derived from his grief. Certainly his usual charm was lacking. Miss Kydd, whose "feminine grace and charm" he warmly recalled in his memoirs, did not think so fondly of him when she left Geneva in spring 1932. In her final meeting with Dr. Riddell she thanked him for his kindnesses but then broke down as she told him how difficult and demanding Perley and Pearson had been. His secretary from that conference recalls how Mike came in early in the morning, rolled up his sleeves, said, "Let's get to work," and most determinedly did so.[44] The record and the reminiscences of the period suggest an ambitious, occasionally imperious, and somewhat opinionated young man. Photographs show his sharp eyes, closed jaw, and the slight forward tilt of his head. He appears sure of himself, confident of his abilities, and devoted to the task at hand. Having cast about for a career, Mike husbanded his many talents and bestowed them fully upon his work. There was not much time for his two young children; he missed them greatly and his eagerness to return from Geneva arose as much from their absence as from the desultory ways of the conference itself.

The best illustrations of his ambition come not from his work in the area of international affairs but from service on two royal commissions which examined the depression's effects on Canada – the 1931 Royal Commission on Grain Futures and the 1934 Royal Commission on Price Spreads. Because the prime minister headed the External Affairs department, foreign-service officers were often conscripted for important domestic tasks. Mike had already caught R.B. Bennett's eye, and Bennett appointed him secretary of the Grain Futures Commission, which would examine whether futures trading distorted the market in favour of speculators' profits. Before choosing an Ontario town boy as secretary, Bennett turned to a British economist and civil servant, Sir Josiah Stamp, to head the commission. Whatever Sir Josiah's familiarity with wheat sheaves, the task did not daunt him for he completed the work of the commission within a few weeks. The hearings took two weeks in April; the report was ready the first week of June, by which time Sir Josiah was back in London, unravelling Britain's railway problems.

The report approved of futures trading to the dismay of the "Pool" interests in Western Canada. This approval was mildly stated, and the arguments of the farmer pools were not criticized directly in the report. Unfortunately, one of the statistical appendices seemed to refute the farmers' case. Faced with irate farm groups, Bennett summoned the commission secretary to his office to subject him to his celebrated rage. Mike pleaded innocence, admitting that he included the appendix but did so only after one of the commissioners, Sanford Evans, approved of its inclusion. He then moved quickly to protect his position, cabling to Evans a strongly worded complaint that he was "at [a] loss to understand" Evans's statement to J.K. Brown, his fellow commissioner, "that you expressed opinion to me document should not be included." He followed with a letter to Brown and a wooing of reporters. It worked. Mike in the 1930s was no pushover, and not always "a nice guy".[45]

On June 3, 1931, just after the Stamp report was completed, George Ferguson of *The Manitoba Free Press* wrote to praise Mike's work on the report, ending his letter: "Out here we starve. The prairies are a barren waste. Gophers and nettles are our daily diet."[46] Mike had seen "drought, dust, depression and despair" when the commission travelled across the prairies in the spring of 1931. As always, the country looked forward to the next summer's crop, but the grasshoppers, the dust, and the markets spoiled each subsequent year as they had the last. No relief was in sight. Mike himself felt little of the depression's sting. The government cut his (and other civil servants') salary by 10 per cent, but the deflation that accompanied the depression meant that Mike's real wages actually went up.* Ottawa was sheltered from the depression's coldest blasts, and he and his colleagues could afford housemaids or nannies, refrigerators, automobiles, radios, and the occasional night out dancing to Benny

---

* The cost of living fell about 19 per cent between 1929 and 1933. Mike's salary increased to $4,300 in 1932 before the cut. His income in 1933 was more than 50 per cent above the average income of a medical doctor in that same year. In real income his salary would be equivalent to well over $60,000 in 1989 dollars, much more than a young officer earns today.

Goodman, at the movies, or at Ottawa's Little Theatre. But the hopeless faces and the hollow eyes were everywhere in Canada in the 1930s. In his generally favourable assessment of Mike, Hugh Keenleyside expresses some reservations. Mike, he claims, made no effort to know the west that suffered so much in the 1930s.* In a broader sense, "something – whether lack of imagination or sensitivity – apparently made it impossible for him to become involved in any intense way with the general tragedy of so many of the lives around him."[47] Certainly Mike's reaction to the human tragedies of the depression lacked the intensity of that of some of his friends, such as King Gordon or Frank Underhill, who turned to socialism and were founders of the Co-operative Commonwealth Federation. They continued, however, to regard Mike as one of their own, recognizing that government service served as a constraint. Commenting on his memoirs in the early 1970s, Gordon told Mike that he was not surprised that Mike had written a remarkably progressive speech R.B. Bennett had given at Rensselaer Polytechnic Institute in 1935, for, Gordon claimed, rumours abounded in socialist circles in the mid-1930s that Mike was one of them.[48] Certainly he was closer to "them" in 1935 than ever before and probably closer than he was later.

The Royal Commission on Price Spreads was the product of H.H. Steven's strong antipathy to monopoly and large business. Stevens, the minister of trade and commerce in Bennett's government, shared Mike's Methodist background; indeed, Ed Pearson had been his minister in Peterborough in 1906. All the enthusiasm the Methodists had earlier expended suppressing sin Stevens threw into his crusade against profiteering. The commission bore Stevens's personal stamp. Mike heard small retail merchants whom Stevens championed complain bitterly about the hardships they faced and the unfair practices of the large corporations and department stores. Mike had to orga-

---

* Keenleyside's statement in Volume I of his memoirs, *Hammer the Golden Day,* that Mike was thirty-six before he saw any part of Canada west of Windsor is a bad slip. Mike, of course, was married in Winnipeg and had visited it several times before he was thirty-six.

nize the hearings, hire staff, and write drafts of the report. The final report possesses a more moderate tone than did Stevens himself. He resigned as its chairman in late October 1934, three months into the inquiry, after continuous disputes with Bennett and other Tories about his attacks on large corporations, especially Simpson's. Nevertheless, the report, which was tabled in April 1935, bears a strongly reformist tone, one with which Mike felt comfortable.[49] He never possessed the hatred of the rich that animated others, but he did recoil from ostentation and obvious inequality. His political outlook was not systematic and, as Keenleyside suggests, he did not relate his political beliefs to individual human circumstances. As part of what Doug Owram has aptly described as "The Government Generation", Mike had a belief in the need for government to act when private initiative had failed. He was definitely a centralist, scornful of provincial claims to a Confederation "compact."[50] Still, he remained more skeptical of what government could do than most.

Just before his appointment to the Price Spreads Commission, Mike gave an address to an Ottawa Study Club on Roosevelt's New Deal. It is the most candid expression of his political attitude during the 1930s and 1940s. He accepts that individualism must be curbed in the interest of society and contemporary circumstances had made "planning" inevitable. Mike, however, was worried.[51]

Now, no such national planning is possible without controls. General Johnson candidly admitted this a few weeks ago. "I think planning for the future," he said, "has proved itself since the war, but planning is no good without some form of control." Further, I think it is clear that in the present "savage" state of the United States such controls must, to be effective, be imposed by the Government. I suggest that this is not possible in the United States under present conditions. I am not sure whether planning is possible anywhere, except in a cemetery, without destroying more than it creates. Certainly it can only be applied to a stable, well organized, and mature political society. It might be done ... in England. I doubt very much if it can be done in the United States.

Planning of the New Deal kind is a middle course between capitalism and socialism. Middle courses are notoriously difficult for intoxicated nations, as for intoxicated individuals to follow. And the United
States is often intoxicated.... And so I feel that while the Recovery
program, born of a crisis, was able to incorporate in its being some
far-reaching social and economic ideas, now that the crisis is past these
ideas are both too radical and not radical enough for permanent acceptance. The socialists will jeer at them as a compromise with capitalism.
The conservatives will damn them as un-American, Red, and retard-
ing recovery.

And so Mike stayed in the middle, pragmatic and now clearly within
the broad avenues of the Canadian liberal tradition.

In the ideological battles of the 1930s Mike's works were neither
cold nor hot. There is a passage in Revelations that Mike knew well:
"So then because thou art lukewarm, and neither cold nor hot, I will
spue thee out of my mouth." Mike's lukewarm caution resulted, not
in being "spued" from the mouth of Canada's political leaders but,
rather, in being taken more closely to their bosoms. The price-
spreads report completed, the commission members wrote to the
prime minister, unanimously commending his work. "To marked
natural ability and technical qualifications," they wrote, there was
added a devotion to duty which won the unstinted admiration and
gratitude of every member of the Commission." His work habits
astonished them: "Since July [1934], all his time was devoted to the
Commission. By 'all' we mean on an average from 9 o'clock in the
morning until midnight, Saturdays and Sundays included." They
requested that Bennett consider giving Mike "some suitable and tangible remuneration". He did so quickly and most generously: he gave
Mike a substantial bonus of $1,800 and invited him to accompany
him to King George V's Silver Jubilee.[52]

Sailing on the French liner *Paris,* sampling the best French wines
(without the press nearby, for "R.B." was publicly a teetotaller), and
forgetting the cares of Ottawa, the prime minister and Mike
improved their already good relationship. Bennett found Mike, as he

later told the House of Commons, "on the verge of a complete break-down" because of his work on the commission.*

Bennett, whose decisions often reflected whimsy more than mature consideration, decided to award Mike a cherished Order of the British Empire (OBE). Knowing the democratic Skelton's dislike of honours, especially British ones, Mike hesitated to accept and suggested a promotion instead. Bennett, who took honours lists very seriously, grunted and told Mike that if he made him change the list again, Mike would get neither an OBE nor the promotion so long as he was prime minister. Mike was silent. A few weeks later after his return Mike was playing tennis at the Rockcliffe Club when a car stopped and Sir Alan Lascelles, the governor general's secretary and a British aristocrat who did not take OBEs so seriously, strolled over to the court, tossed Mike a small case, with the words, "Here's your OBE."[53] Bennett would have been horrified; Mike saw the humour in it.

The irony in the award was, however, lost on Mike. His most notable work in the 1930s came not in diplomacy but in the barbed trenches of Canadian politics. Once again he survived and this time he prospered. Nevertheless he yearned to return to diplomacy. At the Silver Jubilee, the glitter of London and the presence of Europe's greatest could not conceal the rot that was then spreading throughout Europe. Like most Canadians, Mike's thoughts turned to Europe's disorders. Canada's fate, he was coming to realize, would not be decided in Ottawa. Mike returned to London where the truly important decisions were made in the late summer of 1935, and there he began an increasingly horrified watch upon the breakdown of all the dreams peace-makers like his beloved late father had cherished such a short time ago.

---

* Bennett said this in answer to a question about special honoraria asked in the House of Commons on July 3, 1935, by King. King, however, made it clear he had the highest impression of Mike's work.

CHAPTER EIGHT

THE LONDON SEASON

A picnic lunch party in the gardens of Eccleston Square – pickled herrings, meat pies, lemonade and laughter. I shall remember this sunny week in the London season of 1939.... The London season survived the last war and may survive the next. Will there always be cultivated rich girls who have read all this year's books and been to Algiers and will not admit to themselves that marriage is now as tiresomely inevitable for them as it was for their grandmothers? And clever young men in the Foreign Office? And little luncheons of eight in Bryanston Square with an actress, an M.P., a girl three years "out" and getting on with her conversation, an American married woman and a vigorous Edwardian hostess?

– Charles Ritchie[1]

MIKE RETURNED to London for the last hours of what his old officer, Robert Graves, called the "long weekend" between the wars.[2] London in the 1930s retained the white-tie-and-tails elegance of Edwardian days yet offered her residents the various pleasures of modern times, save efficient heating and plumbing. Eccentricity abounded, mad political nostrums were doled out on almost every street-corner, and black limousines and cavernous cabs bore old aristocrats and the *nouveaux riches* to countless clubs and dinner parties throughout the world capital. Although the north, the Midlands, and South Wales that had erected the Victorian foundations of

British grandeur lay desolated by the Great Depression, London's streets abounded with life, the bejewelled pageant of Empire still moved, and unemployment in the Greater London area stood at only 8 per cent, a third the figure in Canada when Mike left.[3] London was to diplomacy what nearby Wimbledon's centre court was to tennis, the highest plateau of a tradition, the arena in which the most talented could most clearly demonstrate their skills.

Mike's apprenticeship had been duly served by 1935, and his background stamped the young Canadian as someone who would neither succumb to the blandishments of the Foreign Office's "clever young men" nor fade into the crowded tableau of London's diplomatic life. The British, whose diplomats maintained detailed files (which were then probably the enemy of action but are today the glory of historians), had good reports on Mike. In 1930, the newly established British High Commission in Ottawa told the Dominions Office that Mike merited "special kindness" while he was at the London Naval Conference for he had "taken considerable risks on several occasions in order to impart to us information which otherwise would never have reached us." Mike had already learned the glories of gossip, and he gave as often as he received. In 1932 the Dominions Office sent the transcript of a speech Mike gave to the Foreign Policy Association in New York with the comment that the speech was "extremely interesting" and drew attention to the "great honour conferred on Pearson in being invited to address ... a most distinguished gathering of United States luminaries."[4] The British Foreign and Dominions offices rarely paid much attention to junior dominion diplomats. Mike, however, won respect, for his ability, candour, and, not least, his sure-footedness in the maze of British social and diplomatic life. Gladwyn Jebb, one of the brightest young men of the Foreign Office in the 1930s, recalls that, from the beginning, Mike seemed "one of us".[5]

Mike, in fact, had become more careful since 1930 when the British High Commission paid tribute to his "friendliness". At the Naval Conference, the Disarmament Conference, and the League of Nations, his Canadian nationalism grew as he saw how little impact

Canadian opinion made upon British decisions, how complicated British interests were, and how often they conflicted with what Canadians deemed their own interests to be. His regular visits to the league and to London led to a characteristically Canadian resentment of Europe's ceaseless quarrels and swelling armaments. Having interred the last bones of the Geneva Conference, Mike returned to Ottawa with a bleak vision of that continent's future. The conference had collapsed, and a new armaments race had begun. The hopes for a collective security system under the league were being undermined by the reality of a pattern of "each nation for itself and ruin for us all". As the memory of the last war's horrors receded, the Europeans once more made trifles of real terrors. Mike told an Ottawa church group in the spring of 1934 that in the 1920s there had been "a chance to build up a better order of things. That chance is now passing, for a new generation is appearing on the stage for whom the sound of the trumpet is a call to adventure rather than a summons to death."[6] For many thoughtful young Canadians, the temptation to close their ears to the European sirens was irresistible. Frank Underhill, Mike's old colleague at Toronto, called on Canadians in 1935 to make it clear to the world, and especially to Great Britain, that "the poppies blooming in Flanders fields have no further interest for us". All of Europe's troubles, Underhill declaimed, were "not worth the bones of a Toronto grenadier".[7]

Most Toronto grenadiers disagreed, and so did Prime Minister Bennett. They continued to regard British international leadership as essential and the Anglo-Canadian alliance as fundamental to Canada's national character and existence. Bennett, moreover, interpreted Canada's League of Nations obligations more broadly than did Skelton, King, and Mike. This division of opinion combined with Bennett's unpredictable ways made Geneva a difficult and undesirable posting for diplomats. In 1935 Skelton became especially worried about Canada's participation at the league. Benito Mussolini of Italy was openly boasting about the war he intended to wage against Abyssinia (now Ethiopia), and the Abyssinians were looking to the league provisions for collective security for protection. In the last case of clear-cut aggression, the Japanese attack upon Manchuria, Canada, through its representative C.H. Cahan, had made a complete fool of itself by appearing to support Japan's "civilizing mission" in China while simultaneously condemning aggression.[8] Skelton regarded the Italian-Abyssinian conflict as potentially even more dangerous. Since Manchuria, Japan and Germany had strutted out of the League of Nations; now an emboldened Mussolini was warning that any attempt to impose sanctions would mean war. Skelton thus drafted instructions to Geneva carefully and tried to keep the Canadian delegates away from the snares that he was certain the British were setting for the unsuspecting dominions.

Skelton especially feared the influence of Riddell, the Canadian advisory officer in Geneva, who he correctly believed was more sympathetic to collective security and sanctions than the Canadian government had traditionally been.[9] The head of the delegation to Geneva for the fall 1935 session was G. Howard Ferguson, the former premier of Ontario, a devout imperialist, and every bit as impulsive and unorthodox as R.B. Bennett. When he was appointed by Bennett to represent Canada in London, Ferguson astonished his socialist British hosts by announcing that he went to Britain on a mission to remould the "old spirit of pride and self-respect" in the increasingly lackadaisical British people.[10] He was a man to be watched – and to be reined in. Mike's qualifications for such a task seemed exceptionally good; he had successfully dealt with the rambunctious H.H. Stevens, and among young External officers his political skills and congenial personality were unsurpassed. He had expressed strong reservations about sanctions and an activist league. Moreover, Ferguson liked Mike. When asked in August 1935 whether he would welcome Mike to Canada House, he responded enthusiastically, declaring that Mike had the "experience, tact and personality" to handle the required tasks. "I am all [for] the idea and all for Pearson." The warm feelings were reciprocated. Mike wrote in January 1936, after the King government had replaced Ferguson with Vincent Massey, that he had "never worked with any man prominent in public life so natural, unaffected, human and friendly in his contacts as he

[Ferguson] is."[11] The parson's son had more respect for such qualities than did Robertson and Wrong, the children of professors.

As the league and Italy moved towards a clash in the summer months, Skelton decided to send Pearson to Geneva so that he could "keep an eye" on Riddell and Ferguson. Mike, who was preparing for his London posting, was furious: he had to leave on "about sixty hours notice", which meant that Maryon had to stay behind to pack, pay the bills, and sell the car, and many old friends would have no time to say goodbye. As for Geneva, he disliked both the duties and the place. The delegation, which included Miss Kydd, was badly prepared and its members "hardly ever saw each other". His solace came in "acting as a golf gigolo to British [diplomats'] wives whose husbands *were* busy." On that score, however, Mike had absolutely no complaints, for he found them (especially Alice Makins) the most charming of women.[12]

Geneva in 1935 was not the dispirited city it had been during the Disarmament Conference. That June, in Canterbury, Eliot's *Murder in the Cathedral* was first performed; in that play ordinary Englishmen are drawn to the cathedral and its spirituality by the political terrorists of the time who threaten its holy purposes. That same month in 1935 ordinary English people rallied to the defence of another cathedral, the Palais des Nations, in Geneva as the 1930s political gangsters assaulted it. The Peace Ballot organized by the British League of Nations Society was a massive public rejection of the claim that the British people would not fight to save the collective system as so many British politicians had said in justifying their weakness in the 1930s.[13] In Eliot's play the knights who murdered Becket complained that Englishmen always favoured the underdog. And they still did: between the swaggering Duce and the tiny Abyssinian king the Englishmen's choice was clear. In 1935, an election year, British politicians responded quickly to the public temper. At the Labour Party conference, trade unionist Ernest Bevin declared that he and his colleagues had had enough of their pacifist leader George Lansbury's carting his conscience from conference to conference, and they replaced him as leader with Clement Attlee, who had a strong war record and a willingness to use force to maintain peace and justice. The Conservative Party under Stanley Baldwin in coalition with National Labour responded by taking a harder stance against Mussolini even though Baldwin had described the league as unworkable a year before. When Sir Samuel Hoare, the British foreign secretary, spoke at Geneva in early September 1935, he stunned the delegates by promising strong British action where there had been none since the 1920s. His Conservative colleague Neville Chamberlain, who had earlier thought the league dangerous and sanctions unworkable, also became convinced they must be tried. When Hoare's strong words were cheered, Chamberlain thought the league was being vindicated, and it was all "a wonderful gain for the world".[14]

The "Geneva spirit" (as the move to sanctions was called) seems to have infected Mike that late summer as well, and some friends aided its spread. Newton Rowell prodded the government and Mike to take a strong stand. The influential Montreal lawyer Brooke Claxton, whom Mike found time to write to before his hurried departure, urged Mike to spend his time in London cleaning up "the mess": "You might begin with Ethiopia. I don't suppose we could ever make up our minds what to do in external affairs sufficiently strongly to have an effect upon British policy but we could at least prevent our negative action on being credited in England with a major share of responsibility for England's refusal to do anything."[15] Britain had argued that its reluctant embrace of collective security came from its need to listen to the opinion of the dominions who favoured the league, where they could parade their newfound autonomy, but who opposed sanctions because they feared war and thought the greatest security came through distance and the British navy. The stance was rational but scarcely inspiring; its expression echoed the legalistic prose of the murdering knights, not the spiritual poetry of Becket. The position was familiar to Mike, but as Hitler and Mussolini spouted their obscenities, he became increasingly uncomfortable with such beliefs.[16]

In Geneva, Riddell and Ferguson were quick to accept the new spirit and to act upon it. Far from being cautious, as their instructions suggested, both pushed the British along in their course. Ferguson, with an old-fashioned imperialist faith in British battleships, even questioned what good was served by having the British ambassador in Rome tell Mussolini that the British fleet in the Mediterranean "had no aggressive intention".[17] Mike heard Ferguson praise Hoare's "strong commitment" and declare Canada's willingness to join "with the other members of the League in considering how by unanimous action peace can be maintained". When the fighting began in Abyssinia, the league moved with unexpected speed, and Skelton's anxiety about what was happening increased. With the Canadian general election taking place on October 14, Skelton's reluctance is understandable. He knew that Mackenzie King, whose views on sanctions and the league were closer to his own, was very likely to defeat Bennett. It was necessary only to keep Bennett restrained. Riddell, Ferguson, and Mike were unwilling to play Skelton's game.

Skelton refused to give the delegation permission to vote to condemn Italy as an aggressor. Ferguson, with Mike and Riddell in strong agreement, challenged Skelton. To them, Skelton's instructions meant that Canada would join Italy's terrified neighbours, as the only friends of the Italian aggressor.

> Mr. Ferguson ... a man of action in an emergency said "nothing doing".... I was only too happy to encourage him in his resistance, and suggested he try to get "R.B." on the phone in Canada and have the instructions changed. He agreed and in two hours [he] was talking to the P.M. It was breakfast time there; lunch in Geneva. I knew RB well enough to feel sure that the result of this conversation ... would depend largely on how the PM had enjoyed his breakfast. It must have been a good one, for the PM was off-hand and jovial about it all; suggested that if the H.C. didn't like the [instructions] he could act as he saw fit.[18]

"Fergie" did as he saw fit, voting to declare Italy an aggressor and, later, agreeing on Canada's behalf to serve on the Committee of Eighteen, which was set up to plan the sanctions. Indeed, Riddell had actively sought a seat on the committee, on which most states that would impose sanctions served, although he knew from Anthony Eden, the British minister for League of Nations affairs who symbolized Britain's renewed commitment to the league, that the members of the committee would be morally committed to sanctions.[19]

Skelton was willing to accept sanctions if the league was united and if Great Britain, France, and the United States took the lead. Paradoxically, the French, the traditional promoters of collective security, were fearful of turning Mussolini towards Hitler. The British did not trust the French enough to follow them to the point of military sanctions, and the United States under Roosevelt was sympathetic to the league's efforts but was not a member. Skelton confronted Bennett about the Geneva delegation's obvious enthusiasm for a hard line against Italy and their disingenuous reporting of their activities. Bennett would have none of Skelton's "hairsplitting". In an angry telephone conversation, Skelton argued that Canada had traditionally opposed any automatic commitment to sanctions and that it should not change that position "merely because Britain has changed". Bennett exploded, accusing Skelton of "chasing moonbeams": "We went into League, took benefits, [and] must assume responsibilities, not try to hornswoggle ourselves out." As the political scientist Donald Story has convincingly argued, Bennett's support for the league "diverged from King to the extent that he had a greater sense of duty or obligation". Mike agreed, and despite R.B.'s astonishingly bad manners, Mike seems to have admired him more than he did his successor, Mackenzie King, and Howard Ferguson, who shared that sense of obligation and expressed it equally vigorously, more than his successor, Vincent Massey.[20]

But after October 15, 1935, Bennett and Ferguson no longer affected Mike's career; Massey and King most assuredly did. There can be no doubt that Mike was caught up in the enthusiasm of Geneva in early October and that he conspired with Riddell and Ferguson in their efforts to make the league work. Just before he left

ABOVE: Pearson was posted to London in 1935, as Mussolini nudged Europe to the brink of war. Left to right: (seated) High Commissioner Vincent Massey and his secretary, Georges Vanier; (standing) Mike, attaché Ross McLean. (NAC C-4053)

RIGHT: The coronation of George VI allowed even greater pomp. Mike wrote on his photograph, "After the Coronation 1937. Gentleman Usher!"

ABOVE: Mike in his office in Canada House, in London's Trafalgar Square. Note the map of Austria behind him. (NAC C-18976) BELOW: Patsy, Maryon, and Geoffrey on an English lawn, before the outbreak of war. The family was split up in 1939, when the children remained in the safety of Canada.

ABOVE: Mackenzie King and Graham Towers, governor of the Bank of Canada, laying the cornerstone of the Bank of Canada Building in Ottawa in 1937, with appropriate formality. Towers was by no means the stuffed shirt he appears here: his parties were celebrated throughout Rockcliffe. BELOW: (left to right) Mary MacKeen, Towers, Gerda Thomas, Molly Towers.

ABOVE: France, 1938: "our gang's" last holiday in Europe before the war. Left to right: Maryon, Hart Massey, Alison Grant, Patsy, Mike, Saul Rae, and Geoffrey.   BELOW: In 1939 the Youngs and Pearsons celebrated Dr. and Mrs. Moody's 40th anniversary, in Manitoba. Norman Young would die at Dieppe in 1942. Note Christopher Young (the future journalist) attaching presents to a "fishing pole".

Geneva he told Mary McGeachy, a journalist for *The Winnipeg Free Press,* that the Canadians would go "all the way" in supporting a league-assembly sanctions resolution. His memoirs also reflect his views in those heady days.[21] In London, however, he had to answer to Massey who was "at one" with King in the opinion that war over Abyssinia must be avoided at all costs. Moreover, Mike knew how close Skelton was to King and how impossible it would be to conduct telephone diplomacy over Skelton's head. In London, Mike's caution returned and, like his superiors, he saw the perils that lay in the league's ambitious course. Since his memoirs emphasize his views at Geneva and have the advantage of hindsight, it is important to set out what he thought at the time. He went with doubts, he admitted in early 1936, but was finally convinced of British sincerity about sanctions. He continues in his extended diary entry of January 1, 1936:

... I was not by any means convinced either of the wisdom or practicality of that policy. My own view was that it should not be forgotten that, while the collective system was worth preserving, Abyssinia was a bad client and Italy, in some respects, at least, had a good case against her, and indeed against the League. Therefore the League should do everything it could to meet Italy's just claims. For that reason I felt that the plan of the Committee of 5 based on territorial exchanges, and international control, did not go far enough to meet the Italian viewpoint. I know that she had turned down better proposals in Paris: that possibly Mussolini was determined to have his fight in any case, but that did not in my mind justify the omission of effort at this time, before Italy had attacked, to meet her claims to a paramount place in any international control over Abyssinia.

I felt this all the more strongly because at the back of my mind, however, there was the fear that later if sanctions were not working, or if they were working too well, or if public opinion should change, then Ethiopia having been encouraged to fight might be abandoned; and, what was of vastly greater importance, the collective system having been put to work would be left stranded by the two chief work-men, England & France, who would fall back on time honoured methods, and do a deal with Mussolini behind the backs of the other League members.

In London, Mike looked out upon a different political landscape, and fog obscured the bright rays of hope that illuminated Geneva. Riddell still basked in their glow on the Committee of Eighteen and took advantage of the chaos that always attends a change of government to take a leading role in the development of the sanctions to be employed against Italy. In early November 1935, he proposed adding oil, coal, iron, and steel to the sanctions. He later claimed to have checked this proposal with Pearson, who told him to go ahead,[22] but we cannot be certain he did so. Within hours, the proposal was dubbed the "Canadian proposal"; within days, Italy was denouncing the proposal as "an act of hostility" that might mean war. Skelton and King were astonished and terrified. They accused Riddell, whom they thought weak and unrealistic, of having been duped by Eden, who was using the league to bring the dominions into line with British foreign policy. On December 1, on King's instructions, External Affairs repudiated Riddell's action as simply an expression of his own opinion and not that of his government. The British were outraged, and a senior Foreign Office official muttered that the Canadians had "lost their nerve". A few days later, however, the British foreign secretary, Sir Samuel Hoare, also lost his nerve and agreed with Pierre Laval of France to a plan to end the Abyssinian War by dismembering Abyssinia. Aroused British public opinion forced Hoare's resignation, but the momentum towards collective security through the league was irretrievably broken. As the British permanent undersecretary put it much later, it was all bluff: "The League was bluff and Britain was bluff and France was not even that."[23] Canada was even less.

Skelton and King sent Pearson to Geneva on December 12 to represent Canada on the Committee of Eighteen, the committee they believed Canada should not be on. The Riddell repudiation and the

Hoare-Laval proposals had created, in King's words, "a horrible mess", but Mike was to take no part in cleaning it up. He was hardly noticed in his debut on the international stage as Canada's fully accredited delegate. He sat beside Laval, the future traitor who "kept puffing away at the inevitable cigarette, with his shifty half closed eyes darting about", and beside Eden whose "brilliant, if somewhat toothy smile flashed on everybody". Mike could never have received the humiliating repudiation that befell Riddell for he "made not a single speech; not even a 'hear-hear,' and you can't repudiate a man who won't even say 'hear-hear.'" Outside the committee chambers, Mike told the many who asked about Canada's actual position on sanctions that he was "a new man only recently sent to Geneva" and was, "naturally, quite ignorant about it all".[24]

In a sense Mike was correct, for Canadian policy was certainly confused. King and Skelton had said that Canada would support economic sanctions, but Mussolini's bluster about an oil sanction made them hesitate and take refuge in ambiguities. Both were shocked by the Hoare-Laval proposals, which King believed sacrificed justice to prevent war, but they also believed the League of Nations would destroy itself if its actions, including economic sanctions, led to war. Just before Christmas a frustrated prime minister wrote in his diary that Britain and France had been perfidious and that Canada should avoid European entanglements in the future. And yet temptation remained: early in the new year King confessed to his diary that he "would be happy beyond words were [he] called on to intervene in the European situation. It would be the greatest joy of [his] life – but it seems too great a mission to expect." How Canadian these contradictions were, and how difficult they made Mike's work at Canada House in the years before the war.[25]

Mike shared many of the contradictions of his prime minister, as Peter Gellman has recently argued.[26] He wanted world order through collective security, but he feared that the league might instead draw Canada into a war in which it had little direct interest. When, in 1935, it seemed that the league would work, he was elated.

When the league stumbled, he supported those who wanted to restrict its tasks. Like King's, his ties with Europe were strong, and he could never consider abandoning Britain in trouble as he could the league; but he remained cautious in making commitments lest they lead to entanglement and to a war over Tanganyika. Canada's relationship with Britain was, for Mike, an affair of the heart, always dangerous, sometimes infuriating, yet at bottom inescapable.

Mike returned from Geneva just before Christmas 1935 with Geneva flu, which, he told Skelton, "consists of a sore throat, a cold, and a general feeling of 'fed-upness'." Maryon, Patsy (as Patricia was now known), and Geoffrey had also suffered various ailments in their first weeks in England. Their rapid departure from Canada and Mike's sojourn in Geneva meant that the early months in London were ones of continuous turmoil. Mike had managed to persuade Skelton and Bennett to boost his salary (including allowances) to $8,000 for his London posting, but it was an expensive city. While they could live relatively well in London with a car, a cook, a housemaid, and a nanny, there never seemed to be enough money or help. Mike's diary, like the more famous one by Labour Party supporter Virginia Woolf, reveals that his egalitarian beliefs weakened when confronted with the legendary London "servant problem": "God, it will be good to be settled," Mike wrote on January 6, 1936. "So far in London, it has been a nightmare. There may be millions of worthy unemployed, but none of them seem to want to work for us. I am rapidly losing much of my sympathy for the 'working class,' but I suppose it is not fair to judge them on the specimens of domestic help that have been paraded for our approval by those London Racketeers – the domestic agencies." Three days later, however, two items in a newspaper provoked his liberal instincts:

At the arms commission session yesterday, the head of Vickers attributed the agitation against "private manufacture" to a "mistaken ideal about the sanctity of human life." That should be enough to run an arms maker out of the country but probably won't even prevent him from being made a Peer shortly. The other item [in the news] was merely that Woolworth's profits over here last year were £25,000,000, and a dividend of 100% was declared! My mind wandered back to our Price Spreads Inquiry and what was uncovered there about the way Woolworth's paid their slaves.[27]

Mike began a diary upon his arrival in London in 1936 and continued it, with some major interruptions, for ten years. The diary for the London years is his finest, for Mike never tired of the city and in the late 1930s he knew that London provided the finest vantage point to watch the great events of the time.* His position at Canada House gave him access to the most senior members of the British diplomatic corps, although his wary superiors in Ottawa sought to keep the fraternization between the Canadians and the British to a minimum. Nevertheless, Mike's personality, his expanding network of British friends, and his growing frustration with the constraints King and Skelton imposed upon Canadian diplomats made him seek out and find those Londoners whose actions and views deeply affected British policy in the three years before the war. And as always, he loved gossip.

The best gossip in 1936 swirled around the Prince of Wales, whose dalliance with Wallis Simpson was the talk of London society. Many were scandalized; some were amused; even fewer felt sympathy for the prince as he became hopelessly infatuated with Mrs. Simpson, an American divorcée of dubious reputation. The Prince of Wales's affairs became a matter of state rather than mere scandal when King George V fell mortally ill in mid-January 1936. On January 18, Mike and Alice Makins, wife of the dashing British diplomat Roger Makins, had taken in a movie, since Maryon was in Edinburgh and Roger in Geneva. When they came out of the theatre, the streets were eerily silent as Londoners crowded around news-boxes. The King

---

* It is interesting to note that Mike kept a diary only when he was outside the country. As secretary of state for External Affairs and as prime minister, he dictated or wrote "memoranda for file" which resembled diary entries in some respects, but were in most respects official documents lacking the personal aspects of the 1936-45 diary.

was dying and the people reacted as one. There was, Mike wrote, "a sense of sadness everywhere – a feeling of the clan gathering together in sorrow", and Mike that evening felt very much a part of that clan. Two days later George V was dead, and Mike marvelled how "a King's life draws peacefully to a close and a new King ascends peacefully the throne; and life goes on."[28] It was a tribute to "the British way".

But life for the new King and for Britain did not go on so smoothly. Mike's doubts about the new king began early when, as Prince of Wales, he ordered the clocks put forward thirty minutes at Sandringham. (Edward VII had made the clocks a half-hour late in order that guests would always be on time, and George V continued the practice.) Mike wondered why the prince acted so quickly: "It seems a strange thing after one's father has just died." There was, he further reported, "a general undercurrent of questioning" how the "new King will accept his responsibilities." Although occupied with his move to a new home on Hampstead hill near the fabled heath and the attendant "servant problems,"* Mike watched the crisis develop. At George V's funeral, Mike's attention was drawn to the new king, who looked "young, lonely and pathetic". He wore a long coat that exaggerated his diminutive stature: "he made me think of a little boy, doing his duty, wearing his big brother's coat and hating it all." And he did hate it all as much as he loved Mrs. Simpson.[29]

Since the crown was, in Mike's opinion, the last tangible link of Empire, the failure to emphasize the imperial nature of the occasion troubled him. The British officials told the Canadians little and involved them not at all, to Massey's considerable distress. Mike, however, had a very well placed and surprising informant: Alan "Tommy" Lascelles, who in 1935 had returned to Britain from Ottawa's Government House to serve as assistant private secretary to

---

* "Personally I would rather struggle with a report on sanctions than talk to these beady-eyed pirates who lord it over mere masters and mistresses in this country. Who said the proletariat were slaves?" Pearson wrote in his diary on Jan. 23, 1936. This was a temporary home: they moved on May 15, 1936, to another home at 7A Ellendale Road.

George V. As Edward and Mrs. Simpson moved towards marriage, Lascelles regaled Mike with tales that astonished him. Unlike his fellow Canadian Lord Beaverbrook, who "stood by" the King and Mrs. Simpson, Mike could not forgive the King's failure to recognize his duty. Nevertheless, he and Lascelles marvelled at the American commoner's mastery "body and soul" over the British king. "From one point of view," Mike wrote, "this power was beneficially exercised, as it was agreed by those who had seen them together, that King Edward was a changed person when Mrs. Simpson was around. She cured him of drinking and most of his nervous mannerisms. Some indication of the measure of his dependence on her is to be found in the fact that when she is not present, he was almost unbearable." Modern morality could not excuse the King's behaviour, nor could the fact that George V had treated his son abominably. "If the King is of such a temperament that he can fall completely under the sway of any single person, if he can lose all sense of responsibility and duty under this influence, then he is obviously no man to be King." Even though Mike accepted Lascelles's reports that Edward VIII was a much better person with Mrs. Simpson at his side, Mike and Lascelles agreed that she was mad to think that a divorced American commoner could marry the King of Great Britain. In August 1936, Lascelles accompanied the King and Mrs. Simpson on a four-week cruise along the Yugoslav, Greek, and Turkish coasts, where he found Mrs. Simpson amusing and intelligent but woefully uninformed about the English character and the place of the monarch. She minimized the difficulties involved for the King, telling Lascelles on the cruise that all the court officials "had to do was to have the King tour a distressed area or a slum or two every six weeks and between times nobody would care what he did."[30] By the end of that year, though, Edward VIII had been forced to give up his throne. In the end, Mike drew a lesson: "in the 16th century the King could be both politically and romantically adventurous; in the 17th and 18th centuries, he could only be romantically adventurous; in the 20th century he can be neither politically nor romantically adventurous."[31]

The abdication crisis did have important constitutional and political implications; indeed that most peculiar Canadian royalist Mackenzie King thought it "the most important historic incident in this country". It certainly was an important incident in British-Canadian relations, but the Canadian High Commission played no part, because of King's distrust of Massey and his insistence on dealing directly with British politicians (Baldwin in the case of the abdication crisis) or the British High Commission in Ottawa.* In summarizing Canada House's activities during 1936, Mike showed his frustration. In the abdication crisis, the High Commission knew little and did less. The other major developments in Mike's opinion were "the international situation" and the Canada-United Kingdom trade discussions. In 1936, Hitler occupied the Rhineland, the Spanish Civil War erupted, and the League of Nations was, in J.W. Dafoe's memorable image, ushered into the night when sanctions collapsed that summer. The situation had never been so grave since the guns stopped firing in November 1918. On New Year's Eve 1936, Mike thought that "the boys" would be in "Spanish trenches" before Christmas 1937. Yet Canada House had little idea what British policy in 1937 was likely to be. It was "the same old story – the Dominions will be informed when something has happened." Mike realized the blame belonged to the dominions as much as to Britain, for some

---

* In his diary entry of Dec. 8, 1936, King deplored "Massey's function being turned into a sherry affair". It was an example of "the thoughtlessness which was responsible for much of the condition of the times". Even though King's diary abounds with critical references to Massey's ostentation and wealth, King himself readily accepted the gifts Massey bestowed upon his friends and often enjoyed the parties Massey gave. A good example of King's effusive response to Massey's gift is found in a letter in which he thanked Massey for "a piece of stone" Massey had sent him from the Palace of Westminster: "Really I have been in raptures about it. By one of those strange coincidences, which have more behind them than appears upon the surface, this British lion arrived at Kingsmere on the day on which an effort was made to frighten King Edward by the throwing of a pistol. I do not know whether or not you noticed the extraordinary resemblance between the expression on the face of this lion and that of King George." In his reply, which is in the Massey Family Papers, Massey did not indicate whether he noticed the resemblance (King to Massey, Aug. 4, 1936, MG32 AI, v. 34 [NAC]).

dominions, Canada included, did not really want to know how dismal the situation was. On the third item, the trade negotiations, Canada House was "completely in the dark". The negotiations were proceeding in Ottawa between the British high commissioner and Canadian officials there. The British, it was obvious, were "willing to trust their High Commissioner ... in a way which the Canadian Government will not trust its High Commissioner".[32]

The Canadian government under King did not trust its diplomats, and the career diplomats such as Wrong and Pearson had little faith in their superiors' support or good judgment. The repudiation of Riddell, Mike's characteristically hasty assignment to London, the suspicious Skelton's extraordinary warning that Mike must not get too close to British diplomats in the Foreign Office or pass on what they told him, and the continuing tendency to make political appointments, as in the case of Massey and Marler, all eroded the morale of the career officers. When the major diplomatic posts went to wealthy ex-politicians such as Marler or prime-ministerial brothers-in-law such as W.H. Herridge, the career men became understandably bitter. Wrong had pleaded with R.B. Bennett's private secretary before the 1935 election to have a special diplomatic service created, free from the restraints of political patronage and staffed with the best and brightest of the time. Wrong claimed that the department had fallen into "a woeful state", unable to recruit, unwilling to take initiatives. Mike was not so pessimistic, but he largely agreed with Wrong. In his view Skelton deserved much blame for the failure of the department to grasp the opportunities that had beckoned in the 1920s. He continued to admire Skelton's "admirable personal qualities and remarkable brain", but lamented that his chief had no interest in or aptitude for "personnel and organization problems". Worst of all, he would not "fight for his men". "Lord," Mike exclaimed in his diary on New Year's Eve 1935, "how I would like to be given the job of pulling External Affairs & the Foreign Service apart & putting it together again, with a few pieces left out." Alas, Skelton could never do it: he was "not ruthless enough; won't hurt people"; and "won't fight for his subordinates". The judgment was too harsh: Skelton in fact had just saved Riddell, whom Mackenzie King (*he* certainly was "ruthless enough") had wanted to fire.[33] Nevertheless, Skelton's faults rested heavily upon Mike at that time, and he resented their weight.

His view of Massey was more complex. Massey was a political appointment but by background and education he was eminently qualified to be a diplomat. Massey's biographer has perceptively noted that Mike's comments on Massey in his autobiography were somewhat "muted in tone as if he were delivering a formal eulogy arising more from respect than admiration". This same tone is sounded in Pearson's private diary as if he were unwilling to criticize one who had been so generous to him but towards whom he never warmed. Massey took Mike to lunch soon after his arrival. Mike wrote in his diary: "He certainly takes his post seriously and his ideas as to its importance and possibilities are not characterized by narrowness or mock-modesty." Certain he smiled when Hume Wrong ridiculed the pomposity of Vincent and Alice Massey. "How are you getting on with Vincent – and Alice?" Wrong asked shortly after Mike's arrival in London. "I imagine that they are having a lively time, and are wearing themselves out in their efforts to obtain an appearance of effortless perfection in their public performances." Massey did seem, as Wrong suggested, a cunning actor who "rehearsed his impromptus carefully".[34] Ferguson's naturalness charmed Mike; Massey's aristocratic ways did not attract him.

Massey and Mike symbolized in their persons the passage from the old to the new in the twentieth century and in Canadian diplomacy. It is worth explaining the differences for they are important in understanding the differences between Mike and Massey, the British and the North Americans. Massey's style harked back to an earlier time when every European country had a *corps diplomatique* made up largely of aristocrats who, in Harold Nicolson's words, "possessed similar standards of education, similar experience, and a similar aim. They desired the same sort of world." Nicolson – diplomacy's keenest student and himself an ambassador's son – believed that egalitarianism, public debate, and direct involvement of political leaders in negotiation undermined the European diplomatic tradition.* Similarly, the distinguished British permanent under-secretary of the 1930s, Robert Vansittart, spoke of the "ruin of professional diplomacy" that followed the First World War when the "general agreement [among diplomats] to behave more or less like gentlemen ended." After the First World War the *corps diplomatique* vanished as surely as the Edwardian collar, billowing gowns, and Windsor uniforms.[35]

Massey never felt so well and fully dressed as in his Windsor uniform, and the coronation of George VI in 1937, where the remnants of European aristocracy gathered, sent the high commissioner on what his biographer aptly describes as a romantic flight on which his equally royalist wife rapturously joined him. He tried to resist the Canadian government's request that knee-breeches not be worn, gloried in his role of royal standard-bearer, and took as a compliment the remark that he "looked like a medieval stained glass window when he carried the standard in the procession".[36] Mike had studied the diplomacy of the past and admired many of its qualities; certainly he loathed the "public diplomacy" of Hitler, Mussolini, and their modern ilk. (He despised vulgarity as much in the 1930s, with Mussolini, as in the 1960s, with Lyndon Johnson.) Nevertheless, Mike found the old diplomacy inappropriate in the modern age. "Striped pants," he once said, "are not a garment but a state of

---

* In his novel *Public Faces* (London: Constable, 1932: p. 9), Nicolson describes the character of a traditionalist in his description of Arthur Peabody, principal private secretary to His Majesty's principal secretaries of state for foreign affairs, in his bath:

> He was a tidy man, and one, moreover, who proceeded in grooves of habit. He called them "my experience." They were excellent habits. He was honest, industrious, clean, truthful, and efficient. He spoke French with a French accent, German with a German accent, and Italian with an accent which was slightly Polish. His memory was frequently infallible; his instinct, quite often, sure; his judgment, on more than one occasion, had proved demonstrably sound. He had received a C.B.E. in 1932, and a C.M.G. in 1935. There was every prospect that in the impending Birthday Honours....
>
> Arthur Peabody moved his sponge hastily: he did not wish, even when thoroughly alone, to anticipate the Birthday Honours.

mind," a state of mind he believed should not exist in the Canadian foreign service. He saw in the Foreign and Dominions offices of the 1930s too many officers who were in "the old privileged mould". In his memoirs, he recalls his resentment when he heard the "caste" of Foreign Office diplomats talk about "a very bright and promising chap in the office who is the son of an engine driver, you know". Mike and Massey would both "know", but Massey, unlike Mike, gave the impression that it mattered.[37]

The coronation in 1937 did matter to Mike, for he appreciated its historical significance and the incomparable British skill in staging pageants. Nevertheless, his memoirs and diary reveal that Mike also gloried in his official role of "Gold Stick in Waiting". The account in Mike's memoirs is so full and humorous that little need be repeated here. The rehearsals for the "Gold Sticks" were exquisitely and ridiculously British ceremonial: "We merely stood around, doing nothing in particular except watch our section commander salute group commanders who would then rush off and salute the Chief Gold Staff Officer who saluted back, muttered a few syllables, whereupon the group leaders rushed back to the section leaders, saluted, and these in turn after returning the salute smartly would return to us and tell us that there would be a few remarks by our commander-in-chief." The anticipated reward, a perfect view of the historic pageant, did not come as Mike in knee-breeches, silk stockings, buckled shoes, with a cocked hat and a sword, took his appointed place behind a pillar while his gold-braided high commissioner regally bore his standard down Westminster Abbey's ancient aisle.

The position behind the pillar annoyed Mike and made him resent the time wasted in endless rehearsals. Other Canadian ushers were much closer to the procession, and Massey's son, also an usher, stood only "a few feet away from the King". Mike's "compensation" was to have "a perfect view of those lavatories which a paternalistic Government has so thoughtfully provided for its peers and peeresses". They would certainly need them since the service in Westminster Abbey would be ten hours in length, and they were mostly elderly. The prospect of seeing them shuffle to the lavatory rather delighted Mike:

"But I have a feeling that the expression of anguish on their faces as they enter and of relief as they emerge will not be sufficient compensation for the duties attached to this office or the five guineas which it will cost me to rent the clown's suit."[38]

Mike's tasks at the coronation were those of a hotel-keeper and social secretary; unfortunately his regular tasks were not much more rewarding. A sample diary entry reveals a sour and critical mood: "There is little of interest to report.... Routine work, and little of that, is all there is to do." "Ottawa" rarely answered any of their enquiries. Things were even worse at other posts. Ken Kirkwood called on Mike and his old friend Maryon and told them the new Canadian minister in Tokyo had organized the legation as a purely social operation. The truth was, Mike's lot was not much different. He did prepare a memorandum on British foreign policy and its implications for Canada for the Canadian delegation at the Imperial Conference that followed the coronation in May 1937. However, he admitted that the memorandum was just a "sideline", his major duty being the allocation of coronation passes to the thousands of Canadians who flocked to London in the spring of 1937.[39]

Mike had expected much more from his work, and Europe's crumbling order suggested Canada needed the best intelligence it could possibly get as it prepared for the most critical decision of its history. Mike's reputation was deservedly high. Massey described him as "extremely able" and an "exceptionally useful member of staff". Alice Massey privately was even more laudatory in a 1936 letter to her sister: "You simply can't think how much in the intricacies of things large and small Mike Pearson means to Vincent.... Mike has a magnificent brain, and he and Vincent think very much on the same lines."[40] Still, Mike courted Canadians, dispensed favours, and carried out countless small tasks that had little to do with war and peace.

Mike and Massey had thought along the same lines in early March 1936 when Alice made those remarks, for both resented the restrictions under which the High Commission acted in its political and diplomatic work. "Never was a special Minister for External Affairs so needed," Alice lamented to her sister. "Can't Queen's make

Skelton its head?" Mike and Vincent, she added, saw "eye to eye" on the problems the High Commission faced. The "say nothing and do nothing" diplomacy of Mackenzie King infuriated others as well. In a letter to Mike, which he circulated widely (but not to King and Skelton), Hume Wrong described the ideal Canadian representative at a conference from Ottawa's point of view: "Our delegate would have a name, even a photograph; a distinguished record, even an actual secretary – but he would have no corporeal existence and no one would ever notice that he was not there." Mike echoed these complaints to the Canadian reporter Grant Dexter who told George Ferguson, a mutual friend, that Mike was "thoroughly disheartened and disillusioned" with External Affairs.[41] Not surprisingly, he was receptive to an offer that came in January 1937 from the newly formed Canadian Broadcasting Corporation.

Mike bargained hard with Massey, Skelton, King, and the Canadian Broadcasting Corporation. He was, as he told his friend Alan Plaunt, who made the initial offer, "deeply interested". He was blunt about his situation: "I don't, and never have regarded my present work in London as permanent. Either it leads on to more important duties and greater responsibility in Canada's External Service or else I leave it and try something else." Mike in the 1930s, if not later, was not one to wait for good fortune to happen.[42] He bargained hard,* and his efforts yielded a rich harvest: a promotion to the post of secretary and a raise of almost $2,000.[43] The parsimonious prime minister himself agreed in order that Pearson be kept in the service.

The CBC offer intrigued Mike as did the media generally. He had a precocious interest in radio and genuinely liked journalists. At the Imperial Economic Conference in 1932 he had handled press relations with considerable skill and made friends with many journalists. In Geneva, he enjoyed the journalists' company best and thought them the brightest of the diverse specimens of humankind one found at the league. He dined often with journalists in London and revelled in the

---

* Jack Granatstein carefully follows the negotiations in his study of the civil service, *The Ottawa Men,* and curious readers should consult that excellent work for the full details of Mike's bargaining which continued until March 1938 when he finally decided to stay in London.

delicious gossip they passed on. He was an early supporter of public broadcasting in Canada and a good friend of Canadian Radio League founders Graham Spry and Alan Plaunt.[44] Nevertheless, diplomacy, though a difficult mistress, was an inescapably alluring one. There are several aspects to that allure.

First, Mike recognized that whatever their faults, Skelton and Massey appreciated his qualities. When Massey informed Skelton of the CBC offer to Mike, Skelton replied quickly to Massey: "It would be a great calamity to lose Pearson from our service. In addition to his intellectual capacity and fine educational background, good judgment and ability to turn out first class work at high speed he has marked ability in getting on well with people and developing friendly relations with representatives of other governments without losing his distinctive Canadian point of view. We are all proud and very fond of him."[45] Skelton paid no higher tribute to any officer at any time. Mike never read these comments, but he knew how valued he was, especially in Massey's eyes. Massey, moreover, did support his staff. He backed up Mike's requests for promotion and higher salary with strong arguments. He was personally generous as well, often bestowing gifts and small favours upon the Pearson family. When the Canadian author Elizabeth Smart called upon Mike and Maryon in February 1937 she found David Milne paintings encircling the room. They belonged to Massey; Maryon and Mike exhibited them, and occasionally made a sale to friends who called.[46] Massey, an energetic promoter of Canadian art, in effect used the Pearson home as a gallery – to the Pearsons' delight. Massey even gave them paintings, which they treasured.

Secondly, Mike and Maryon loved London, especially after good servants and schools were found. There were the Saturday soccer games for Mike and Geoffrey, and drives through the charming English countryside with its quaint villages with their narrow, ancient streets, which the Pearsons' Chevrolet could barely negotiate. They acquired a taste for country weekends with their rituals of early morning tea, dressing for dinner, and port and spicy conversation after.[47] In the city Mike and Maryon went regularly to the theatre, so often that Mike became a critic in his diary with his most damning comment: "the Ottawa Little Theatre could have done as well." After theatre, they dined at the Café Royal on Regent Street or went dancing at the Café de Paris. The company was splendid, and the food and wine far beyond the wildest imaginings of the chef at Ottawa's Château Laurier, much less the diners. Soon after his arrival (to give but one example) Mike lunched at Boulestin's, Evelyn Waugh's favourite London restaurant, with Bruce Lockhart, a renowned columnist; Harold Nicolson, "one of the most clever and attractive men of his generation"; Maurice Peterson of the Foreign Office; and Moir-Mackenzie, "a Scot, 220 lbs, hearty, sporting, booming Secretary of the Federation of British Industries". The crowd was delightfully British, the food exquisitely French, the ambiance definitely not Canadian.[48]

Nevertheless, Mike was thoroughly Canadian, reacting quickly to British slights and retaining the Canadian accent that many of his countrymen quickly lost. Yet he and Maryon fitted London's ways closely, better than they did Ottawa's and Toronto's in the 1920s and 1930s. Literature and theatre mattered ever more to Maryon, and household chores attracted her much less. In Britain she could afford servants who, however troubling, were much superior to no help at all. The children went to public schools; at other times, because of the ever-proper Alice Massey's prodding, there was a nanny, whom Patsy still recalls with some resentment. There was, then, a freedom for a woman – and a wife – that Canada in the 1930s granted grudgingly. There was also a lightness and even a libertinism to London in the 1930s that Ottawa lacked. The city and the times excited Mike and Maryon. It was, social historian Philip Ziegler writes, "a golden age for the party-goer" in which "beauty, breeding, money and the ability to amuse could provide admission tickets".[49] The more attributes one had, the more invitations one received.

Mike and Maryon received more invitations than most. Mike's ready wit and boyish face, which broadened quickly into an unforgettable smile that spread completely from his tousled hair to his wide Irish jaw, made him a delightful dinner companion or cocktail-party guest. His bow ties, which he now wore more frequently, enhanced his youthfulness and informality. He danced well, knew the theatre and the court gossip, and was drawn to attractive women as quickly as they were to him. In London, the setting provided more opportunities for the social life he enjoyed, such as the time in 1933 in London when he called up the youthful and beautiful Elizabeth Smart and asked her to go dancing after a concert. She rushed back to her flat and changed into a "red dress and black velvet puff-sleeve little coat and rushed to Quaglinos feeling like a devil. Cute little Mike waiting." Four years later she had become closer to Maryon than Mike – "I love being Canadian vulgar with her" – and Mike was rude rather than cute, neither rising to meet her nor bothering to fix his tousled hair when she came to visit Maryon. Elizabeth, the daughter of an Ottawa lawyer, and a fine writer, did note, however, that "there was a moment with Mike before the others came up when I was glad of my physical womanly growth and rejoiced to own such a powerful and easy weapon. Because Mike can be so rude when he is bored."[50] One should not make much of these remarks, for the encounter is simply a tale of the times, when women first tasted the fruits of political equality and economic opportunity. Friendships between men and women and a new ease in conversation and companionship were noticeable everywhere and have been recorded in a hundred novels and movies. Maryon, like Mike, attracted much attention from the opposite sex. She possessed the full-figured beauty the 1930s favoured and a sharp but not conventionally attractive face. She came alive around clever and charming men and found their attention at a party some consolation when Mike was closeted in the corners with Foreign Office types. Both flirted; both enjoyed the intrigue; each hurt the other occasionally, but it really meant little. They lived like most they knew with constraints and freedoms they well understood.[51]

Finally, and most importantly, Mike stayed in External because by late 1937 he knew that another war was likely, that Canada probably would be involved, and that he could serve the nation best in London where the critical decisions involving war and peace were made. By mid-1937 Skelton and King paid little attention to Massey's analyses even though Massey often agreed with them. Norman Robertson was still tied up in trade negotiations; Hume Wrong was in dreary exile in Geneva; and Loring Christie, who had returned to the department in 1935, had a deserved reputation for erratic judgment. To promote Mike the department had posted Vanier to France, leaving Mike with complete responsibility for political reporting from London. Never was political reporting so significant; and no one had a better vantage point than Mike. After the Imperial Conference in May 1937 where the new British prime minister, Neville Chamberlain, began his policy of "appeasement" of Germany, a policy applauded by Mackenzie King, Mike became the major interpreter of Britain's aims to Ottawa and vice versa.

From May 1937 to the spring of 1939, Mike saw Europe fall apart and many of his hopes and beliefs with it. The Abyssinian débâcle, the impotency of the league, the final collapse of the Naval Conference in 1936 and the outbreak of the Spanish Civil War caused Mike to lose all faith in the possibility of disarmament and collective security. He flirted with the notion of Canadian isolation, primarily because the thought of another war repelled him so much. Unlike many, including Mackenzie King, he had no illusions about the new dictators. He was as skeptical when Sidney Webb waxed eloquent about Stalin's magnificent accomplishments as when Foreign Office officials told him what honourable chaps the Nazis were.[52] Yet his own position was muddled. What he said about an Anthony Eden speech in early 1937 could apply to his own predicament:

> It was the same old stuff – why cannot everybody be as highsouled and peace-loving as we are? Eden is not as impressive a speaker as he is a personality and I felt last night that his words did not command in the House the attention they once did. He had lost the sympathy and admiring interest which his youth, his enthusiasm and his sincerity for the cause of peace once gained for him.... He is also forced to play a very thankless game; to keep his head and maintain his courteous composure midst the shrieks and threats of the demagogues on the Continent. A mediator can never be popular and a moderate can never be stimulating. Eden is both.[53]

Faced with Skelton's isolationist tendencies, on the one hand, and Massey's anglophilia and the British assumption that Canada would come when called, on the other, Mike tried to mediate and to stay in the middle.

The centre did not hold. Mike realized the British were hopelessly overextended, unable to defend India, Singapore, and Hong Kong against the Japanese, doubtful of American assistance in a European war, and overcommitted through history and alliance on the continent. He initially deplored the British rearmament program, repeating the disarmament movement's slogan that more armaments never brought security. He also resisted and, as a nationalist, resented British assumptions that Canada would rally automatically to its defence. In his own words, he "tore into" speakers who urged imperial centralization for defence purposes. By the fall of 1937, as Hitler's bluster increased and newsreel scenes of Germans bombing Spanish villages made Mike "almost physically ill", he realized that Britain had to prepare for war. He continued to hope that Britain would "stay out of the European mess" but knew that British isolation from the continent was as difficult as Canadian isolation from Britain. Nevertheless, as late as December 1937, Mike, in one of a series of dialogues on the BBC in which he participated, placed limits on his commitment to Europe, which his partner Dr. Geikie-Cobb, a London physician, did not.

> Geikie-Cobb: ... we've all got to come to our senses ... and realize that there's no country in the world that can afford to be uninterested in what happens elsewhere. We've got to pull together and to grasp the fact that what happens in [Czechoslovakia] *does* matter to *me* and to *you*.
> Pearson: Speak for yourself....

In the next few months, however, Mike began to see more substance in Geikie-Cobb's arguments.[54]

In March 1938, Mike was "so blue about the international situation" that he "almost [felt] like reserving a cabin on every C.P.R. ship leaving in the next six months, so that when the crash does come, at least I will be able to get my family out of the way." He realized that the crash would come not because Germany wanted equality and France denied that claim but because Nazism was "evil and savage and an immediate menace to freedom and peace". He had passed through Germany on his Christmas holiday in Switzerland and had found the atmosphere oppressive. Entering France and hearing and reading the French slander of their politicians was like entering the open air after a confinement in a windowless, stuffy cell. Britain as the dominant democratic power finally had to step forth to confront the Nazis. Churchill now impressed him more than Chamberlain, and he told Skelton that Churchill's view that Britain should take steps "to impress upon the dictators that [Britain] will soon have the strength and will to stand up to them" was commanding more and more support. The argument that Hitler's appetite was now satisfied did not convince Mike: "Even if you accept the view that the boa constrictor, as Churchill picturesquely put it, will now uncoil and rest while the process of digestion goes on, events in Austria show that this process is pretty fast in our mechanical age. Furthermore, I simply cannot feel that this particular boa constrictor's appetite is going to be satisfied by the most recent sheep." Skelton, who like Mackenzie King was no admirer of Churchill, told Mike that it was easier to be philosophical in Ottawa. He added that more people in Ottawa believed that the boa constrictor was satisfied than that Hitler's war machine was gaining momentum with every success.

Although Mike's major work that summer was on an international wheat agreement and the organization of a trade fair at Glasgow, his attention remained fixed upon Central Europe. Then came the fall and Munich, and he could think of nothing else. He thought first of his family, now settled in a new home, "Fairacres" in Roehampton. On September 27, the day before Chamberlain flew to Munich, the Pearson family packed Geoffrey's and Patsy's trunks – and wept. That weekend they went to the country and saw "a long steady stream of vehicles going out of London ... like a refugee procession". When Chamberlain returned with "peace in his hand" Mike was relieved because "peace seemed to be a pretty important thing to come back with", if only because it purchased more time. We know

now that "Munich" did gain time for the weak democracies and that Chamberlain's diplomacy infuriated Hitler who had wanted war over Czechoslovakia. Still, the agreement appalled Mike in 1938 and later and made him – but not Massey* – convinced that he must prepare Canadians for the boa constrictor's next strike, which would mean war.[55]

In his memoirs, Mike quotes at considerable length his letters to Skelton, written in the aftermath of Munich. Unlike Mackenzie King's telegram to Chamberlain on September 29, which declared that "the heart of Canada" was "rejoicing" at his "success", these letters convey the pessimism of a former soldier who hated the next war that he knew was coming soon. Those letters should be read by all students of international affairs in the 1930s; one letter is worth repeating here because it reveals that Mike's mind had cleared but his heart was sad:

> My first emotional reaction to the events of the last two months is to become an out-and-out Canadian isolationist. Yet when I begin to reason it out, it isn't as simple as that. I just can't find the answer to a lot of questions. For one thing, critical though I may feel of British policy leading up to the crisis, I can't sincerely quarrel with the decision taken last September not to fight. That being so, I have no right, I suppose, to assume that the present government is not as aware of past mistakes and present dangers as I am, and will not take effective steps to right the situation. In the second place, would our complete isolation from European events (if such a thing were possible) save us from the effect of a British defeat; and, even if it did, could we stand by and watch the triumph of Nazism, with all it stands for, over a Britain which, with all her defects, is about the last abode of decency and liberty on this side of the water?
>
> If I am tempted to become cynical and isolationist, I think of Hitler

---

* Alice Massey described Chamberlain upon his return: "that calm, quiet face full of purpose and character. Something great and something very spiritual had somehow altered his whole being." She added: "The tragedy of Czechoslovakia no one can minimise, but it was going to be a tragedy anyhow."

screeching into the microphone, Jewish women and children in ditches on the Polish border, Goring [*sic*], the genial ape-man, and Goebbels, the evil imp, and then, whatever the British side may represent, the other does indeed stand for savagery and barbarism. True, as Mr. Massey often tells me, there are seventy-five million decent Germans, who love peace and, apparently, revere Chamberlain! They may eventually, with the help of friendliness and restraint on our part, cast out their own evil spirits. That's a hope, I admit. But though I am on the side of the angels, in Germany the opposite spirits are hard at work. And I have a feeling they're going to do a lot of mischief before they are exorcised.

I think that this is the general feeling in this country. Certainly it is among men of my own generation in all walks of life whom I have talked to lately. There hasn't been one of them who has not sneered at the idea that Munich meant peace with honour; or who has felt that Germany and England can now be good friends; or who has not sworn that, if this country does not soon put herself in a position to stand up to the next German challenge, the present government will pay the penalty. Events are going to move swiftly in the domestic and international spheres during the next few months.[56]

Mike wrote his friend Graham Towers, the governor of the Bank of Canada, at the year's end: "Thank God 1938 is finished! The only people who will regret it are those that are convinced that 1939 will be infinitely worse." It was; it was worse than he ever imagined.[57]

CHAPTER NINE

IN LONDON
AT WAR

This was the new society of one kind of wealth, resilience, living how
it liked – people whom the climate of danger suited, who began, even,
all to look a little alike, ... The very temper of pleasures lay in their
chanciness, in the canvaslike impermanence of their settings, in their
being off-time – to and fro between bars and grills, clubs and each
other's places moved the little shoal through the noisy nights.
            – Elizabeth Bowen on London at war[1]

A FTER MUNICH, Mike went down to the House of Commons
to hear Winston Churchill, whose oratory he continued to
admire and whose arguments had ever more merit. Munich, Churchill declaimed, was only "the first sip, the first foretaste of a bitter
cup which will be proffered to us year by year...." For Mike, too, the
taste of appeasement had grown increasingly sour, and the case for
rearmament ever more compelling. From his Canada House office
on Trafalgar Square he looked out at Nelson's monument and knew
that, in this war, the square was only a couple of hours away for the
Luftwaffe's bombers and that the British Navy could offer little
defence. Canada was thousands of miles away, but by 1939 he could
no longer believe that Confederation Square in Ottawa was much
safer than Trafalgar Square. Britain and Canada now faced a common danger.[2]

When, in April 1939, the isolationist Frank Scott asked Mike what he thought about a declaration of Canada's right to independence, Mike had little patience with his friend's suggestion because, he warned Scott, it "would be seized on in Berlin and Rome as important evidence of disunity in a front that is finally being formed against Nazi brutality and aggression". For Mike, as for the swelling forces behind Churchill and Eden, one issue transcended all others: "the menace of a tyranny that is worse than anything else the modern world has known".[3] Mike did not want war, but by New Year's 1939 he regarded it as inevitable and necessary. What made Mike and most Britons come to this position so soon after the last war, when memories of its carnage remained fresh and the evidence of its effect on British power was so obvious? The historian Paul Kennedy talks about "the weight of accumulated prestige and habits of mind, together with the domestic pressures". The psychologist Carl Jung would have talked about the collective unconscious, the elements in the individual's unconscious derived from the experience of the race. In Mike's case, those elements included the Methodist hymns that called on God to save his children "from vice, oppression, and despair", the Ontario schoolbooks that spoke of the burdens the British Empire had to bear, the recollection from the 1920s of the goose-stepping German children outside his Heidelberg rooms, and his own children whose coughing kept him awake at nights and whose future had become so much bleaker than it had seemed when they were born.* The bombast from Berlin, Rome, and Barcelona deeply offended all whose instincts were democratic and liberal, and Mike's were increasingly that way. "Isn't it too bad," he wrote to eleven-year-old Geoffrey in January 1939, "that General Franco has captured Barcelona?" No longer would he pass on "cheerful" news to Skelton to satisfy the under-secretary's isolationist tastes. Although Massey continued to remind him that there were "seventy-five million decent Germans, who love peace", Mike could only see demonic "spirits"

---

* "Patsy has a terrible cough and I couldn't sleep tonight, because of her own inability to sleep," Mike wrote in his diary on Feb. 18, 1936. "Poor kid, it was anguishing to listen to her cough and then whimper. It's rather terrifying to have one so small and helpless mean so much to you."

"hard at work" in Germany. Those who grasped at Hitler's occasional pacific gestures were simply deceived and their action was itself "a mirror of our deterioration".[4]

Another mirror of deterioration was the stream of refugees who passed through Canada House. In their criticism of Canadian policy towards refugees, particularly Jewish refugees in the 1930s and 1940s, Irving Abella and Harold Troper place blame upon the Immigration department, Massey, External Affairs, and, not least, an intolerant Canadian public. Mike, officially and unofficially, saw many of these refugees whose tales horrified him and whose circumstances troubled him. In one of his BBC dialogues, Mike responded to a comment that the Jews caused their problems by not mixing by pointing to the success of British Jews, such as Disraeli. He added, when challenged further: "But even if that were true, who's responsible for this tendency? It wasn't so many centuries ago ... when Jews were forbidden to be anything but Jews, no matter how long they'd lived in a country; they were herded together into separate communities, they were kept there as a separate people...." He said that the problem of admitting Jewish refugees to Canada was the fact they were not agricultural.[5] The Canadian Immigration department restricted entry to agriculturalists, which had the effect of barring most Jews, who were urban dwellers. This technicality served well those Canadians, especially deputy-minister of immigration F.C. Blair, who wanted to keep Canada off limits to Jews. Between October 1938 and April 1939, Mike dealt with the Czech embassy in an effort to settle some of the German social democrats and Jews who were fleeing Nazi persecution. Their plight touched his conscience. He wrote to his mother and Vaughan on St. Patrick's Day 1939, perhaps recalling those Irish refugees ninety years earlier:

> In an hour or so I am going to be visited by a man who was until yesterday one of the senior officers of the Czech Legation here and as such worked with us in arranging for the movement of Sudeten-German refugees to Canada. Now he is a refugee himself and will, I think, ask me if I can get him into Canada as an immigrant. I'm afraid

most of our Sudeten-Germans will never reach [Canada]. Some of them are out of the country but those who are still there will probably be in concentration camps. I have some pretty pathetic interviews these days with refugees who want to go to Canada. I wish we were a little more generous to them. It's distressing having to tell so many of them you can do nothing for them.

The Czech diplomat Dr. Frey did ask Mike to help him emigrate to Canada; Mike in turn asked Skelton to help. Frey, though "penniless", had "qualities which certainly [would] be of value to our country". "Unfortunately if he goes to the Immigration Department here they will reproach him with the fact that he is not a trained agriculturalist and hold out no hope for his entry." We do not know what happened to Frey, but for most, hope died at the Immigration department under the impassive gaze of the clerks. Mike was successful in a few cases, such as that of Leon Koerner, whose half-Jewish background led him to flee Czechoslovakia in 1939. With Mike's assistance, the wealthy Koerner, the timber controller of Czechoslovakia in the Benes years, settled in Vancouver and introduced kiln-drying of spruce and hemlock to Canada. He never forgot to help Mike Pearson's future causes.[6]

Frey became a refugee when Hitler marched into Prague in March 1939 in defiance of the promises he had made at Munich. Britain had not fought for Czechoslovakia in 1938 even though it was a democracy, had been a pillar of support for the league, and had a defensive alliance with France. Chamberlain believed, rightly, that Britain was ill-equipped to confront Hitler in Eastern Europe and, wrongly, that Hitler's appetite would be satisfied when all Germans were included in his Reich. As Mike told Skelton, that last theory "ceased to have any meaning" after March 15, 1939. Nor did Mike hold out any hope for the "economic appeasement" efforts Britain had avidly pursued in an effort to halt Hitler's aggression in Europe and to assure the Americans and Canadians that Britain was doing all it could to avoid war. A government and Federation of British Industries mission to Berlin offered little comfort, he warned Ottawa, which had placed some faith in it. Ottawa had to recognize that the "long term trend" was "steadily downwards. How could it be otherwise when Germany and Italy are States organised primarily for war, on a foundation of hyper-sensitive and deified nationalism; and when Great Britain and France can only meet this menace by a policy of rearmament, which in fact is not a policy at all, but merely an instinctive reaction to danger."[7]

Part of Mike's new duties as counsellor included regular reporting to Ottawa on the press, and he wrote his reports with a bias towards those papers that demanded stronger action and mocked those, such as Lord Beaverbrook's *Daily Express,* that claimed "that all is peaceful and calm, and that if we will only bury our heads cheerfully in the sand, we will see nothing unpleasant". The temptation to bury one's head in the sand was even greater in Ottawa, and Mike worked incessantly to keep those frightened heads in the air.

It was difficult. Skelton, King, and Loring Christie concentrated upon Canada's divisions: between French and English Canadians, between imperialists and "North Americans", between rich and poor. Christie, once an imperialist and now an isolationist, privately told an American friend that Canada's membership in the British Empire was a "bad and vicious thing for Canadians both materially and morally". He dreamed of an Anglo-Saxon union with Britain, detached from Europe, but had no faith that the dunces who ruled Britain would see its wisdom.[8] Skelton similarly ranted about British stupidities, emphasized the internal weaknesses of Canada, and thought the British Empire meant little to Canada apart from the wars it drew Canada into. For him, Canada was a North American nation; its true interests lay in stronger political and economic links with the United States. After Munich when the cabinet and King seemed ready to go to war, Skelton clung to King's traditional statement that Parliament must decide, and hoped it would balk. He carefully recorded each time that Britain stumbled, ignored the burden Britain bore, blamed the British for failing to consult Canada while telling Canada's representatives in London not to get near the British, and believed that a fifth column within Canada was plotting

Canada's involvement in the next war. It was his belief that most Canadians were opposed to participation in "British wars" but that an "imperialist minority" who possessed a "greater share of wealth, influence, assurance and public position" would never allow the majority to rule. The call for democracies to "rally around" was phony; "at bottom the attitude was based on instinctive racial sympathy" and was centred in Toronto, which Skelton had always regarded as responsible for the moments of madness in Canadian politics.[9]

Vincent Massey came from Toronto and was very rich, very assured, very anglophile, and Skelton naturally distrusted him. In a caustic exchange in June 1938, Massey took issue with Skelton's charge that Britain's ambassador in Washington was worrying more about making propaganda than preventing war. "I am unable to believe," Massey wrote sharply, "that it is in the Ambassador's mind to accept the 'blind drift to war as inevitable' although the danger of conflict in the near future is apparent to all those in close touch with the rapidly moving events in Europe." Skelton was not there; Massey was, and while he hoped peace might be maintained he submitted "in all deference" that there was little to be done "except to strengthen the democratic front". For Skelton, Canada's relationship with the European system now reflected only "technical dependence" and Canadians today had to treat with "great reserve" any declarations emanating from Europe about the "cause of democracy".[10] Massey had supported the old British policy of appeasement; he now supported the new policy of the guarantee to Poland; and his government's attitude embarrassed him. Although a Canadian nationalist who emphasized Canadian distinctiveness in his public activities in London, Massey could not imagine Canada without Britain, and he retained that respect for British statesmanship that Skelton and Christie lacked. Close consultation was a prerequisite for a satisfactory Anglo-Canadian relationship as well as an activity he prized. How proud he was to say that he spoke for Canada at Whitehall, Downing Street, and the Palace. The problem was that King made certain that those eminent Britons realized he did not.

Although King had decided in 1937 that Canada would go to

Britain's defence and the cabinet had agreed during the Munich crisis, he never informed his high commissioner of those decisions, leaving him adrift in uncharted waters, uninformed and unused. Nor did it help matters when Queen Elizabeth, on the Royal Visit of 1939, told King that Alice and Vincent were exactly the "kind of people" Canada should have in London.[11]

Massey seemed to hover above the High Commission, rarely descending to debate the issues of the day with his colleagues. Mike and he now shared their views rarely, although on some issues the events of 1939 brought them to a common position. Mike thought Ottawa's hesitancy to use its diplomats deplorable and its attitude to the European situation naïve. Like Skelton and King, Mike believed that the British hardly respected the spirit of Empire when they made commitments without consultation and regarded Canada's war effort as automatic. Although Mike did privately believe that Canada must and would go to war at once, for him British arrogance justified keeping them guessing. In a broadcast in May 1939, Mike replied evasively to a question about Canada's "isolationism" by emphasizing the "great division of opinion" in Canada that arose from the fact that its population was "a collection of various races". But when asked directly whether the "attachment to the Commonwealth" was greater than "the attachment" to the United States, Mike responded quickly, "Oh, of course.... Education and tradition and sentiment would make for that inevitably." They certainly did so for Mike and Massey, if not for Skelton and Christie. More importantly, they did so for Mackenzie King. King frustrated the British and the Canadian High Commission in London with his evasiveness. But the evasiveness was purposeful: "Passionately committed to avoiding divisions, particularly between English and French Canadians, King steadfastly resisted moves to clarify Canada's legal, political or moral position in the event of a European conflict. Such action, he believed, could disturb the delicate balance that was the source of his political strength." Yet when tested King was consistent. He told his political protégé Norman Rogers during the Czech crisis that if Britain entered the war, it was a "self-evident national duty" that Canada had to fight. It would be for Canada to decide what form and extent that participation should take, but on March 20, 1939, Mackenzie King told the House of Commons that "if there were a prospect of an aggressor launching an attack on Britain, with bombers raining death on London," Canada would regard that attack as an act of war against itself. Those words brought relief to Mike Pearson, who saw war coming and wanted Canada in it.[12]

That last summer before the war there was little to do but wait. In May, Mike and Maryon holidayed on the Isle of Wight, golfing, sailing, and exploring with Patsy the many coloured sand-dunes on the island. The family couldn't wait for their first Canadian leave, which began on June 30. Before they left, Mike and Maryon were invited to dinner at Buckingham Palace, an event he reported in detail to his royalist mother and brother. Although Mike told the under-secretary that the Canadian enthusiasm for the royal tour troubled him, Mike's letters home leave no doubt that, in royalty's company, he could be "plus Royalist que le roi", as he had once intimated that Massey tended to be.* The invitation caused Maryon to buy a new dress, "a lovely light blue and silver affair", which made her (Mike proudly reported) "the most gorgeous person there". He even "went to the lengths of pressing [his] trousers and taking special steps to see that [his] white tie and [his] medals were on straight." The royal couple charmed them, and Mike beamed when King George, asked whom he wanted to speak to first, said "Pearson". (This was the work of Mike's friend, the King's secretary, Tommy Lascelles.) He warned Annie and Vaughan that they would be telling tales of the dinner with the King and Queen "for years to come".[13] Certainly, at the Moody household, on the shores of Manitoba's Lac du Bonnet, that evening at the Palace made a splendid story.

The Pearsons left Britain on the *Duchess of York* on June 30 and stopped in Ottawa and in Toronto before travelling on to Winnipeg.

---

* Mike may have been trying to conciliate Skelton, who was not a royalist, with whom he had a dispute over Skelton's refusal to allow him to keep Vanier's driver and car after Mike was appointed to carry out Vanier's functions.

In Ottawa Mike and Maryon went to a dinner party at Kingsmere, King's retreat in the Gatineau Hills. The Skeltons were there, as were Arnold and Peggy Heeney, and Joan Patteson, King's frequent hostess and fellow spiritualist. In King's view, "the dinner went fairly well, [the] table looked pretty, but [he] felt it was just not the right company...." The Pearsons probably felt the same.[14]

Lac du Bonnet and the large farmhouse where the Moody family gathered in the warm midsummer of 1939 to celebrate Dr. and Mrs. Moody's fortieth anniversary made European quarrels and Canadian politicians seem far away. Herbert Moody, Maryon's brother, now a successful architect, came with his young family from Winnipeg. Norman and Grace Young, whom Mike and Maryon had rarely seen after the double wedding, came with their four children. One of them, Christopher, who later became a distinguished journalist, recalls the old farmhouse, the swimming, and the baseball games, which Mike "enjoyed enormously". At those times with children, Mike removed his tie, loosened his belt, rolled up his trousers, and threw himself into the game, and his world became the children's world.[15] The respite was brief, for in mid-August Mike rowed over to the post office and saw a headline: "Nazis Threaten Danzig and the Polish Corridor". Before he had left in June Mike had warned a newly arrived officer, Charles Ritchie, that "if the Germans attack the Corridor, Poland will fight, and so will France, and then we shall be in." That prospect became inevitable when the Soviet Union and Germany signed their non-aggression pact on August 22. The pact did not surprise Mike, who had viewed British and Soviet efforts to negotiate an accord earlier in 1939 with skepticism. The two dictators, Hitler and Stalin, were much more compatible than were Britain and the Soviet Union. In Ottawa, Mike was none the less rather surprised that the pact pleased Mackenzie King because it meant that Canada, through Britain, would not be allied with the Soviet Union and that Britain and France might now hesitate to defend Poland. King, who had once compared Hitler "the mystic" to Joan of Arc, continued to have faith in Hitler's pacific instincts and told Pearson as they wandered among the curious "ruins" he had erected at

Kingsmere that war would not come. Nevertheless, King and Skelton agreed to Pearson's request that he return to London at once, although Skelton was nonplussed when Mike said he wanted to fly to London via the new Pan American Superclippers, which had begun service to London via New York. On August 25, *The Winnipeg Free Press* reported that Mike had left for London; he arrived a few days before the war began.[16]

Also aboard the "American Clipper" were a Polish and a German reservist who joked with each other about the coming war throughout the flight. The giant seaplane glided into water at Southampton and the passengers disembarked and travelled by train to London. Everywhere, newspaper headlines proclaimed war's inevitability, but, unlike earlier ones, this crisis had brought an eerie calm to London, and the parks and streets were crowded with people enjoying a late-summer evening. The city, however, was ready for war: traffic lights had only small green and red crosses, black and white stripes marked the curbs for black-out driving, and anti-aircraft balloons hovered overhead. Mike spent his first two nights with the Masseys. Vincent clung to the hope that war might not come and worried whether the Poles were not using a trick to drag the British into war. Alice flitted about Canada House, repeating "I know, I know, it's going to be alright." Her words, in Mike's view, were as pathetic as Chamberlain's initial weak response to Hitler's invasion of Poland. On the morning of Sunday, September 3, Mike joined Massey and the emergency staff at Canada House to hear Chamberlain's "tired" but inevitable declaration of war: "It was all very quiet and matter of fact. But we all knew our world was at an end."[17] Indeed it was.

An air-raid siren wailed that first day, and Mike and the staff "tumbled" into the shelter in the cellar and waited for the "all clear" call on the special telephone installed for that purpose. This preferential treatment, however, was hardly preferable, for when they escaped the overheated shelter into the summer they saw the "general public", which had learned the sirens were simply a "false alarm", feeding the pigeons in Trafalgar Square. Massey and Mike, who now was second-in-command at Canada House, left the square and walked through St. James Park where they saw bunches of men cheerful despite the gas masks they carried. Massey left Mike sitting on a park bench; he counted 152 silver balloons threaded together across the sunset. That night Mike drove through blacked-out London to a friend's house, where he was staying. All the cinemas and pubs were closed. "Where will the soldiers on leave go in this war?" Mike asked himself. The last war offered no guide-posts, and Mike had little patience with those who recalled those old battles too quickly and fondly. His colleague Charles Ritchie spent the war's second Sunday with Mike and the Masseys. Mike told Ritchie that he had gone to a night-club on Saturday night (when Maryon was absent Mike was nocturnal) and saw some RAF men drinking and "pretending to fight over girls", which seemed as it should be. "But he was disgusted by a group of middle-aged men, survivors of the last war, back in uniform again, singing the old songs of the last war, trying to fancy themselves heroes to the night-club hostesses, trying to get back the glamour of their own youth." Old soldiers deserved to die when they looked ahead to another war.[18]

Mike did not welcome the war but he had no doubt that it was necessary, for Britain and for Canada. No hesitation about the war's purpose appears in his diary although great frustration with Canadian and British officialdom developed quickly.[19] Canada's official declaration of war was delayed until September 10; while the delay made no difference in terms of Mike's activities, it satisfied his nationalist's sensitivities. He did admit to some equally puzzled reporters, however, that he was unaware that Canada had not been at war since September 3! (The matter did not end there. The written submission did not arrive from Ottawa until much later and constitutionally Canada, in fact, may not have been at war until much later.) When, on September 12, he broadcast (anonymously) to the Empire and Germany on Canada at war, Mike emphasized Canada's full commitment to the struggle. Crowds of Canadians fleeing, trying to join the forces, or simply seeking news packed Canada House and were making Mike's days very long. Matters were not made easier by Alice Massey who "exhorted" the Canada House staff constantly, news of which reached Mackenzie King and further reinforced King's dislike of the Massey family.* King's firm decision not to send a Canadian cabinet minister to London, as had been done in the last war, nevertheless enhanced the authority of the high commissioner. Massey had more access to British officials, and his work and Mike's gained immeasurably in significance. They also worked more closely together in those first months of war. Mike shared Massey's exasperation with "Ottawa", with its quickness to complain and its constant suspicion of the high commissioner's activities.[20]

King and Skelton tried to maintain control of Canadian-British relations from Ottawa, partly because of their fear that the anglophile Massey would make too many commitments to Britain and the war and partly because King believed Britain would try to entrap Canada in an imperial snare that only he was sufficiently wily to escape. Again and again, Mike expressed bitterness in his diary at King's idiosyncrasies:

> Mr. King has been sending personal telegrams on the [wheat negotiations] to the P.M. [Prime Minister] – a stupid procedure – as some of them deal with details that not even a P.M.'s private secretary should be worried about. But it suits his amour propre to send personal messages to his opposite number. He would die before using this Office or is it this [high commissioner] for such a purpose. He feels probably more strongly about that than winning of the war. It's a strange phobia, this insistence on direct communication by one who in so many respects prides himself on his ardent nationalism. If we were really independent we would act through our own representative here – and not directly or through a United Kingdom Department.

This style of diplomacy was strange and most certainly stupid, a reflection of the failure of King and Skelton to build a diplomatic

---

* When the governor general suggested Massey as a possible successor, King told him that he did not think it acceptable. He wrote in his diary on Dec. 6, 1939: "I might have added it would be intolerable." On Jan. 20, 1940, he noted that he had told the governor general that Massey's service was "vitiated by everyone realizing he was overzealous for recognition and titles."

service consonant with the responsibilities of a modern sovereign nation. It made a mockery of Canada House "when the British know more of and know sooner, what our Government is doing".[21] At times it was comical; at other moments, it was embarrassing and injurious to the interests of Canada and its war.

London played the game as fully as Ottawa. The massive British Commonwealth Air Training Plan grew out of a Massey proposal put forward at a meeting of high commissioners on September 16, 1939. Massey and Stanley Bruce, the Australian high commissioner, suggested that the Canadian, Australian, and New Zealand air forces should be trained in Canada. Within ten days the Dominions Office, which Mike's sometime tennis partner Anthony Eden now headed, had prepared a telegram proposing fifty-two training camps, which could produce tens of thousands of pilots and make Canada, in Mike's words, "the centre of all Empire air training during the war". Massey even helped in drafting the British telegram in order that it not arouse King's delicate sensitivities. Mike was fully supportive of Massey's intrigue and of the "stupendous programme" proposed, but he was pessimistic about Canada's response to it: "To carry out such a plan will require vigour, imagination, drive and, above all, 100% enthusiasm for the war. I don't see that combination of qualities in the East Block." The proposal, in fact, seemed a godsend to King, who saw the training of pilots and a concentration on the air force as a way to avoid a large expeditionary force, which, in a protracted war, would (and did) lead to conscription. Mike and Massey took little part in the negotiations, which were conducted, with considerable rancour, in Ottawa, but both must have obtained quiet satisfaction at the success of the proposal. When King learned after the war that Massey had first proposed the plan, he was outraged and felt all his suspicions fully justified.[22]

King co-operated with Britain on the air training plan, but his pre-war reluctance to meet and discuss with British politicians and diplomats continued into the war years. King and Skelton feared consultation with the British because it meant commitments and the possibility of blame being attached to Canada; to Mike and to

Massey consultation had now become essential and the lack of it irresponsible. There was another difference: in 1939 and 1940 King wanted a war of "limited liability", but Mike was fully committed to the war. Strategic necessity now outweighed Canadian nationalist emotion. For Massey and Mike Canada's greatest interest lay in winning this war, not in observing constitutional proprieties.

"I think Winston Churchill is one of the most dangerous men I have ever known," Mackenzie King wrote in his diary on the eve of war.[23] Mike completely disagreed. Even then Churchill had become for Mike the symbol of British resolve and democratic resistance; he was pre-eminently the man of the hour, as Lloyd George had been in 1915. Not that Churchill was faultless; his old-fashioned imperialism was as offensive to Mike as to King. Mike saw Churchill on November 20, 1939, at the Cabinet Office, where he looked as "cherubically juvenile as ever" and expressed views that were themselves often juvenile, ending the meeting with a pledge that the mistakes of Versailles must not be repeated: "We must really 'fix' Germany this time; not fall for any disarmament bunk; keep two British fleets in being, one for Europe and one for Asia, and never forget that during our lifetime and our children's lifetime our only security would be the British navy and the French army."

"What suicidal rubbish!" Mike wrote in his diary.[24] And yet Churchill had become Britain's, the Empire's, and Mike's hope, just as Chamberlain was the symbol of decline and lassitude; in Mike's words, "an obstinate old man of limited vision" and "about as uninspiring a leader of a democracy, as was ever offered to a long suffering people." Hitler's first peace offers might have tempted the British, Mike thought, were it not for "the deep and heartening effect of Churchill". Unfortunately they also seemed to tempt Mackenzie King, and, as a Canadian, Mike was embarrassed that they did.[25]

No peace came, and the winter of 1939-40 was hard. The "phoney war" scratched upon the exposed nerves of the Canadians and the British as they kept waiting for Hitler to strike and for their war effort to gain momentum. Hume Wrong arrived from Geneva in October, much to the consternation of Massey who recalled all too well their difficulties in Washington. Mike and Wrong met continuously to work out their respective responsibilities and got on well. Wrong was senior to Mike, but Mike's position in Canada House ranked above Wrong's undefined position. Wrong told Ottawa that Mike was helpful and that he would accept nothing that would affect Mike's position. Nevertheless, his pride would not permit him to accept an inferior position. On November 10, he asked Massey directly who would be acting high commissioner in Massey's absence. Massey answered, "Pearson", and Mike wrote in his diary: "This has been an easier day." Matters became even easier as Mike and Wrong attended meetings together and golfed together on weekends, this combination of work and play breeding respect.[26] Wrong treasured style "in everything from the way he [wore] his coat to the prose of his memoranda". In London in 1940 Mike had style, infinitely more than Wrong on the golf course and tennis court, and because of his familiarity with Whitehall and music halls, he cut a very stylish figure in London social and political life as well.[27] Wrong eventually demanded that his function be defined, and that he be given a title, a staff, the authority to correspond on policy with British departments, accommodation, and funds.[28] King granted these requests grudgingly; Wrong did acquire the title of senior economic adviser, although his functions remained unclear until he returned in 1941 to Ottawa. Mike and Wrong grew much closer, and, on many weekends, inseparable, especially after Maryon arrived in London in January 1940.[29] Joyce and Hume Wrong were, very simply, splendid company for the Pearsons in bad times.

Mike's work was better defined than Wrong's and Massey's. He completed the wheat negotiations, which had been a major concern for him for some time, and assisted a Canadian mission, headed by T.A. Crerar, the minister of mines and resources, that arrived in London to deal with economic and financial questions. Mike grew fond of Crerar, who had served as a cabinet minister during the First World War and had a storehouse of anecdotes to fit every occasion.

Unfortunately, Crerar and the High Commission were not equipped to handle the intricate details of the economic web the war was weaving across the Atlantic. The governor of the Bank of Canada, Graham Towers, was admirably equipped, and, on short notice, he agreed to come to help out in November 1939. Mike was much relieved on two counts. Towers quickly cut through the British arguments and made clear to the British what Canada was prepared to do in this war. Towers found the British were hesitant in working with Canada because they thought there were distinct limits on Canadian willingness to make sacrifices. There were several, such as "no conscription", but in the economic realm not so many as the British thought. He showed the British that the Canadians were not easily tricked; treated fairly they would do their part. During the negotiations, Towers bore himself with the cool reserve and meticulous dress of a city banker; after hours, he loosened up dramatically. He enjoyed lively parties more than anything except his work. The Rockcliffe hostesses' favourite dinner guests, Towers and his lively wife, Molly, had become quick friends of the Pearsons after their arrival in Ottawa in 1934. Mike's correspondence with Towers in 1940 is his best – biting, witty, and personal. The nature of their relationship is apparent in a letter Mike sent to Towers in September 1940 after Maryon had returned to London: "I hope you are looking after my wife and keeping her out of mischief.... Tell Molly that as the incendiary bombs drop all around, my thoughts turn instinctively to her." Mike's relationship with Towers cooled somewhat, as Maryon and Graham became very close. But Towers had great charm, and to his female friends he was every bit as attentive and caring as he was to Canada's exchange rate.[30]

Social life in London was surprisingly normal when Towers arrived in late November. Mike had tired of driving home to "Fairacres" every evening through the nightly black-out and had moved into a flat just off Piccadilly Circus with his good friend Harry Crerar, who was organizing Canada's military headquarters and playing Chinese chequers with great skill. He took quick advantage of the location to go to three shows in the first week: "a good old honest

English variety", a "frothy" French sex comedy, and a "leering" English sex revue. Mike now had "the rare and plutocratic privilege reserved to really rich Londoners, visitors and prostitutes of being within walking distance of all the places one goes to – including the Office". In the theatres and the restaurants Londoners acted the same as usual; the women again wore evening dress rather than the uniforms that were everywhere during the war's first week. The contrast troubled Mike: "Why," he asked, "can the Germans be holding back?"[31]

In the new year, the Germans began to move and the Londoners soon realized that the "phoney war" was ending. Mike was drawn into military work because of his good relationship with Harry Crerar and General A.G.L. McNaughton, commander of the First Canadian Division, whose arrival in December 1939 stirred Mike's patriotic fervour. Despite Mike's personal friendships, the civil-military relationship was not always easy because of the military's ever-increasing demands. The Canadian military needed the High Commission to penetrate the maze of British bureaucracy. In January 1940 he asked Skelton for assistance; not only had the paperwork increased exponentially but the personal side of diplomatic work had become more demanding because of the appearance "every day of Canadian officers and men who knew me, or my father, or my great uncle, or a friend of any of the above...." Massey was now of little help. Mike told Skelton that the high commissioner had taken the view that all the "Women's War Work" should be supervised by and closely connected with Canada House. Massey would, Mike warned, be "sorry" for it some day. For his part, Mike "would rather battle the whole of the Treasury over the financing of the Air Training Scheme than try to co-operate with the embattled hosts of Canadian war women."* He was equally reluctant to get directly involved with the growing Canadian military establishment in Britain and carefully

---

* Massey was, in fact, protecting his wife's position. She moved into Canada House to organize "women's war work" but within a month there was a rebellion against her control. She responded by invoking the high commissioner's authority. Mike was troubled by this use of the office, but did not intervene. Privately he grumbled.

restricted his work to liaison functions.[32] McNaughton offered him a position as his special assistant, but Mike turned it down, partly because he thought his work in Canada House of at least equal importance but mostly because of his doubts about McNaughton's leadership.

Mike liked "Andy" greatly; his blunt Western-Canadian style, gregarious personality, and "unkempt" ways were a refreshing contrast to the spit and polish of the British officers. He delighted Mike as he raged against the stupidities of "Ottawa", with its fear of being informed and its complaints when it was not. He confronted British inefficiencies with a brusque Canadian nationalism that demanded equal treatment. Mike approved, for these sentiments were his own, oft thought but only privately expressed. McNaughton gave Canadians a powerful voice they could recognize as their own. But Mike had deep reservations. One April evening in 1940, after hearing McNaughton predict, with unpardonable enthusiasm, a series of wars lasting forty years, Mike expressed doubts about the general: "As I get to know McNaughton better in war-time I find myself in some doubt as to his judgment, both in respect of men and in respect of policy. He is an amazingly efficient soldier but it is surprising how far off the rails he goes at times in his opinions on persons and his analysis of events."[33]

On that very evening, April 11, 1940, events were moving very quickly in Denmark and Norway, and McNaughton acted without authorization to order the dispatch of Canadian troops to help the Norwegians. Initially Mike agreed with McNaughton's orders, but then, after studying the legal aspects, he agreed that McNaughton had gone too far. The temporary presence in London of Norman Rogers, the Defence minister, eased some difficulties. Rogers was an Oxford acquaintance of Mike, and Mike spent much time with the increasingly influential politician. Rogers knew "McNaughton perfectly – both his strength and his weaknesses" and agreed with Mike that McNaughton's impulsiveness required a careful watch. He too asked Mike to consider a position on McNaughton's staff to handle "political and constitutional matters", but again Mike refused. Mike and Rogers discussed McNaughton's problems on a jaunt to their beloved Oxford, a journey that broke the wartime tensions for both of them. Mike's comment about Rogers's attachment to Oxford was a reflection on his own attitude: "I have more than once been struck by the fact that some of our most ardent nationalists are Oxford graduates who find it quite easy to reconcile their Canadian nationalism with a devotion to Oxford which is as deep [as], and probably deeper than that of most British undergraduates."* Rogers never saw Oxford again; he died in a plane crash in Canada six weeks later. On his death, Mike wrote: "I've lost a good friend, Canada as unselfish and intelligent a public servant as she has ever had."[34]

Canadian nationalism ran strongly through Mike's thoughts in April 1940 as British failures in Norway coincided with a marked reluctance to involve Canadians in decisions about the war's conduct. It was a period of fear and, occasionally, depression. Then, the real war began as Hitler stormed through the Netherlands, and Belgium and France reeled before the *Blitzkrieg*. In London, Charles Ritchie wrote, "One has the dazed feeling of being dragged in the wake of a runaway destiny," and on May 13, the date of that comment, destiny seemed decidedly on Hitler's side. Gas masks appeared in the streets again. The only good news came in the House of Commons with the fall of the "tired and pathetic" Chamberlain and Churchill's acceptance of the office of prime minister.[35]

As the Maginot line crumbled and French morale collapsed, the thought of defeat appeared in London "in whispers and averted glances". Mike's nerves were raw, his temper short: "If I didn't know what was going on behind the scenes, it would be easier. But to know, to watch the telegrams, to get from Harry [Crerar] the latest

---

* According to Mike's diary entry for Apr. 21, 1940, Rogers and Mike went to Rogers's Oxford college where they immediately met the porter who "of course" remembered him. He wasted no time on congratulating Rogers on his success but rather "delved at once into an ancient black book, from which he emerged with the information that Mr. Rogers still owed the College 13 / 7 and would he pay up?"

dismal bit of news ... to watch the German arrows moving over the war map, and to be able to do nothing about it – well, it's an exhausting business." The public in that second-last week of May 1940 still talked about the French counter-attack. But Mike began to notice "uneasiness" about it. "Can it possibly be," he asked himself, "that the French can't counter-attack, and, if so, are the B.E.F. surrounded? What happens then?"[36]

The French did not counter-attack, and the worst happened. On June 2, he and Charles Ritchie went down to the sea at Dover to see the remnants of the British Expeditionary Force and the tattered French army scramble onto Britain's free soil. It was a Sunday morning in a beautiful English spring. In the harbour a fine mist and the "eternal gulls" hung over the dozens of old trawlers, yachts, barges, tugs, and warships going back and forth between Dunkirk and Dover. In Dover, old ladies came out of Sunday service and chatted in the sun, but in the field young boys wrestled – wearing their gas masks. The Canadians returned to London consoled and determined, more so than they should have been, for we now know that Britain was very near defeat. Too many of her guns were museum pieces; her military had men but few arms; her people, according to the Ministry of Information, ran "around looking as if they want to put their heads in a gas oven".[37] Mike was morose; but the challenge made him more determined than ever. He could forgive the British everything as long as they did not crave peace as the French had. He told Ritchie after France collapsed: "If this country makes peace I hope Canada will become a republic and that will be the end of this business of our duty to the Empire."[38]

Britain did not make peace, and Churchill's defiant promise that he would never surrender inspired his people and Canadians, too. That defiance begat pride, a sense of duty – and fear. Mike, Wrong, and Crerar agreed in late May that the fall of France made the invasion of Britain possible, if not likely. The three husbands agreed that they would approach their respective wives with an ultimatum: they must leave London at once. Maryon and Mike argued long into the night about the decision, but, finally, Maryon under protest agreed to return to Canada where the children had remained at school when she had left for London in January. The trunks were packed, and the three wives proceeded to the ship that would carry them to Canada. Maryon bade Mike farewell and boarded ship, where, to her astonishment, she learned that Joyce Wrong had ordered the porter to remove her trunk and had taken the train back to London. A day later Joyce showed up at "Fairacres" where Mike and Hume had planned to stay alone. Maryon was not amused; and Mike knew it.[39]

On June 25, Mike wrote Maryon a letter on some scraps of paper as he waited for Canadians fleeing the *Wehrmacht*. Probably the second letter he sent after Maryon's departure, it is the only one that survives of Mike and Maryon's correspondence from the 1930s and 1940s and therefore deserves to be quoted in full, not only because it is unique but also because it captures the flavour of that dramatic month.

1940
June 25th

It[']s 8:20 A.M. at Paddington station – a funny place and time to be writing a letter. George Vanier was to have got in at 8 but his train is 2 hrs. late – and won[']t arrive till 9.20. So while Pauline and her 4 are having breakfast I bought myself this pad (6 p) at the book stall and decided to seize the opportunity to write – goodness knows if I'll have any other time today.

I seem to have been spending a good deal of time in Paddington lately. Thursday night we received a wire that a Canadian official party of 37 had been evacuated from Bordeaux and next morning we got a wire from Alfred Rive that they had landed in England after an exciting trip and without money or luggage! They would arrive at Paddington said Alfred at 11 P.M. So at 10 to 11 I was there, with Pierre Dupuy and some of the men who had come by destroyer and had arrived that afternoon in London.

When we got to the station, the station master said the train was very late & might be in any time after midnight. We waited till 1.30 and then I phoned the flat – just in chance something had gone wrong and Alfred might have phoned there. Hume answered and said Alfred *had* phoned at 9.30 and by now the party were presumably in bed. No one had met them, naturally, and they didn't know what to do etc. It was a dismal ending to a pretty terrible trip – about 2000 packed into a small ship – mostly women and children. They were bombed as they went up the Bay of Biscay and were all in a state of nervous exhaustion when they arrived.

Pauline was I believe very upset – and all next day was in a state of nerves. I managed to convince her though that we had even more of a grouse than they did – first at Alfred for saying they would arrive at 11 and then at the Station authorities.

The party consisted of Pauline and her 4, Mme [Pierre] Dupuy – 2 children, the Manions and infant, sundry wives & stenographers etc.

Next evening I invited them all to Fairacres for cold supper 12 turned up! and Nellie & Thomas did themselves proud. Only Mmes Dupuy & Manion were still too exhausted to go out. Then Sunday evening Mrs. Massey had them to the Dorchester. Next week all the women folk go back to Canada. It[']s just as well that Mesdames Massey & Vanier will be far apart. Sparks have already flown freely. Mrs. Massey started it by insisting as soon as she met Pauline that the latter must be off to Canada *at once*. One of those cases where she may have meant well – but Pauline was angry at this order to depart. Then Sunday night there was a real row at supper. Mrs. Massey started attacking the French (we all over here felt pretty bitter about them that evening) and Pauline burst into tears and launched a counter attack. Mrs. Massey – more or less hysterical – ordered me to defend my chief. I broke in by saying that I despised beyond words the French govt & some of their military leaders but I wouldn't say *one* word against the French people. Whereupon Mrs. M. hissed "disloyal" in my ear & I almost felt like strangling her. This unpleasantness was soon cleared up and we all became calm or relatively calm & friendly again. But on leaving Mrs. M. with simply incredible stupidity – said goodnight to Pauline as follows "When you are safely back in Canada will you think of us being bombed to pieces over here."

A lovely evening to close one of the most tiring & tense weeks I have ever spent.

9.20

George[']s train hasn't yet come in but the Vanier family, who were sitting in the car with me during the last two pages of this letter have left to walk up and down the platform, so I may be able to finish this in peace.

What a week we have had – it[']s been almost too much – the combination of depression of spirit because of the news and the millions of jobs that one simply can't get done at the office has been a pretty difficult one. After this week it will be quieter because the rush of Canadians back home will have ceased and by that time surely *all* of my acquaintances here will have phoned me to see if I can get the wives & children of their friends and relations into Canada. For the last week I have literally had a queue outside my office and by evening I'm ready for bed after dinner and a game of Chinese Chequers.

Last night about midnight the sirens went (first time since last September) but I stayed in bed – and listened to the drone of aeroplanes far up. I was furious at this particular interruption in my sleep because I had just picked up Myrna Loy at a country club and she had agreed to have dinner with me!

I was so glad to get your letter over the week-end & one from Patsy & Geoff. I'm afraid I may not have time to write the children this mail because it[']s going to be an awful rush when I *do* get to the office. Tell Geoff I'm very satisfied with his report which came yesterday & Patsy's marks – which she wrote me about – were fine. Also please tell your mother I'm so grateful for her letter and the snaps. I shall write her just as soon as I can.

Jack Holland has been enlisting my help lately to get his children away. Saturday he asked me if I could get someone to take them to Winnipeg from Montreal! He thought I might know somebody on the boat who was going there. Then yesterday he phoned to say they mightn[']t be going which means possibly I may have to ask Jack Patteson at the last minute to cancel his passage.... This rush of children on Canada is terrific & it[']s driving Jack Patteson & me nearly crazy....

Well, darling, I must stop. Latest news is that the train will be in in 5 minutes. I should have been at the office an hour ago. I hope Mrs. Massey doesn't think it disloyal of me to spend so much time meeting a Vanier!

It will be wonderful at Keewatin – but I know you would be sooner here with me. But you are doing your job too and it[']s a harder one than mine. I'm sure it[']s easier for Joyce here than for you there. That[']s why I still get rather mad at the thought of Joyce still being here.

But we are all a happy group at Fairacres and get on well together. Thomas has taken complete control of the kitchen and Nellie seems quite happy under his sway.

noon

George got here safely and looks very well.

Heaps of love.

That siren that disturbed Mike's dreams sounded nightly as the Battle of Britain began. If his sleep was interrupted, so, regrettably, was his diary, which did not resume until February 1941. He probably slept little during Britain's "finest hour" as the Royal Navy, "5000 pink-cheeked young pilots", the rag-tag British army, the First Canadian Division, and motley other imperial forces stood alone against catastrophe. Canada was now the front line if Britain fell, and Britain's defeat was now most assuredly Canada's as well. The challenge inspired Mike and most of his countrymen. Yet the great warlord, whom Canada cheered and who himself held the Empire so dear, was not disposed to share his thoughts with the dominions. Eden's successor as dominions secretary, Viscount Cranborne ("Bobbety" to Massey), complained to Churchill about his excluding him and about his "not know[ing] what was going on" since he could tell the dominions little. Massey and Mike were annoyed but they realized that it was King as well as Churchill who thought the high commissioners a nuisance. On great matters, the leaders dealt directly; on others, wartime justified many oversights. As a result Massey's role became increasingly one of publicity and formality. He greeted visiting Canadian politicians with exceptional grace and trotted them through the appropriate clubs and displayed them at court when occasion permitted. His thespian skills served him well in the myriad ceremonials wartime presented; and one supposes that this most aristocratic Canadian was a useful counterpoint to the Canadian soldiers who were acquiring a rather beastly reputation as they socialized in their own way in the English countryside. Alice Massey, too, became less an irritant and more an asset. She finally quelled the rebellion against her authority in women's war work, and bravely worked herself to death, helping the wounded in war. Her faults were forgotten as her good deeds mounted.*

With the Masseys occupied, the High Commission's work fell largely upon Mike's desk. He now had superb colleagues with whom to share the tasks of drafting telegrams, cajoling visiting Canadians, smoothing relations between the Canadian military and British, sorting out the financial details of the Canadian presence on British soil, and thinking about the future. After the fall of France, Wrong's duties, which were mainly concerned with economic ties to continental Europe, became much less since nearly all of Europe was now occupied. He and Mike now shared their complaints each evening, and they had many. In November 1940, Mike gave Graham Towers a blunt assessment of how poorly the Canadian government was using Wrong and him. "There must be a lot tougher jobs [in Ottawa] than mine, tougher on the brain, anyway. I've got lots to do God knows, but God knows also – though you needn't spread it about – that it's easy enough work. I wish it could be made a lot harder and more satisfying, by the Canadian government asking our views about anything. Hume Wrong feels the same – only far more so, because he has much less to intrigue him in the way of mental activity, than

---

* For Alice Massey, no embarrassment could halt her commitment to the cause. In a letter to her sister, Maude Grant, of Nov. 9, 1941, she revealed that while touring a Canadian base, she "felt something slip in my clothing. I kept hitching it up, but got nowhere, and finally got behind a garbage pail, and in a great hurry took off my black bloomers, which were the culprits, went up to George [Ignatieff] and said: 'George, put these in your pocket and say nothing'!"

I have. It's a crime that he is not given a really responsible hard post." Mike's own job was "to join in holy but uneasy wedlock the Canadian civil and military powers – which means, among other things – keeping McNaughton and the High Commissioner as far apart as possible." The job was not easy, and it was important, as the First World War experience had shown, but it scarcely taxed Mike's intellect.[40] Nor did it change his view about the many stupidities of the Canadian government's approach to the war. As in pre-war days, Mike's strongest denunciation was directed towards the Immigration department. In his letter to Towers, he wrote

> It seems to me obvious that we should now encourage emigration of all those people who are able and willing to work, but our Immigration Office in London – carrying out orders received from Ottawa – are applying the present regulations just as strictly as they did in the days when their sole object in life was to keep people out of Canada. Some of the things they are doing are almost unbelievable in their absurdity. I have no doubt you hear of this in Ottawa, which is the fountain-head of bureaucratic ineptitude in these matters. These may be harsh words but no harsher than are deserved.... A Polish, a Czech, a Belgian or a Dutch refugee might be an expert mechanic in the manufacture of aeroplanes or any other vital engine of war, but the questions they will be asked are – When does a hen first begin to lay eggs? How many teeth has a full grown cow? and What is the best way of ploughing? If they can't answer these questions, nothing else matters (unless they have friends at court). If they can answer these questions they will probably be allowed into Canada at a time when the Government should be discouraging, rather than encouraging agricultural production. I suggest that one of the most important things that can be done in Ottawa at the present time would be to pull our Immigration Laws and Regulations to pieces, and the Department with them.

In their indictment of Canadian immigration policy in *None Is Too Many,* Irving Abella and Harold Troper are severe in their criticism of not only Immigration but also External Affairs. They do not criticize Pearson but they do imply that he, an External Affairs officer, deserves many of the criticisms they make. In the case of Pearson, at least, the implied criticism seems unfair.[41]

Whatever the complaints about the Canadian government and the nature of their work, Mike and his colleagues had a memorable time. Those days in London in the blitz bonded together a small bunch of Canadians in an intimacy they would always treasure. Three decades later Mike recalled that extraordinary winter of 1940-1. "Life became more difficult and dangerous. Yet the spirit of the people was never better, their morale never higher than in those weeks of night bombing. There was no sign of panic. Instead, there grew up a sense of solidarity, a community of suffering and sacrifice, and cheerful cooperation. There was the attitude you find in the face of a common danger, and which unhappily dissipates when the danger is past and you return to the competitive, acquisitive society where men are unequal and insecure."[42] In Canada House, as in Britain, this precious "spirit" thrived as the danger grew. Charles Ritchie, aware of the danger, was so quick to mock it. "The Ritchie," Mike wrote, "is as cheerful as ever, in spite of his bombed flat, his amatory complications and his job." Every morning the Canada House staff met to compare their harrowing experiences of the night before and "The Ritchie" always won. Because of his "amatory complications", Ritchie slept in many beds, and his stories were always the best. In August he claimed he was "practically riddled with shot and shell from the air". Ritchie's "story was exciting at 9:30 a.m. – by 6 p.m. it had beaten any war thriller that ever was invented." When his flat actually was demolished in November, Ritchie admitted to his diary that he enjoyed "the publicity attendant on this disaster, particularly the idea which I have put abroad that if it had not been for the chance decision to go to Aldershot I should have been killed". He recovered quickly and his thoughts soon returned to the American ballerina whose coyness frustrated the libidinous Ritchie in a setting where there was not world enough or time. Mike liked to "shake up" Ritchie: "He was telling us of a young lady who was going to have a baby. I looked hard at him for a moment but he replied cheerily, 'It's alright, I haven't seen her for ten months.' I asked him if he had ever heard of time bombs. Now the poor chap is worried again."[43] Charles Ritchie, then as ever, was wonderful company – and a first-class diplomat.[44]

"I did not think I was still capable of the friendship I feel for George Ignatieff," Ritchie wrote of the "new boy" who arrived at Canada House in 1940. Son of the Education minister in the Russian czar's last government, Ignatieff had gone to Oxford as a Rhodes scholar when Mike first met him. He urged Ignatieff, as well as many other bright young Canadians whom he met, to consider the foreign service as a career. Ignatieff signed up and was sent to London immediately. Mike developed a high regard for Ignatieff's abilities and a warm personal relationship with him. Ignatieff's affection for Mike brims over in his memoirs and personal conversation, and the "Mike" he recalls is the person he knew in London in 1940-1. At work Mike was the mentor; after hours they speculated about the shape of the future and partied with a group of young attractive male and female Canadians who lived in wartime London.*

One of the most attractive was the Masseys' favourite niece, Alison Grant, whose charm and generosity left their mark on all she encountered. Even her brother George, an Oxford student who came down to wartime London as a conscientious objector, extolled his sister's virtues in a most un-brotherlike fashion. Alison, he told his mother, "is turning into one of the finest and nicest people I have ever seen. She is becoming more and more feminine – more and more subtle and altogether so nice it kills me that anybody can be so nice." She was the emotional ballast for George as he went out in the evenings to the East End of London and, as alternative service, helped

---

* James Spence of Canada House's Press Office gave a vivid description of how Canada House operated in a letter to Pearson on Mar. 2, 1942, just after Mike's departure: "Mr. Massey flits silently to and fro on dark errands like a fasting Pope wrapped in a shadow. Ritchie's laughter is the exception that proves the rule of raucousness and the vacant mind – I beg you to read that phrase carefully, since it does not imply the heresy of a Ritchie who is anything but brilliant – while the Ignatieff uncoils himself gently here and there with the gentlest of smiles (Pale hands pink-tipped, beside the Samovar!) and the most remote of interests. I often feel that he looks through one to the great Caucasian steppes beyond."

London's poorest as German bombs rained upon them. Alison charmed Mike (and me when I interviewed her four decades later), and she drew him into her circle of attractive young friends. The group invigorated him. Mike described to his mother and Vaughan a London evening with Alison during the blitz that captures well the way they lived there. After reassuring his mother in the same words he used in the First World War ("I've never slept better.... In fact I lead a life of perfect security"), Mike contradicts his assurances.

> One effect these nightly bombings have had – apart from disturbing sleep and transportation – is that when you have anyone to dinner – he arrives with tooth-brush & pyjamas – expecting to spend the night. In the last 10 days we have had 6 different people occupy our spare bed. Similarly, I was out for dinner Tuesday night at Alison Grant's flat (Mrs. Massey's niece) which she shares with Mary Greey, a Toronto girl. Major Basil Wedd from Headquarters was there too. It was pretty noisy outside and I was a long way from [home] so I decided to accept the offer of a sleeping bag in the cellar for the night.... Well, before I could get into my bag, a Molotov Bread Basket affair descended on us, and showered incendiary bombs all around – one on the next roof. It was exciting for a moment but the A.R.P. [Air Raid Precautions] people soon dealt with the one on the roof while it was easy to put the others out on the pavement.... That's what a dinner party in London is liable to develop into these days.

Alison worked in British intelligence, lost her boyfriend, the brilliant Frank Pickersgill, when the Nazis captured and garrotted him in 1944, married George Ignatieff at the war's end, named one of their two sons Michael, after Mike, and, in her own way influenced Canada's future as much as did her distinguished diplomat husband. When I asked her, too boldly, what she thought of Mike in those days, she said simply, "I loved him."[45]

Alison's group adored Mike although George, who was on the left politically then, thought his politics too simplistic because Mike told him it did not matter if Wendell Willkie defeated Roosevelt so long as American foreign policy was handled satisfactorily. George was also annoyed when he learned that Mike had said of his decision to give up his conscientious-objector status that it was "nice" that George had "grown with the years out of a childish preoccupation". Mike thought George too brittle, and George had reservations about Mike. The blitz created a temporary closeness. Indeed, one night Mike even bathed George after he returned from the East End. Others in the group were embarrassingly enthusiastic about Mike. One day in midwinter 1941 a letter to the editor appeared in *The Globe and Mail* from Elizabeth Greey, sister of Alison's roommate, Mary Greey. She took strong issue with a *Globe* criticism of External Affairs and expressed regret that Canadians did not know their diplomats. Dr. Skelton had died in late January and his eulogies pointed to the shy public servant as one of the most influential men of his time. But there were others Canadians should know, most notably "L.B. Pearson ... familiarly known as 'Mike,' [and] possibly the best loved Canadian in London. His energy and personality have not only won him his reputation, but they are the mainstay on which the greatly expanded work of Canada House rests." Mary and Elizabeth Greey were constant companions in London. Canadians living in England, Mary and Elizabeth moved in with Alison in 1940. George told his mother that Alison's new companions "the Greeys are ANGELS". Elizabeth returned to Canada to sing Mike's praises. Women and men were equally attracted to Mary, who remained. Alison said of Mary: "When she looks limpidly through her blue eyes people go absolutely weak." Mike found her thoroughly admirable and magnetic, and she was a scintillating companion in the absence of his family during the "siren years".[46]

Elizabeth Greey was a biased source to be sure, but her letter to *The Globe and Mail* accurately reflected the solid reputation Mike had acquired in wartime London. He craved new work because he knew how significant his work could be. Skelton's death, however, threw External into disarray, especially since Loring Christie, Canada's minister in Washington, had fallen mortally ill in early 1941. These events affected Mike's position immediately.

Mike, Wrong, and Robertson had spent many hours detailing Skelton's liabilities, but his sudden death shocked them and made them realize how, in Robertson's words, "we all lived & worked secure in the shadow of a great rock...." By the time he wrote, three days after Skelton's death on January 27, Robertson had already been appointed acting under-secretary by Mackenzie King. The appointment made Robertson, six years Mike's junior, uneasy. He admitted his discomfort to Mike: "I did not really write to praise or bury Caesar [Skelton] but to say you have been on my conscience for the last year – and now worse than ever – for if you had come back with the other visiting firemen you would undoubtedly have been asked to carry on in O.D.'s place rather than I." Mike unfortunately did not receive this letter until February 27, and he was annoyed. He thought Robertson's letter was "very friendly and very apologetic", but the suggestion that he could go to "the Argentine or Brazil as Minister" was not welcomed. When Maryon heard from some friends about Argentina, she was "indignant". She thought, and Mike agreed, that he should be Skelton's replacement.[47] And Maryon did not hesitate to voice her opinion.

Mike took several days before replying to Robertson and began by indicating that Robertson's letter had taken a month to arrive. He, too, was friendly, but the letter has an impersonal tone and does not respond to Robertson's "apology" about his elevation above Mike.* He did respond directly to the suggestion that he go to South America: "Under present conditions I would be unhappy if I were sent there, though on principle I do not think anybody has any right to refuse any post offered. That is why I hope there will be no such offer to me. To leave London and bask in the sun of Rio or Buenos Aires these days would seem to be like deserting the battle-field. I would

---

* In his memoirs, Mike admits he was disappointed that he was not appointed under-secretary. He does say the disappointment was lessened by the friendship between the Robertsons and the Pearsons. He also points out that Wrong was overlooked even though he was "superior in intellect" to himself. He was not, however, "superior" in his ability to get along with people.

certainly have no objection to leaving London for a post which means as hard work and as much opportunity for real service; but not otherwise." In other words, he would return as under-secretary or not at all.[48]

Nor was Mike pleased when King appointed "a 71 year old businessman", Leighton McCarthy, to Washington and then sent Hume Wrong there as his counsellor. It was insulting to Wrong (who, incidentally, favoured Pearson over Robertson as under-secretary) and an indication once again that Mackenzie King did not take the idea of a professional foreign service seriously. King's eccentricities left an increasingly bitter taste. Quite apart from his refusing to deal with Canada House, King's requests sometimes had a touch of madness. The most outrageous of them was made in a secret telegram and demanded that Canada House secure a few stones from the ruins of Westminster Hall, which King had heard was bombed the previous night. The ruins of the Mother of Parliaments seemed an especially worthwhile addition to his growing collection of ruins at Kingsmere. Joyce Wrong and Mike were playing Chinese chequers when the telegram arrived, but a prime minister's needs had to be served. British officials whom Mike approached were bemused but co-operative and packed up the stones to be shipped by submarines to Canada. Not surprisingly, when Mike heard a rumour on March 26, 1941, that he would be returning to Canada as King's private secretary, he wrote in his diary, "God protect me from that!"[49]

Three days later Mike received "shattering news from Ottawa". A long telegram from King to Massey announced that he wanted Pearson to return to Ottawa, "probably as an additional Assistant Under-secretary". Mike set out his position in his diary.

> I ought, of course, to be both excited and delighted at the thought of getting back to Ottawa. But I don't feel that way about it. If it were not for the family being there I just wouldn't go.... One hates to leave London at this time, and the only real compensation – apart from family considerations – would be that the work I was going back to was more important than that which I am now doing, from the point of

view of the war. That may be the case, but I am not quite sure. Like so many telegrams from Mr. King there is a good deal that can be read in between the lines and much that is not clear cut and explicit. Of course I don't like the idea really of going back to the Department, except as Under-Secretary, and I am not quite sure what this post of Joint Assistant Under-Secretary means. My own view is that it means that Mr. King wants Norman Robertson as a sort of super personal assistant and is going to give him the rank of Under-Secretary for that reason, while I am to be brought back to do the work that the Under-Secretary would normally be doing, without being given the rank.

Mike, in those days, was modest about neither his ambition nor his talents.[50]

Mike and Massey acted jointly to advance his cause. Massey told King that Mike was ready to leave but added that Mike was "a little worried about his recall to Ottawa because he leaves an important and well defined appointment to assume a position as yet not definitely decided." Massey strongly hinted that the position should be the under-secretary. Massey added some gratuitous comments about Mike: "As you know, Pearson has great capacity for all kinds of work in our External Affairs service, and combines in an unusual degree qualities not often found in one person. He has impressed me as having first rate administrative ability with excellent initiative.... Pearson can now bring to any task the advantage of wide and varied experience and he is I believe entirely competent to assume any position within the sphere of our External Affairs service." Mike, who saw these kind words, sent a separate note to Robertson in which he bluntly complained about leaving London "unless I were satisfied I was required for equally responsible work in Ottawa". In this sense, Mike pointedly added, "I am not much enamoured of the proposal", especially "if I am right in interpreting the telegram as meaning that the Under-Secretaryship is closed."[51] Hume Wrong had taught Mike lessons in more than Chinese chequers.

The under-secretaryship was closed. The King diary makes no mention of Mike as a possible under-secretary and as time passed

King's respect for Robertson grew.* Robertson did clarify Mike's status, indicating that he would be one of three under-secretaries, that he would deal with British and Commonwealth questions, and that he would not receive an increase in salary. "At least Norman has been frank," Mike wrote on reading the telegram. His doubts were scarcely removed. Moreover, he realized that the transfer would cut his income "by more than one half" because of the loss of allowances.[52] Still, he knew he had to go. Regretfully, he booked his departure and bade goodbye to London.

Mike's youthful infatuation with Britain and Britons had been rekindled during Britain's "finest hour". Graham Spry, who had become an even closer friend during the London years, organized a farewell dinner at the Coq d'Or restaurant for about fifty colleagues. Mike spoke wittily and sentimentally. He paid tribute to Massey, the Canada House staff, and the spirit that animated their work together. Then, he spoke of the British people: "God knows those people are not perfect – They have defects enough. At times their methods seem to me to be based on Plantagenet ideas, applied with Victorian ease.... But, by and large, I feel that this country represents the furthest and finest stage mankind has yet reached in political and social development." For Mike, Canada's identity still rested upon the line that ran politically from Magna Carta to the report of the Rowell-Sirois Commission and culturally from Chaucer to E.J. Pratt. Those roots brought forth the efflorescence of greatness Mike encountered in Londoners in those treasured wartime years. But now Britain's future, like his own, lay westward. He knew when he left that Britain's proud defiance was costing her more than she knew and that power was ineluctably passing to America, a land less developed politically and socially.[53]

---

* It was not initially so. On Apr. 5, 1941, King complained in his diary that "External men" were tending to believe they could "settle everything" and ignore politicians. On the same day, Mrs. Patteson told King, to his horror, that Mrs. Robertson at a party had expressed the hope that Britain would be destroyed and that Robertson said nothing. King resolved to "rely upon his own judgment" in making decisions. The story is apocryphal.

Mike, in fact, left London at the proper moment, for Canada's relationship with the United States now required more attention than Canada's relationship with Britain. Indeed, we shall see in the next chapter that even his most important work in London in the spring of 1941 dealt with the United States and its role in the war. He returned to Canada with a clearer sense of what Canada's part in a future international system should be, and a commitment to educating Canadians to their new responsibilities. And he had new confidence in his country. In his final broadcast from Britain, he ended with a story about a Canadian soldier on leave who was in a building bombed by the *Luftwaffe*. There he remained, unmoving beneath a pile of rubble, fearful that any movement would bring death. An arm remained exposed but in the night it became cold. When the rescue squad member felt the arm in the morning, he murmured "This chap's gone." Beneath the rubble came a "short sharp reply in good Canadian: 'Sez you!'"

There were many other memories as well: of the Sunday morning when his caddy told him when teeing off to slice more than usual because an unexploded bomb lay in the middle of the fairway; of the nervous and mousy Canada House typist whom the blitz transformed into a determined and enthusiastic patriot; of the Marble Arch eccentrics orating beside fresh bomb craters; of the late-night speculations with Hume Wrong and George Ignatieff about how the shattered pieces of the world could be glued together again; of boys playing in gas masks and old ladies chattering outside church when he and "The Ritchie" left Dover on Dunkirk morning; and of the walks with Alison Grant and Mary Greey through blacked-out London while broken glass crackled beneath their feet, silver balloons thronged the sky, and the black dust from last night's raid settled on their skin. Those who knew Mike best then say he changed later: the public face concealed more of him and his private self became even more elusive. The judgment seems correct, but that transformation affected others too.

In the most evocative novel about wartime London, Elizabeth Bowen, who came to love Charles Ritchie then, and he her, said that, in autumn 1940, Londoners began an instinctive movement to break down indifference "while there was still time". The "wall between the living and the living became less solid as the wall between the living and the dead thinned." Saying goodnight was harder because you hoped not to die that night, "still more not to die unknown". Those times were precious, for "That autumn of 1940 was to appear, by two autumns later, apocryphal, more far away than peace.... That particular psychic London was to be gone forever; more bombs would fall, but not on the same city."[54] The city would never be the same, but neither were the people who had dwelt in it.

CHAPTER TEN

WASHINGTON
AT WAR

All the talk is of peace these days, with the Germans apparently retreating headlong before the Russians. Unfortunately, thoughts of victory in Washington are accompanied by a recrudescence of political style. My own view is that American policy after this war is not going to be much more intelligent than it was after the last. The fact of the matter is that most Americans are natural isolationists, and only international co-operators in an emergency. We are in for a sticky time.
– Lester Pearson at "the turn of the tide" in 1943[1]

LESTER PEARSON'S training as a historian was, perhaps, one factor that led him to see "time as a stream".[2] It was his habit to recall the past while confronting the present and considering the future. He had read Gibbon on Rome's decline, and Spengler's *Decline of the West* had been fashionable among undergraduate history students and, hence, their teachers in the 1920s. He knew that great empires waxed and waned, and Britain's "dominion over palm and pine" was, as Matthew Arnold had warned many years before, an orb too vast for the Island kingdom to uphold. At his first international conference in 1930, Mike saw the British government appease American demands that imposed considerable restriction upon British strategic freedom. She could no longer defend her great base at Singapore while warding off attackers from her Mediterranean interests. Britain's historic mission was now more than ever an "Atlantean load", especially since her dominions seemed reluctant to bear their share and the United States stood in defiant isolation from the old world's concerns while badgering British statesmen to maintain the interests of freedom and democracy. "It is always best and safest," wrote a suspicious Neville Chamberlain in 1937 as his appeasement of Germany commenced, "to count on *nothing* from the Americans except words."[3] As with appeasement, many Canadians agreed.

Britain needed far more than words after the fall of France in June 1940. There was a mood of desperation to which a sympathetic American president, Franklin Roosevelt, responded. Mike was elated when Mackenzie King and Roosevelt signed the Ogdensburg Agreement in August 1940, setting up the Permanent Joint Board on Defence between Canada and the United States. He told Brooke Claxton, now a Liberal MP, that the new accords were "something to cling to and ... something which, in the long run, will prove decisive". In Mike's view, the agreement, which had "far reaching implications", was "one of the wisest and most astute things Mr. King has ever done, and it has been so skilfully engineered that no possible criticism can arise."[4] And little criticism did arise, but as the Americans negotiated a deal whereby the British traded bases in the western hemisphere (including Newfoundland) for destroyers, Mike felt some wistful regret. In early 1941 he represented Canada during the United Kingdom-United States negotiations in which the latter held all the high cards and the former had only its tattered silk shirt. The British looked "pathetically" across the table at the confident Americans and gave in. In late March the agreement on the Newfoundland bases was signed, Mike had Churchill autograph a copy, and then heard Churchill call for champagne. As he waited, Churchill paced the floor "like a caged lion, puffing away at his cigar, occasionally stopping and bursting forth with an expletive of some kind or other". The champagne arrived, the glasses were filled, Churchill then toasted the King and the President of the United States. Mike sensed how symbolic the moment was and shared the relief all Britons felt.

But he wrote in his diary: "No matter how much we may applaud [the agreement] now, or toast it in champagne, it is a victory for the United States and means the beginning of the end of British rule in the West Indies."[5]

Looking back, historians confirm what Mike felt and Churchill feared: that he had become the prime minister of England who would preside over the liquidation of the British Empire.[6] To be sure, the liquidation came later, but its inevitability derived from the events of the war years. The war acted like an x-ray, penetrating the Empire's ermine robes to expose the malignancies in its extremities and the weakness at its heart. The United States' rise to superpower status was accelerated by the rapidity of Britain's decline, and this circumstance left a strong residue of resentment not only among the British but also with some Canadians. While Mike never shared Donald Creighton's laments about the decline of British power and the rise of American globalism and its impact on Canada, he did express much private irritation when confronted with American statesmen, intoxicated with schemes to reorder the world, who treated British statesmen with the disdain due last year's sporting heroes. The celebrated bonhomie between Churchill and Roosevelt could not disguise the desperation and even political diffidence with which the old world's greatest leader of this century made his appeal to the new world's greatest.[7] As a recent study of the transfer of great-power status has pointed out, the Americans caricatured the British and vice versa. To the Americans, the British appeared not only arrogant but "tricky and devious too", and "this hostility was exacerbated by the conviction of all right-thinking Americans that Britain's wealth was immoral, since it was based on colonialism, which reduced millions to servitude". Britain, of course, saw her imperial role as a mission to spread principles of individual liberty and the rule of law, a role she could fulfil far better than could the United States, "a country not yet civilized, but uncouth and raw".[8]

Canadians, of course, tended to reject both stereotypes, for they had themselves felt the icy disregard of British imperialists even as they served their cause; and they knew well that, by the 1940s, most Canadians were irredeemably American in their styles, their accents, and their geography. Skelton, of course, had affirmed this truth most enthusiastically in the 1920s and 1930s. When Mike's friend Frank Underhill did so just after France fell, pointing out that Canada's loyalty to "North America" now would and should matter most to Canadians, he faced a threat of dismissal from the University of Toronto. What probably saved Underhill was the effect such a dismissal would have upon American opinion. Keenleyside, Skelton, and Brebner rallied to Underhill's defence, and Mike would probably have done so had he been in Canada.[9] Yet it must be added that Underhill's sneers towards the British and his warm embrace of North Americanism did not reflect Mike's own attitude. Canada's status, he wrote Massey in January 1942, was more respected by the United Kingdom than by the United States.[10] Like Massey, he never lost that view, but unlike him and Creighton, he never came to symbolize it. It lurked within his private thoughts; publicly such doubts were suppressed as what *Time* publisher Henry Luce called "The American Century" began.

Ottawa in 1941 had changed considerably from the peacetime city Mike had left six years before. Compared to London, Ottawa retained a frontier and ramshackle flavour, which the string of "temporary" buildings along the Ottawa River cliffs only enhanced. The Château Laurier cafeteria, where wartime civil servants dined, must have kindled fond memories of those exquisite lunches at Claridge's (although certainly not of his Travellers' Club whose fare was notoriously English). Ottawa's wartime atmosphere was nevertheless more to Mike's taste than he had expected when he left London. The war had swollen the bureaucracy and had spawned in Ottawa a greater variety of people than had gathered there before. "Dollar-a-year men" recruited from business to administer various cogs in the economic war machine, university professors eager to apply theory to practice, and journalists and film-makers convinced that their frivolous crafts could, in wartime, rally a democratic populace to victory made Ottawa a different city. All of them worked very hard, and in that atmosphere of commitment and long hours, unusual friendships formed between bureaucrats and businessmen, socialists and conservatives. Even socialists could forgive the hard-headed business views of C.D. Howe when that most able wartime minister was organizing Canada's contribution to the destruction of Fascism.[11] The Canadian "mandarins", that group of public servants who so influenced Canada's development in the 1940s and 1950s, got to know each other and to learn how the state could intervene in the economy and society for the betterment of all Canadians in wartime Ottawa.

Certainly Mike's Ottawa stay, brief as it was to be, benefited him greatly. He renewed old friendships, made important new ones (notably in the business, academic, and journalistic worlds), and made an impression on Mackenzie King, whose diary reveals that he barely took notice of Mike's existence before his return to Ottawa. In his first interview with King upon his return, Mike's hope of securing the under-secretary's position never was raised. Mike wisely offered what King preferred. He "reported his readiness to begin work at once." Then he quickly added, perhaps knowing King's unusually close ties to his own mother, that his first request was that he be allowed to go to Toronto to see his mother. "Very modest, unassuming," King wrote, "He is going to be valuable to Robertson." Mike knew that his future reputation now depended on being "valuable to Robertson", and he quickly and publicly squelched rumours that he wanted Robertson's job himself and thought his appointment unwise.[12]

In fact, Mike, who complained so often about Skelton's lack of organizational skills, did think poorly of Robertson's as well. He was not as critical of Robertson's abilities as was their colleague Hugh Keenleyside, who later wrote in his memoirs that "the selection of Norman Robertson was, of course, a mistake". Mike was much more generous, saying that administration and personnel matters were, for Robertson "a burden which, I knew, he did not like and in consequence bore with only partial success". Moreover, Mike liked Robertson personally, and it was easy for him to help out Robertson in a wide variety of tasks. Keenleyside, who did have considerable interest in personnel matters and who worked out a plan for the reorganization of the department on more clearly defined lines, thought that Mike's work on the department's new personnel board was "of great benefit" and that, in most matters, Mike "had a much greater understanding [than Robertson] of what was humanly important and how human beings should be dealt with."[13] Mike himself was inclined to blame King more than Robertson because the former asked the latter "to do far more than any one man can do effectively". Robertson had to spend "two hours each day" worrying about such items as the cost of linen or the newest stenographer's salary. Small wonder there was little chance for improvement.[14] There was, in fact, some improvement to be had from Keenleyside's plan to have the department divided into four sections, one of which was Commonwealth and European. Mike headed that division.

Duties, however, failed to follow these new divisions, and Mike found himself involved in myriad activities that were only indirectly related to his supposed area of responsibility. He represented External Affairs on several of the interdepartmental boards that proliferated in wartime Ottawa. Some were especially interesting, such as his position on the National Film Board, where he watched the work of the great documentary film-maker John Grierson with a mixture of respect, amazement, and puzzlement. At the urging of Canada House's staff secretary, Ross McLean, Pearson had been instrumental in having Grierson come to Canada just before the war began. Grierson quickly became a fabled figure, too outrageous to contain within the normal confines of bureaucracy. He fascinated Mike, who recommended him to become the head of the government's faltering Wartime Information Board, but each succeeding encounter with "St. John and his disciples" baffled Mike more.[15]

Mike also dealt with internal security questions and was troubled when the RCMP persisted in keeping communists interned after June 1941 when the Soviet Union entered the war as an ally. The rapid volte-face of the Canadian communists after Hitler attacked the

Soviet Union did not impress Mike, but he thought that further internment served Canada's broader interests poorly. Mike personally negotiated an accord between Canada's communists and the government. On a boat trip on the Ottawa River Mike and Fred Rose, a communist leader and later an MP and a convicted Soviet spy, agreed that the communists, who were now vigorously pro-war, could have their freedom if they gave themselves up and served a short time in jail. Both the meeting on the Ottawa and the agreement were evidence of the bizarre character of wartime alliances. Other duties were equally peculiar, none more so than Mike's chairmanship of the Associate Committee of the National Research Council, which supervised the "Examination Unit", an intelligence unit that tried to intercept enemy messages and share this information with the Americans and the British. The Canadians had little experience in these matters and accordingly sought the help of the U.S. Signal Corps. Its chief recommended in the spring of 1941 that Canada appoint H.O. Yardley to organize a cryptographic (code-breaking) bureau in Ottawa. Yardley came to Ottawa in May with his assistant, Edna Ramsier, and immediately set up the unit, using the name "Osborne". Yardley had been the leading American cryptographer in the First World War and in the 1920s but lost his position in 1929 when U.S. secretary of state Henry Stimson refused to maintain an intelligence service, declaring that "Gentlemen do not read other people's mail." A few years later Stimson and other gentlemen read in horror Yardley's book *The American Black Chamber,* which revealed how the United States had read Japanese diplomatic despatches in the early 1920s. The book sold especially well in Tokyo. Yardley, who had first fled to Hollywood where he wrote a novel, took refuge in China with Chiang Kai-Shek and once again broke the Japanese codes. Except for the work during the First World War and in China, the Canadians apparently knew nothing of Yardley's notoriety. They soon found out, first from the British who had "blacklisted" Yardley in the 1920s and who, with some relish, pointed out the Canadians' stupidity in hiring him. The United States, where Stimson had recently become secretary of war, of course agreed. (Stimson, it must be said, now did believe in reading some other people's mail.)[16] It fell to Mike to fire Yardley, which he did with some trepidation, recalling Stimson's fate when he dismissed him in 1929. Yardley did protest; in fact, the unit's records suggest that he had done all he could and his days in Ottawa were numbered. A golden handshake was arranged for Yardley / Osborne and his "assistant", and they departed, pledging to serve the cause of liberty in some other far-off place. On July 10, 1942, Mike, now in Washington, received a message from Tommy Stone, his successor as Examination Unit chairman: "Osborne, nee Yardley, now reported operating very successful restaurant in Washington and making, according to his own statements in Ottawa recently, ten thousand dollars a year.... Miss Ramsier is his principal assistant. How is that for an Intelligence service?" One doubts that Mike dined at Yardley's restaurant.[17]

Upon Yardley's firing at the behest of the Americans, the British quickly sent out a replacement. In a sense this bizarre incident symbolizes the growing difficulties Canada and External Affairs faced as the British and the Americans moved closer together. Mike had seen how Canada's interests could be ignored as Britain clamoured for American aid; and he resented the pattern. In the Newfoundland agreement, what especially troubled Pearson was the fact that the strongest objections to Canada's position came not from Britain, which, after all, was the proprietary power in Newfoundland, but from the United States, which clearly had new long-term interests of its own.[18] Canada moved quickly to establish its own position in Newfoundland in response to the American challenge. Still, Canada, and in particular Mackenzie King, revelled in the work Canada had done "in bringing about the closer relationship between the United States and the British Commonwealth". It will, King said after Congress passed the historic lend-lease bill in March 1941, "seal the spiritual union of free peoples everywhere".[19] The Hyde Park Agreement, which followed in April and which protected Canada's wartime economy, similarly seemed an act of unselfish generosity to most Canadians.* Disturbing signs soon appeared that the Canadian "linch-pin" had become irrelevant and that Roosevelt and Churchill regarded the war as theirs to wage while others, including Canada (in the words of one well-informed observer in Washington), were "looked on somewhat as poor cousins who can be depended on to do whatever Uncle Sam wants...."[20]

On the Sunday morning the Japanese attacked Pearl Harbor, Mike was working at the office. General Crerar, however, was strolling through Rockcliffe that Sunday morning and dropped in on the Pearsons. Twelve-year-old Patsy casually opened the conversation, asking what he thought about the attack on Pearl Harbor. The startled general ran out, no doubt ready to court-martial his intelligence unit, which had failed to contact him. Both Mike and Crerar lamented the casualties but celebrated the American entry into the war, which they thought might clarify the ambiguities that had sometimes marred Canadian-American relations. The hopes were quickly dashed. Churchill and Roosevelt immediately met at the so-called Arcadia Conference, where they jointly and exuberantly established the new machinery that would direct the war effort. The Combined Chiefs of Staff and the Munitions Assignment Board, the Combined Shipping Adjustment Board, and the Combined Raw Materials Board were set up; their members were exclusively British or American. As these events transpired, a side-show took place off Newfoundland's shores when General de Gaulle's Free French forces occupied St. Pierre and Miquelon. The American government exploded in anger, blaming the Canadian government for this

---

* Mackenzie King, however, was troubled in the midst of acclaim the Americans received in Canada. It all meant, he wrote in his diary on Apr. 23, 1941, that "the defence of this continent is bound to be increasingly that of the United States itself. Just what may result from this line it is difficult to say. I, personally, would be strongly opposed to anything like a political union. I would keep the British Commonwealth of Nations as intact as possible. Canada, in time, and sooner than we expected perhaps, would become centre." This statement would have astonished Mike, not to mention Massey and Churchill.

"invasion", which threatened the United States's so-called Vichy gamble. The Americans, who disliked de Gaulle, had sought to court Vichy, the bastard offspring of the fall of France. American secretary of state Cordell Hull issued an angry public statement that spoke of the "so-called Free French" and "inquired" of the Canadian government what steps it was prepared "to take to restore the status quo of these islands". At 10:15 on Christmas night Mike telephoned the strong Canadian response to J. Pierrepont Moffat, the American minister in Ottawa.[21] Mike reflected on these events two weeks later in a letter to Massey. Canada, which had stood by Britain in her finest and most perilous hour, increasingly was left alone:[22]

> ... United States-Canadian relations present a very difficult problem indeed in present circumstances.... There are very definite and discernable [sic] tendencies in the latter capital to consider us either as a part of the British Empire to be dealt with through a British Empire spokesman from the United Kingdom or as a North-American colony.... I am ... enclosing a short note I prepared on the absence of Canada at the forthcoming Rio Conference. There is no question that the United States did not wish us at that conference. The United States is also not anxious for us to play too big a part in deliberations in Washington. Mr. Churchill's visit showed that. Their view was that he was quite qualified to speak for the British Empire and that too many voices would complicate matters. I feel certain that if any Allied Council is set up there we will have to fight hard for our place in it, but so far as the officials of the Department are concerned we are certainly willing to make that fight....
>
> But the really serious difficulties we have had with the United States have been, of course, over St. Pierre.... St. Pierre gave me one of the busiest and most exciting Christmases I have ever had. I was at the Office all day and until 1.30 a.m. next morning – in fact I have been at the Office every day, including Sundays and holidays, for the last month, along with the other senior people. The time is coming when we must get a rest or the work will suffer. But to get back to St. Pierre.

In our view the conduct of the State Department in this latter is entirely inexcusable. We know Moffat well enough here personally to tell him exactly what we think about the way his colleagues handled this matter. I am afraid we are not out of the woods yet, though the earlier and wilder plans of Washington to use us to drive the "so called Free French" (that reference was one of the worst things they did) out has been abandoned. However, there is very little we can do to influence American policy on this matter. I am afraid they do not treat our views with any great deference or respect and I am, also, afraid that we have ourselves partly to blame for this. Great Britain will have to fight the battle of the Free French and it looks as if we will have to accept any arrangement agreed to by Great Britain and the United States. Mr. Churchill was very sound on the matter when he was in Ottawa and his speech in the House of Commons in his references to Vichy was very helpful though it infuriated the State Department. However, I understand Mr. Churchill reacts somewhat differently in Washington under American pressure than in Ottawa....

Hugh Keenleyside talked about "American imperialism" in an angry memorandum he sent to Robertson in April, and Robertson himself warned King that the Canadian legation in Washington was not equal to the difficult tasks it would face. Indeed, it was not. It was in a state of near chaos, with Hume Wrong once again the centre of controversy. When Loring Christie fell ill, King appointed the wealthy Toronto lawyer Leighton McCarthy as Canada's minister to Washington. McCarthy met King in February 1941 and asked that Hume Wrong be sent to Washington to replace Escott Reid whose well-known leftist views probably offended McCarthy. McCarthy said he was "very fond of Wrong's wife" and had "known Wrong too all his life". Within a year, McCarthy was denouncing Wrong and his wife and demanding that either they leave or he would. At this point in late winter 1942, Mike (rather unwisely) sent a long memorandum to Robertson strongly urging "the reconstruction and extension of our representation in the United States". The legation, Mike told

Robertson, "made little impact on the mind or life of Washington....
Indeed, Canada and the Canadian war effort makes little impact on
the life and mind of the United States, except when [Ontario pre-
mier] Hepburn accuses the American Navy of hiding from the Japs
and we fiddle over a plebiscite while Singapore and Java burn." Mike
made it clear that he thought McCarthy should go and Wrong stay.
Mackenzie King naturally disagreed.[23] McCarthy stayed, Wrong
went to Ottawa, Mike to Washington.

Mike, the above comment suggests, was a supporter of conscription. Other evidence seems to confirm this interpretation. In a
memorandum to Robertson he dismisses the need for "home
defence" and says Canada must focus on the defence of Britain, and
he extols the benefit of compulsory military service on national psy-
chology in a letter to Brooke Claxton.[24] His views were not those of
the prime minister, and perhaps it was wise for him to go to Washington.

Mike knew the importance of the Washington tasks, but he certainly saw little attraction in going to Washington as McCarthy's
second-in-command. In his memorandum to Robertson, Mike had
recommended himself for the position of Canada's first minister to
the Soviet Union! But Mike knew he could not refuse Washington
even though he would not receive ministerial status and, it seemed,
could never become the minister there himself (this was perhaps the
reason behind the peculiar suggestion of the Moscow posting). The
disadvantages appeared great. Mike and Maryon had bought a comfortable house in the bureaucratic fastness of Rockcliffe; the children
were at home; and social life in the few hours of free time wartime
exigencies allowed was richly satisfying. Mike and Maryon also
needed the time together after their wartime separation, a separation
that some feel created strains in their relationship.[25] Still, they sold
the house, packed their trunks, and left for Washington just in time
for the dreadful Washington summer. It was a melancholy spring
and summer, most of all because Norman Young, their brother-
in-law, died leading Winnipeg's Cameron Highlanders onto the

beaches at Dieppe.[26] The war was good to Mike Pearson, but this loss was a deep wound.

The appointment as minister-counsellor in Washington brought no increase in Mike's salary of $6,240, but he was now eligible for $4,275 in allowances.[27] He would need it, for wartime Washington was expensive. They searched in vain for a house that would not exceed the housing allowance. Fortunately, C.M. Drury (better known as Bud Drury, and as a Liberal politician in the 1960s) left his post as military attaché to go on active duty, and the Pearsons inherited the home "in a nice quiet district, with some trees, a garden, mice in the cellar, and a good cook."[28] The city – more even than in Henry Adams's day – was "a political camp". It was also, despite the New Deal, a southern city and hence a divided one, two-thirds white, one-third black. The major difference between Washington and Atlanta and Birmingham was that Washington blacks could ride its buses, at least until the buses passed over the Potomac into Virginia and they had to get off. David Brinkley, then a young reporter in the capital, recalls that the blacks were out of sight in a government whose face was almost entirely white, except in the elevators and at night when the janitors came in. The geography and the sociology made it a peculiar capital; never more so than in wartime when it became, Malcolm Cowley wrote on the eve of the Pearsons' arrival, "a combination of Moscow (for overcrowding), Paris (for its trees), Wichita (for its way of thinking), Nome (in the gold-rush days) and Hell (for its livability)".[29]

Mike's brief memory of one summer in Washington did not prepare him for what he encountered. Like most Canadians of his class and background, he was most familiar with the Northeast. Again like most Canadians, he had American relatives and was always careful to distinguish his affection for individual Americans from his doubts about the United States as a nation and about the American way of life. Duke, of course, was now an American, and an increasingly wealthy and patriotic one as he rose in the Armour organization in the Boston area. To American audiences Mike emphasized these connections as well as his distant blood relationship to the American poet John Greenleaf Whittier.* These ties, however, did not bind Mike emotionally to the United States as history and blood had bound him and most other English Canadians to Britain. This difference is critical in understanding the distinction between the Anglo-Canadian alliance of pre-war days and the Canadian-American alliance that developed during and after the Second World War.[30]

Mike's years in Washington are the most crowded of his life and, in many ways, the best documented. He began his diary once again (a sure sign that he considered what he was doing and seeing significant – it always stopped in Ottawa) and commented freely on America, its policies and its peculiar ways. He found McCarthy every bit as difficult as he had feared and Hume Wrong had warned. His interest in administration was negligible, his knowledge of diplomatic reporting non-existent, and his interest in his duties minimal, with one significant exception, the relationship with President Roosevelt. King had appointed McCarthy not only because he was wealthy and Liberal but also because McCarthy was a friend of Roosevelt. Mike, who was at first skeptical of that relationship and its value, saw the warmth between the two frequently and recognized its value. Roosevelt held an extraordinary sway over Washington, and access to and friendship with the president were as rare and cherished then as today. McCarthy was a loyal friend to Roosevelt. When Mike drafted a letter to Ottawa, criticizing Roosevelt for not following through on agreements, McCarthy refused to sign it.

---

* Whittier, fortunately, was an anglophile who wrote:

O Englishmen! – in hope and creed,
In blood and tongue our brothers!
We too are heirs of Runnymede;
And Shakespeare's fame and Cromwell's deed
Are not alone our mother's.

This poem "To Englishmen" was splendid material for wartime Washington.

He said it was a reflection on the President's personal honour to suggest that his promises would not be carried out.... The Minister is as jealous of the President's reputation – and, indeed, as sensitive about everything concerning him – as his wife or mother could be. He has a far higher regard for him than, I gather, for any other statesman, and yet, with this loyalty to an American President he combines an almost colonial attitude toward Great Britain. It is a strange contradiction, that he should be a follower of the American President and a Toronto Tory at the same time.

Mike was none the less familiar with that contradiction, and he and McCarthy got on well. Very soon McCarthy was pressing King to choose Mike as his replacement. Mike's charm and good manners and perhaps hypocrisy had concealed his profound doubts about McCarthy's diplomacy.[31]

Because of McCarthy's frequent absences, Mike ran the chronically understaffed embassy. Mike has a reputation as a bad administrator; certainly his years as under-secretary and prime minister offer some evidence for that view. His years in London and Washington, however, provide support for the contrary view. He was a popular, inspiring leader who accomplished a multitude of tasks with skill and efficiency and raised the morale of those around him. Perhaps the position as second-in-command to a superior who was indifferent or aloof was most congenial for Mike. Whatever the reason, Massey and McCarthy both praised Mike's administrative skills and so did others who worked with him in London and Washington.[32] By mid-1944 McCarthy was almost always absent, and Mike performed nearly all of his tasks. In the early summer of 1944 Mike's work was recognized by a promotion to the new and grandiose position of envoy extraordinary and minister plenipotentiary. McCarthy, now an ambassador because the legation had become officially an embassy, was publicly recognized as the one responsible for "the more ceremonial functions connected with a diplomatic mission".[33] Mike handled just about everything else. On January 1, 1945, Mike became ambassador, the first career diplomat named as Canada's representative to the United States. It was a tribute to the foreign service but most of all to what he had accomplished in wartime.*

Mike, as much as Dean Acheson, was "present at the creation" – Acheson's description of the rapid shift of influence, and the desire to use it, to the United States. He had left Ottawa concerned about how Canada would fit into the new world being created. By winter 1943 it was clear that the United States and the Soviet Union, which had turned the tide on the Eastern Front, would dominate the post-war world. The prospect troubled Mike who believed British restraint, calmness, and international experience were badly needed at the conference table. These values, he believed, were not those which the United States held in highest regard. Their nationalism, in his view, was noisy, with too much the touch of show-business and fashion and with too little of the mature consideration of the nation's opportunities and responsibilities. A scene at a January 1943 luncheon at a Washington restaurant, for example, provoked this comment: "During luncheon at this fashionable and society-babbling restaurant, the radio kept blaring the President's speech to Congress, but no one seemed to be listening to it, though it was a pretty important pronouncement. When he finished, the radio played the National Anthem and the guests suddenly realized they were patriots and self-consciously got up to their feet, some of them without interrupting their conversation."[34] Later in that same month the Pearsons attended the President's Birthday Dinner at the Mayflower Hotel. Again Mike's diary entry is interesting: "It was a noisy, crowded affair, juvenile, boisterous Rotarianism, notwithstanding the

---

* Gordon Skilling's *Canadian Representation Abroad: From Agency to Embassy,* the standard history of the Canadian diplomatic service, describes the minister plenipotentiary's duties: "The Minister exercises a general supervision of the work of the Embassy officers and liaison with other Canadian agencies in Washington; he also represents Canada on international bounds and agencies such as the United Nations Relief and Rehabilitation Administration, the Interim Food Commission and the International Wheat Council, and in connection with mutual aid and lend-lease questions."

presence of the dignified diplomatic and political world, who were, in any event very definitely second string to the film stars, who graced the head table, 20 or 30 of them." Al Jolson entertained, successfully so, "thanks to his determination not to allow the distinction of his audience to interfere with the crudeness of his jokes". When Lord Halifax laughed, Jolson stopped the show and said: "I'm worried. There must be something wrong with my stories. The British Ambassador is laughing at them."[35] Mike and especially Maryon were personally very fond of Halifax, and they felt the wound.

These anecdotes are of no significance in themselves, but they – and numerous others in Mike's diary and letters – reveal the doubts Mike had about American society and its politics. American society was often crude, and this meant that many would be hurt because their feelings were not respected. Celebrity was too much the product of physical beauty, of dubious accomplishment, or of an ephemeral craze. Hollywood, with its simplicities and romantic nonsense, had cast its spell over a democratic people whose political élite catered so quickly to the popular taste. Mike was liberal and democratic in outlook, but his reaction to American democracy in the 1930s and 1940s has a Tocquevillean reserve to it. In speaking about the New Deal in June 1934, he was skeptical about its future success because it was a "middle course between socialism and capitalism" and "middle courses are notoriously difficult for intoxicated nations … to follow". He quoted Henry Wallace as saying, "We are a people given to excesses." Wallace, who was increasingly viewed as a future president in the war years, may have meant that as a compliment; Mike Pearson most certainly did not.[36]

By the time Mike arrived in Washington, the fears about the demagogic character of Roosevelt's New Deal had disappeared for all but a few. Mike none the less continued to see that American politics was much more a matter of manipulative technique than were other democratic political systems. During his years in Washington, Mike fumed continuously about the American press and the symbiotic relationship between the false currency so prevalent in American politics and the sensationalism of the American media. Paradoxically,

Mike proved himself to be a deft manipulator of the press, and one of his most useful assets in Washington was his personal association with some American newspapermen, such as James Reston of *The New York Times*. Mike respected these journalists and used them most effectively to promote Canada's "message".[37] Nevertheless, his reservations remained. At a Washington reception, Mike saw Drew Pearson in attendance. He commented in his diary: "It was a little nauseating to me to note how so many important public men greeted this irresponsible columnist in such a friendly, almost deferential way."[38] In short, Mike believed that mass communications could prove a valuable tool for educating a democratic public to accept civic responsibilities. His support for John Grierson's work reflects this, as does his respect for Reston. To have a public voice was a privilege that too many Americans, including Drew Pearson, abused.

During his tenure in Washington, Mike faced numerous problems in diplomacy. The disposition of Americans to ignore Canadian interests frustrated him regularly. In March 1943, after a winter in Washington, he had pointed to the particular difficulties that Canada had with the United States.[39]

> ... the very intimacy, informality, and friendliness of our relations with the United States, though it has great advantages in many ways, notably in the field of defence and war supplies, does in another sense constitute a difficulty. The American authorities often tend to consider us not as a foreign nation at all, but as one of themselves. This is flattering, but leads occasionally to misunderstandings. Because they take us for granted, they are perplexed when we show an impatience at being ignored and an irritation at being treated as something less than an independent State. They make sudden demands on us, for some concession or co-operation which they consider to be required by the war emergency, and they do not understand why we would not respond, as the Governor of a State would.

For Canada, this situation was dangerous:

Suspended, then, somewhat uneasily in the minds of so many Americans between the position of British Colony and American dependency, we are going to have a difficult time in the months ahead in maintaining our own position and standing on our own feet.

This difficulty in merely "standing" should make us particularly careful in choosing our direction each time we start to "move." If we don't exercise such care, our role of "interpreter" will result in bringing the United States and United Kingdom together but in such a way that we find ourselves uncomfortably squeezed in between. In a postwar world, where power is going to count for so much and where the little nation may possibly receive less consideration than formerly, we should certainly try to avoid a squeeze play of this kind.

Mike's task was to educate the Americans about the sovereignty of Canada. Preoccupied with global problems, even knowledgable Americans such as the State Department's Jack Hickerson lumped Canada together with the rest of the British Commonwealth. With others the attitude was sometimes patronizing. Secretary of state Edward Stettinius told Mike in 1945, "You people in Canada really have nothing to worry about [in the U.N. discussions]; you are in a sense part of us and you are also part of the British Empire. You are really very fortunate because you have such good and strong friends." Mike commented: "I neglected to reply that our preoccupation with these matters was not as part of the United States or as a part of the British Empire, but as Canada. It seems to me that this is a point that will have to be made clear more than once to the Secretary of State, who, while always amiable and friendly, does not, I feel, really wholly understand our independent interest in international affairs."[40]

By this time Mike had come to realize that the structure of decision-making of American foreign policy made it difficult for American diplomats and political officials to understand the "independent interests of other nations in international affairs". In describing a dinner in 1943 at the British first secretary's residence, Mike noted that all "agreed that the Russians were winning the war

for us and that the American organization in Washington and overseas was deplorable. There is a good deal of talk around here now,
especially in Congress, about the British paying back some of the
assistance they have received from the States by handing over bases,
etc. That kind of talk makes even the most polite Britisher in Washington mad – quite justifiably so."[41] This idle "talk",* which Congress so quickly reflected, continued to plague the work of all diplomats in Washington as did the relentless jockeying for positions
about the president who distrusted his career diplomats and concentrated power within his own office and person. Information was
withheld from those who needed most to know. Assistant secretary
of state Dean Acheson, for example, complained that even though he
was in charge of economic matters in occupied territories, James
Dunn would not tell him what the terms of Italy's surrender were.
Mike told him "that he ought to come up to the Legation occasionally and we would tell him what was going on!"[42] In fact, they probably could, for Americans were quite willing to report their difficulties
with their own colleagues to others. With so much effort expended in
internal politics, the policy-makers had insufficient time to devote to
study of international problems. Mike was most disturbed to learn in
October 1944 from Jack Hickerson, who had become the State
Department official responsible for British Commonwealth and
Canadian matters and who had been generally sympathetic to Canadian complaints, that the "view at the top" in Washington was that
"on general political questions the views of the parts of the British
Commonwealth should be co-ordinated and received through the
United Kingdom".[43] The result of American disorganization was a
tendency to seek simplicity in international relations rather than to
recognize the inherent complexity of such relations. In the post-war
world that complexity would be so much greater and simplicities so
much more dangerous.

---

* Mike added in his diary, on Feb. 13, 1943: "How are the Americans going to pay
back the Russians for the millions of lives lost in their defence; or the British for having held the fort in 1940...."

From 1943 to 1946, the Canadians in Washington pressed hard to make Americans at all levels aware of Canada's independent interests. As he carried out his tasks, Mike came to accept and even to appreciate the flexibility of the American political system. If the Americans paid too little attention to some important traditions and interests, that very inattentiveness made it easy to accept new departures. Mike reflected this view in his comments on a 1944 memorandum by a young External officer, R.M. Macdonell, which, in Pearson's opinion, had emphasized the negative aspects of the Canadian-American relationship. He warned:

> We certainly do not want to debase our coinage by too frequent protests, which people in the State Department will come to think of as unnecessary and often frivolous. This is, I think, particularly true in wartime, when nerves are frayed and tempers occasionally strained. When we are dealing with such a powerful neighbour, we have to avoid the twin dangers of subservience and truculent touchiness. We succumb to the former when we take everything lying down, and to the latter when we rush to the State Department with a note everytime some Congressman makes a stupid statement about Canada, or some documentary movie about the war forgets to mention Canada.[44]

Pearson agreed that the American administrative machinery often functioned badly, but this was partly the result of the influx of so many inexperienced people who had caused many of Canada's problems but who had also been "of the most tremendous help". This applied not only to the new people but to the U.S. government as a whole.

What Canada must show, Mike argued, was a "wary sensitiveness". Then he used an interesting metaphor to make his point: "I suppose there is no person in the world against whom a married man can develop so many grievances as his wife, but that does not mean that he thinks less highly of her than he does of the strange woman across the street." Pearson quickly abandoned this particular illustration. He did express agreement with Macdonell's final conclusion, which suggested that Canada should try to keep minor slights in perspective but take "a firm stand on important issues" whether they be bilateral or multilateral. No issue was of more importance in this respect than the shape of the emerging international institutions.

In 1944 Mike was solidly in Roosevelt's camp as he sought his fourth presidential term. Seeing the American political system so closely, Mike came to admire the president's mastery of that system. Without Roosevelt, America's war effort could never have been glued together. Even Duke, who criticized Roosevelt's economic policies, agreed with Mike that a different wartime leader was unthinkable. In the fall of 1943, the Four Power Declaration at Moscow had committed the United States, Britain, China, and the Soviet Union to the establishment of a "general organization" which would ensure "the maintenance of international peace and security". In the spring of 1944 Roosevelt began to sell the plan to the American people, who a quarter-century before had rejected Woodrow Wilson's league as a bad bargain. Never was the master salesman so badly needed. Mike admired Roosevelt, in part because the president's approach to diplomacy increasingly resembled his own. "I dream dreams," Roosevelt declared, "but am, at the same time, an intensely practical person."[45] Mike too dreamed, but in 1944 his aims and Roosevelt's aims were practical.* The disasters of 1919 could never be repeated; American isolation would be even more catastrophic now.

The Americans' fascination with their own development made them natural isolationists in Mike's view. Paradoxically, the success of that development in economic and military terms had made that isolation impossible, just as it had transformed the United States internally. The enhanced role of military people and thinking in American public life had been criticized in Macdonell's memorandum, and Mike had agreed that it was a troubling trend. The

---

* Mike's aims were not always practical. In a letter to Harry Crerar on April 5, 1944, he requested that he be allowed to join the First Canadian Army. Crerar refused to take his request seriously.

construction of the massive and permanent Pentagon structure across the river from Washington symbolized the change in American life. Nevertheless, his experience in working with the architects of the post-war order, particularly in his position as chairman of the Interim Commission of the Food and Agriculture Organization, led him to become skeptical of Soviet goodwill and more admiring of American intentions.[46] He came to see that the American officials' desire to play "a real part in post-war international cooperation" was strong and sincere, but that it was based upon relatively little knowledge about previous attempts at co-operation and too much assurance that U.S. plans should be universally accepted.[47] Above all, there was the danger that the United States would withdraw in pique. American public opinion clearly supported international organization, but it was notoriously fickle.

In the late summer of the election year 1944, the great powers met at Dumbarton Oaks to sketch out the new international organization. Canada was excluded, although the British kept Ottawa informed and Mike learned some details from Americans. He worried about what he heard, especially the impression that "three or four powers" would be "controllers of the world's destiny". Mike expected more information and sympathy from the Americans, but when he complained, Jack Hickerson became testy. Hickerson, who knew about British consultation with the Canadians, complained that he was annoyed that the Canadians passed on information about the Americans to Great Britain. Mike "reminded him that we often reciprocated by giving the Americans the British point of view when we were able to obtain it. Moreover the British welcomed Canadian ideas and gave them serious consideration. [Mike] was not sure the Americans did."[48] Certainly on the issue of the new international organization the Roosevelt administration heeded its own intuition and had little time for others. In criticizing the Dumbarton Oaks proposals for international organization, Mike admitted to the Americans that he feared the public discussion would create great political difficulties for them. (The Americans knew Mike's views; perhaps the Soviets did as well for the views are found in Alger Hiss's papers.)[49]

It became a careful task to manage American opinion, which was not an educated one. Indeed, private State Department polls taken six months after Dumbarton Oaks ended revealed that only 30 per cent of Americans knew what the conference had accomplished! This management of public opinion meant doing some things that were unfortunate and would alienate the Soviet Union. However, "management" was essential: the United States, it seemed to Mike, was the essential actor in the new international drama that was beginning.[50] The Canadians and other middle states would have to moderate their demands in order to secure the commitment of the U.S. government and its people to the new international organizations. The extent of the great power veto, which in December 1944 Mike had described as leading to a farce, came to be reluctantly accepted in 1945.

Mike saw that the United Nations, which took form in the late war years, was probably as much as could be expected but certainly less than was needed. If the league had failed because the great powers abandoned it, the United Nations could be defeated if the great powers sought to dominate it, as they had its creation. With the great powers divided – and it became increasingly clear in 1945 that such division was likely – the best that could be hoped for was continued international commitment on the part of the United States. With Roosevelt's death and Truman's accession to office, the responsibility and continuity of American leadership was by no means assured. Canadians should be worried, and the San Francisco Conference where the United Nations Charter was hammered together in the spring of 1945 only heightened Mike's fears: "Between Russian deviousness and U.S. ham-handedness, this Conference is going to have a bad time.... I wonder if the Russians are manoeuvering for the position of a leader of a democratic front here. I wonder also if the obvious stiffening of the U.S. attitude is on instructions from the White House. I think so. The British are just tagging along...."[51] It became clear that all others would often have to tag along in the post-war world. The best answer was an institutionally strong international economic and social fabric, one that enmeshed the new superpowers, the Soviet Union and the United States, and taught them the habit of co-operation. By the end of the conference, Mike more than ever preferred the ham-hands of the Americans to the devious grasp of the Soviets.[52]

Ham-handed Americans and Canadians came together each spring in mortal combat on the baseball field. The first challenge came from Mike in a letter to Ted Achilles of the State Department, on April 29, 1943:

> I have been requested by Their Excellencies, the various Canadian officials now serving in the penal settlement of Washington, to throw at the State Department a challenge to a test of strength or skill on what is, I believe, known as a baseball diamond. This game of baseball is understood to be the national sport of both the United States and Japan and though unknown in Canada, it is consistent with the well-known chivalry and generosity of the challengers to offer to participate in this game in preference to one of the more familiar Canadian games, such as snowshoe running, ludo, bull-baiting and "I spy Dominion status."

Achilles accepted the challenge and "Les Panzers Canadiens" took the field against the "[Cordell] Hull Hillbillies". Les Panzers took a quick lead of 10-0, but then, in a spirit of sportsmanship, "withdrew their best pitcher and substituted for him the aged and inefficient Mr. Pearson". Mike reported the aftermath to the under-secretary:

> It would, of course, have been inappropriate if the Legation had won; it would have been humiliating if it had lost. With the score 17-13 in favour of the Legation and two out in the 9th, it appeared that our desire to ensure permanently friendly relations with the State Department might not be achieved. However, four errors in quick succession, and a tremendous, but accidental three base hit by Mr. Hickerson permitted four runs to be scored. The game thereby ended happily for all concerned, who immediately adjourned to the residence of Mr. Theodore Achilles, where hospitality was accepted and aching muscles assuaged.

The British Empire may have strengthened its sinews on the playing fields of Eton and through allegiance to the King, but the American Empire, where Canada was concerned, gained strength in Yankee

Stadium and through allegiance to Babe Ruth, Lou Gehrig, and, especially in 1943, Joe DiMaggio.[53] Mike had long shared that allegiance – and others.

Reading Mike's diaries for these years one senses along with the regular irritation with the Americans and the apprehension about their political course, a growing fascination with the country. One gets the feeling that John Cheever had when he read his old stories, "of a long-lost world when the city of New York was still filled with a river light, when you heard the Benny Goodman quartets from a radio in the corner stationery store, and when almost everybody wore a hat".[54] Mike and Maryon liked that flavour of America, and the taste once acquired endured.

Lester Pearson's American experience changed his views of the United States. His presence there coincided with significant changes within the United States itself. He came with many doubts about the nature of American society and politics. These did not fully disappear. Nevertheless, he came to admire the flexibility and the openness of American life and politics. This contrasted strikingly with his increasingly negative opinion of the Soviet Union, which by 1945 he had concluded was "a force which we simply do not understand".[55] A Canadian could understand the United States; even more, he could influence Americans, if only in a minor way. Indeed, considering the stakes there was no choice. The U.S. vision remained too limited but was the product of deeper forces in American society: the populist democratic faith, the worship of progress, the wariness of tradition, the suspicion of the "foreign", the sensationalist media, and, not least, the enormous wealth. Pearson's critique of American society bears only a small resemblance to that of the many European intellectuals and artists who landed in America in wartime and who have had a profound influence on the intellectual's perception of America. Unlike Theodor Adorno, Bertolt Brecht, and Herbert Marcuse, Mike did not recoil in horror from American mass taste, whether in the arts or politics. Like them, he did find much that was offensive in the raucousness of American public life, but he liked baseball, adored Ginger Rogers, and revelled in the political gossip of the day. His critique bears more similarity to that of the young

Daniel Boorstin* who argued, from the position of an amazed admirer of his native land, that the United States had used its wealth, its literacy, its technology, and its progress to create "a thicket of unreality which stands between us and the facts of life".[56] This "thicket of unreality" had blocked off America in 1919. The Second World War cut away some of the thickets, and Pearson desperately hoped that regrowth would not occur. A Canadian might and must assist in cutting away some of the underbrush; the larger task was America's own. The United States had won Pearson's sympathy but had not eliminated his fears.

Certainly the Pearsons had good memories of their years in Washington, especially after Mike took up his ambassadorial duties. Maryon returned to Winnipeg in December 1944 and gave a rare (perhaps her first) interview to a reporter in Winnipeg. She told her that she had been doing sixty hours' a month volunteer work in a hospital as a nurses' aid, but that this work would have to end with her new duties as hostess at the Canadian embassy. She liked the embassy: "The rooms are spacious and a number of them have beautiful oak panelling." Ever the cultural nationalist, she added: "I want to have some Canadian paintings hanging on the walls to show what fine artists we have in Canada."[57] In fact, the embassy at 1746 Massachusetts Avenue no longer was suitable as a residence because official functions were now too numerous, and during the Pearsons' stay in Washington plans were made to build a new residence for the ambassador.

Maryon managed the embassy with the skill with which she handled the family budget. Her talents were needed because the McCarthys had discharged all their staff when they left Washington. When Maryon and Mike arrived back from Winnipeg there was no food, and a full wine cellar but no corkscrew. With so many social responsibilities, Maryon had to find staff immediately and turned up an exceedingly British butler named "James", who set about educating the Pearsons on the appropriate manners for a diplomatic couple.

---

* Boorstin, a distinguished historian and the Librarian of Congress, began as a leftist and became a strong and conservative nationalist. He was in Washington in 1942-3.

He was exquisitely discreet. When one of the royal family dined at the embassy he asked the name of the wine. Rather than utter the German name "Liebfraumilch" in wartime, James replied, "Milk of the Virgin, Your Royal Highness". Alas, James liked the milk of the virgin and various other alcoholic concoctions all too well. At one luncheon James failed to appear, and Maryon found him prostrate and called for help. The Emergency department, misinterpreting Maryon's words, believed that "the ambassador" rather than "the ambassador's butler" had been stricken and rushed out a fire-department rescue squad complete with respirators. "Disappointed, no doubt, because the Ambassador was in good health", they simply hauled James off to the emergency ward, which was far too busy to deal with drunks. A penitent James was returned in a few hours. He promised to be a teetotaller but soon failed. Mike and Maryon, no doubt aware of their own straying from Methodist teetotalling ways, tried to be tolerant but eventually gave up and dismissed James.[58] He endured in their memories as a good story of a time they both later treasured.

For Mike, the Washington years were especially rewarding. He believed that he and his nation had achieved a great deal in wartime. In navigating the rapids that led on towards American post-war pre-eminence, Mike believed that he and his colleagues had been skilled boatmen, moving with the current and not simply drifting aimlessly. Later, when critics charged that he and King sacrificed Canadian independence in the Second World War, he responded angrily. The journalist Charles Lynch, for example, once asked how a historian such as Donald Creighton could say "that all that happened" in the war "was that we reverted to colonial status". Mike exploded in response: "That is absolute rubbish and quite unworthy of anybody who professes to be a distinguished historian." In revising for publication his comments about his former colleague at the University of Toronto, he made only one change: he erased "distinguished". For Mike, Canada's wartime performance was "magnificent", and that was one opinion his pragmatic mind was never willing to change.[59]

CHAPTER ELEVEN

THE
WORLD STAGE

The thought in this I [was] probably right that if Pearson could be brought into public life, he would make the best of any successor to myself. This, however, is something which only the future can settle....

— Mackenzie King in October 1946[1]

Mike, like most public servants, had long laboured in the obscurity of diplomacy, unable to shed the cloak of anonymity or to participate in political rough-and-tumble. When absent from Canada, he could not even vote because diplomats were then denied the franchise. (Neither, however, did they have to pay taxes.) Mike knew many Canadian politicians, but he was emotionally remote from Canadian political issues, save those that touched upon Canadian foreign relations. In those areas, however, he was extraordinarily well informed, perhaps better than any other Canadian. And in 1946 no area mattered more to Canadians than Canada's relationship with the world beyond its boundaries. Charles Ritchie, recalling Canada's isolationism and puritanism, wrote in his diary in February 1942: "I cannot imagine going back to the old small town Canada with its narrow, intense local interests and sitting down under it again."[2] By the war's end, that Canada was almost gone, even if a few of its relics continued to occupy some prominent places. This change in the heart and face of Canada made living there and working for it more congenial for Ritchie and Mike. Canada now honoured its diplomatic sons (there were no women until 1947), and with plans for peace congealing, the diplomats not the soldiers were becoming the glory of those times.

Still, the thought of Mike Pearson as Mackenzie King's successor is astonishing, most of all because the notion was that most politically sagacious prime minister's own. Since he left Canada to fight in the First World War at the age of eighteen, Mike had spent more time outside of Canada than in it. (To be specific, he had spent just over eighteen years residing in Europe or the United States and since 1935 had been outside Canada except for his brief stay in 1941-2.) Nevertheless, Mike's concerns had become Canada's, and his skills were those his nation now thought it needed most. The new public-opinion polls confirmed what Mike had most strongly argued: that Canada could not go back to "the so-called, but mis-called, 'good old days'; insisting that the poppies blooming in Flanders Fields have no longer any meaning for us; determined, like Ulysses, to sail by the European siren, our ears stuffed with the tax bills of the last war."[3] Canada after the war no longer moved cautiously into the chill winds of international change[4]; indeed, it audaciously tried to tame them.

Mike moved ever more confidently on the world stage. The contrast between Mike's first stint as an official Canadian delegate in post-Riddell Geneva, when he maintained complete silence lest he be repudiated, and his assertive performances in wartime Washington is striking. What Mike had thought would be a dreary and thankless task, acting as the puppeteer for a puppet ambassador in Washington, gave him a unique opportunity to display skills honed by a decade and a half in the diplomatic service. The opportunities came through representing Canada in the creation of a new international structure whose foundations were crafted in the United States. It was through Mike's work in the formation of the Food and Agricultural Organization (FAO) and the United Nations Relief and Rehabilitation Administration (UNRRA) that he gained a public prominence unique among Canadian diplomats and, indeed, among Canadians generally. And Canada, as all Canadians know, admires most its sons and daughters who perform well on the world stage: Mike Pearson and Barbara Ann Scott; Ken Taylor and Elizabeth Manley. A decade after Elizabeth Greey's 1941 letter complaining that no one knew who Mike Pearson was, he was the best-known Canadian in Canada and beyond.[5]

The frequent and, for Mike, fortunate interpretation of his rise as accidental, simply a case of "good luck", is largely false. Mike's career after 1943 succeeded because he saw his opportunity and devoted himself wholly to grasping it. He was, in fact, extraordinarily ambitious, able to work twelve-hour days year after year, to deny himself pleasures he savoured, and to mingle with and even flatter those he loathed. Readers will recall that this description of Mike does not apply to earlier years, to the 1920s when he seemed so unfocused in his aims or to the 1930s when he had so many doubts about his country's course and his diplomatic career. It also may not apply to his prime-ministerial period when age, frustration, and circumstances sometimes took their toll upon his commitment. The impression one has in following Mike through the 1940s and 1950s is of the integration within himself of past and present beliefs and of public aims and private feelings. His British-Canadian and Methodist past, which had seemed so anachronistic in the 1930s and in External, could now be seen as an antecedent to a desired future. The Anglo-Canadian tradition became for him the liberal-democratic heritage that wartime horrors made Canadians treasure more than ever. Similarly, his reinvigorated internationalism recalled the old images of Methodist universalism: the Sunday-school painting of Christ surrounded by children of the world, and the hymns that asked God "to make the nations one, one in the bond of peace". And as political scientist Reg Whitaker has perceptively observed, there was a strong whiff of the old-time moralist in Mike's righteous denunciations of the Soviet Union. A psycho-historian might carry these thoughts a longer distance, and debt to Erik Erikson should be acknowledged in what has been said already, but the direct evidence offers support for only these limited conjectures. Let us simply suggest that the part he played in the 1940s and 1950s was, unlike earlier times, consonant with his identity, and that he approached that part with (to use Erikson's terminology) a "disciplined devotion".[6]

There were costs, however, especially in his private life. Diplomatic life meant no home in the sense most Canadians knew. It brought so many separations. Geoffrey and Patsy had to be fitted into a crowded life, and after 1939 the family was seldom together. Both Geoffrey and Patsy came to cherish the memories of their early years in Ottawa when, after work, Mike ran down Ottawa's Russell Road to meet them, swinging them in his arms and clinging to them as only a young father can. In the 1940s Geoff and Patsy were away at school most of the time. Mike, now middle-aged, missed them more than ever, and his only consolation, as trite as it was true, was his belief that his work would make their future better. Mike was at the San Francisco Conference when Geoffrey graduated from Trinity College School. All he could do was write:[7]

> I can understand that you must be feeling pretty sad at leaving T.C.S. [Trinity College School] but I think you can take a great deal of pride at what you have done there. If you are too modest for that, you may get some satisfaction out of knowing that your mother and I are proud, very proud indeed of what you have done. Parents – at least most parents – don't talk much – possibly not enough – about these things and if I were with you I probably wouldn't be a notable exception, but I can at least write what would be more difficult to say; that you have made us both very happy and proud of the part you have played at school....
>
> All the best for Friday. I would give anything to be there but as we discuss and discuss and discuss things here – all day – I'll be thinking of you and sending my graduation blessings.
>
> Best love – old man
>
> As ever
>
> Dad

For Patsy the partings were even more difficult; and it is not surprising that the truest portrait of Mike Pearson came much later from her in the year he became prime minister.

Although they spent so much less time together than most Canadian fathers and daughters did, Mike and Patsy shared an extraordinarily deep affection. At a very early age, she cut through his dignity and won his heart. "My marks in school are quite good," she wrote Mike from Winnipeg in 1940, "but it[']s the Arithmetic … even you aren't very good are you daddy dear."* Mike replied to "Dearest Patsy":[8]

I'm writing this note to you from our living room at Fairacres. I'm sitting in front of the fire while Mr. & Mrs. Wrong and Mr. Ritchie are chatting – and making it difficult for me to write. I thought the mail was leaving this evening and that I wouldn't have time to write you but it's not being collected until 10:30 A.M. tomorrow so I can pop this note in with Mummy's. I was so glad to get your note with Mummy's letter of Oct. 28th which arrived today. Are you liking Rockcliffe School? I'm very glad Mummy asked them to put you back to Grade VI. I thought Grade VII was too high & might be too difficult and make you worry. I remember once when I was just about your age, I skipped a grade and I had a very hard time trying to keep up with my Arithmetic in the new grade. How I used to worry about my sums. Then, the more I worried, the worse I did. So I decided to work but *not* worry and then I did much better. But, oh, how difficult I used to find those sums. My oh my, much more frightening than the racket of the guns going on right now. I tell you, Patsy, I'd sooner dodge a whistling bomb any day than try to work out how many strips of carpet 3″ x 8″ are needed to cover a room 20′ x 10′.

My goodness, I can't write while that Mr. Ritchie is talking – he is making more noise than the guns.

---

* She probed another weakness in another letter: "I forgot to tell you that I am getting housepoints for French, which I bet is more than daddy would."

I had lunch with Mr. Liesching today and he said he had two girls at Rockcliffe School – do you know them: Jane is the one and I forget the name of the younger.

I must close now, dear, & write a few lines for Geoffrey.

Much love

from

Daddy

The next month, December 1940, he wrote again, the chatterbox Mr. Ritchie presumably absent: "How are you and how is school and is it snowing in Ottawa and are you skating and do you still think Daddy is your 'bestest' friend (I hope so) and will we win the war (yes)."[9] And Mike made certain that they knew he was helping to win the war for his country and for them:

... I work all morning – a few letters to the King, Mr. Churchill, or Lord Halifax giving them advice on the war – then a modest war lunch of water soup and a piece of lettuce – then more work – then the long drive home in the blackout – then more watery soup and Ryvita – then the 9 o'clock news and to bed with a good book.... Then I turn out the light and maybe I dream of Mummy and you and Geoff. I had a lovely dream a few nights ago – that you two "young 'uns" were diving from a rock to show me how good you were while Mummy and I looked proudly on. I remember Geoff did an especially exciting sideways flip ... while you went right into the water like a Silver Arrow.

All my love Patsy

Daddy

As Mike's station rose and she saw him even less, she worried: "Please Daddy," she wrote in 1945, "take it easy for a while, eh? After reading about [Wendell] Wilkie [sic] dying like that you ought to realize how important it is for you not to work too hard and for you to rest often." His faults still did not escape her. After a 1945 nation-wide speech by Mike that garnered much praise, sixteen-year-old Patsy deflated him: "I heard your speech Daddy – although I wasn't so interested in what you were saying as hearing your voice! Gosh, you know something – you *have* a lisp!" Patsy spotted this political liability, which even Mackenzie King had missed.[10]

The letters slowed drastically as Mike "got busier and more involved with politics and the United Nations and NATO". For Patsy, Geoffrey, and Maryon, satisfaction with Mike's public career gave solace for the loss of his company. Mike knew what he had lost. On Patsy's twenty-first birthday he wrote: "It's hard, and a little sad to think that tomorrow you'll be 21. Why oh why did you have to grow up so quickly? My mind wings back to when you arrived ... and when you used to play in the sandpile in the little yard on Russell Ave. and your brother was accustomed to hit you over the head with his shovel ... the few words I could hear across the transatlantic telephone on the first Christmas of the war ... our holiday trip to Hollywood ... how we thought you were growing up too quickly ... and now you are 21, very old, very responsible and very grown up."[11] Increasingly, such private and personal moments were memories, but Mike, now in middle age, was not alone in that circumstance. At the time there seemed to be no alternative. Even in retrospect, his children agree. Accepting their father's absence was their form of service.

In July 1943, Mike received a note from Georges Vanier:[12]

I read in yesterday's "Times" the news that you had been elected Permanent Chairman on Food and Agriculture.

Warmest congratulations – you are becoming a very important person in the International world....

Do you remember when you spoke about leaving the Service and I told you not to be stupid!

Various other tributes followed and the indices of both of the great *Times* newspapers, London and New York, start to contain many references to L.B. Pearson. There is some irony in Mike's celebrity for it is doubtful that anyone expected less of the conference in Hot Springs, Virginia. In 1943, the victories of the Soviets and of the

Allies in North Africa turned the thoughts of Americans and Canadians towards peace, and they quickly became aware how little in pursuit of that goal had been done. Mike shared this sense of disappointment and badgered all he saw with the need "to translate" the theory of the United Nations into non-military practice.

Roosevelt was facing an election in 1944; the popular mood in the United States was leftist and internationalist; and his Republican opponent of 1940, Wendell Willkie, was evoking a vision of "one World", in a book that sold two million hardcover copies. Roosevelt instinctively responded with the idea of a conference to deal with one of his four cherished freedoms, the freedom from want. With Roosevelt, ideas came like sparks off a flint, few of them igniting a flame that would last. In this case, the spark came from a meeting Eleanor Roosevelt arranged with an Australian, Frank McDougall, who had written a memorandum on "a United Nations programme for freedom of want of food". Unlike similar Australian initiatives in the 1930s, this memorandum took a global approach, emphasizing the need for adequate diet everywhere, not simply in the advanced countries. Just as Keynes had discovered when he discussed his new economic theories with Roosevelt, McDougall found Roosevelt vague, uninformed, and unlikely to act. Then, as with Keynes, he acted.[13] He summoned the United Nations to the unlikely spot of Hot Springs, Virginia, for a conference on food and agriculture. Its members would have the task of fanning the spark into a flame.[14]

Mike did not think much of the idea and saw the proposal as the product of the muddled moralism and political grandstanding that too often characterized Roosevelt's foreign policy. He was horrified when McCarthy reported that Roosevelt was "all mixed up about the forthcoming United Nations conference on food. He thinks it is going to discuss relief also...." When he asked Dean Acheson about the conference, he found that senior State Department officials were "completely at sea". More disturbingly, Roosevelt told a press conference that no date for the conference could be set because all replies to the invitations had not come in. The truth was that no replies had come in because no invitations had been sent out! In frustration

Mike suggested to Acheson that the Americans delegate some of the chores for the U.N. conference, but he knew that nothing would come of it. On April 27, 1943, a month before the food conference began, Mike and some friends met with McDougall, whom Mike knew from Geneva days. All agreed that the forthcoming conference was a fraud: "We had a lot of fun kidding McDougall about [it]. We all agree that he is really the father of this illegitimate child. He was over here last autumn and I think managed to convince the President that food was the first subject the United Nations should discuss. Now that they are discussing it, nobody knows quite what to do." The laughing ended a couple of weeks later when Mike learned he was to be one of the hapless delegates to the conference. There was nothing to do but pack his golf clubs, tennis whites and racket, and go.[15]

Fortunately, the British, who had had nothing to do with planning the conference, sent the usual superb delegates headed by Mike's old Oxford friend "Dickie" Law. "Dickie" with characteristic grace (a quality Mike saw in the British but not very often in the Americans) invited Mike to a meeting of the British delegates and asked him to explain the Canadian policy for the food conference. It was a difficult task since Canada had no policy so far as Mike knew; but he "babbled on in generalities for about ten minutes". Then they all agreed that the forthcoming conference would fail unless "something unforeseen happens".[16]

A few days later, the special conference train departed from Washington's Union Station for Hot Springs, crammed with five hundred delegates and overflowing with pessimism about the conference. The last fifteen miles were uphill and Mike feared the train would go off the rails like the conference itself. Eventually the massive "Homestead", famous later as the locale for Peter Sellers's brilliant portrayal of an empty-headed president in *Being There,* loomed before them. Mike wondered what the Russians, "who had just flown here from their hard-pressed country, or the Ethiopians from Addis Ababa, think of this haven of peace and luxury, so very remote from blood, sweat and tears."[17]

The next day Mike wisely headed first for the tennis courts, where photographers, who along with reporters were banned from the conference, snapped photographs. Mike feared these photos might appear on the front pages of *The Ottawa Citizen,* where Mackenzie King might glimpse his diplomat at play. The conference opened in the evening in an extraordinary fashion as the chairman, Judge Marvin Jones, tried "to marry the Congress of Vienna to a Rotary meeting". Amid Confucians, Hindus, Moslems, and atheists, Judge Jones began with a silent prayer and "The Star-Spangled Banner", which Mike, like most others, refused to sing. In his introductory speech, Judge Jones "managed to pack practically every cliché in the English language into twenty minutes." The Russian delegate, who understood no English, sat beside the judge with "the most perfect deadpan countenance" Mike had ever seen. Then, just as at Rotary meetings, Judge Jones asked each delegate to stand up and give his name and where he was from. For a few moments at least Shanghai could be exactly like Kansas City. After this ceremony, Mike left the conference to return for a few days in Washington where King, Churchill, and Roosevelt were meeting; his diary records not a word about the conference.[18]

On May 23 he returned and, discovering no progress had been made, escaped at once to the golf course. The next day Mike discovered the Americans were proposing an "interim commission" of forty-three to "continue" the work the conference had not done. Mike forgot the tennis courts and the golf course and huddled at once with the British, Americans, and Australians to head off what he thought was an ill-conceived notion. The British produced what Mike described as "a very advanced and far reaching document" looking towards international control in food and agriculture. The Americans, as expected, were more pedestrian, but Mike saw that there was room for fruitful compromise and made suggestions to both great powers. Mike's initiative led to his appointment to the drafting committee for the conference communiqué, where he put forth strong arguments for "a short, non-technical" political statement that could set a precedent for future U.N. conferences. He also

ABOVE: In London, in 1940. General Andy McNaughton (third from right) in postprandial flight; General Harry Crerar beside him, watching; Anthony Eden listening but not watching; and Mike, farther up the table, enjoying war stories.

RIGHT: Mike had great respect and affection for the royal family. "Mike beamed when the King, asked whom he wanted to speak to first, said 'Pearson.'" (Canadian Gov't Motion Pictures Bureau)

ABOVE: After an Ottawa interlude, the Pearsons were posted to Washington in 1942. Here Mike (seated, centre) is a member of the Canadian delegation to the Hot Springs Conference on food and agriculture. This was the first function to win him international attention. (NAC PA-117605)

LEFT: Mike addresses the San Francisco Conference of 1945, where the United Nations was established. "I heard your speech," Patsy wrote her father. "Gosh, you know something – you have a lisp." (NAC C-18532)

RIGHT: Mike admires the huge, ornate doors of the U.N. building. In 1946 he almost became the U.N.'s first secretary-general, but was vetoed by the Soviets. (NAC C-18975)

BELOW: Mike was appointed ambassador to the U.S. in 1945. The Pearsons visited Hollywood to pay an official call on American "royalty"; here they meet Dennis Morgan, star of *The Time, the Place, and the Girl.* (Warner Bros.)

ABOVE: Roughing it at the cottage of Hume and Joyce Wrong in the Gatineau Hills, in 1947. (The convertible is not the Pearsons'.) BELOW: In 1948 Mike and Maryon set out on the campaign trail for the first time, as Mike contested a seat in Algoma. Although he had never won an election, he was already a senior cabinet minister, and secretary of state for External Affairs.

urged that the conference produce a pamphlet that would inspire public debate on the food issue. The idea took hold, and Mike was appointed to head a smaller group to work on the pamphlet. By this time he had become not so much an interpreter as a mediator between the adept British and the clumsy Americans, who had come to feel that they had called the conference "but the British had captured it". Mike agreed with the American analysis but argued that this occurred "because the British on the whole work better and produce more than the Americans".[19] The other great power, the Soviet Union, hosted a final vodka party. The host, Comrade Krutikov (whom the British dubbed Inskrutikov), tested the capacity of his guests by passing around glass after glass of vodka, to the accompaniment of many smiles but very few words. After five quick shots Mike staggered back to the lobby.[20]

To everyone's surprise, the conference ended with a strong sense of accomplishment. Mike, who had wanted a general U.N. conference before any technical conferences took place, changed his mind. "There is no doubt," he wrote, "that the atmosphere has been extremely good, the co-operation ... most encouraging, and that a fine foundation has been laid for future United Nations conferences." Certainly it laid the foundation for Mike's future. On his return to Washington, the Americans asked him to chair the Interim Commission on Food and Agriculture, which was charged with creating the institutional framework for carrying out the tasks the Hot Springs conference had deemed essential. Mike readily accepted and thereby forfeited his summer vacation in 1943.[21]

The Interim Commission laboured in undeserved obscurity. Mike's knowledge, which he had acquired handling Canada's interest in the international wheat commission, gave him some advantages, but fundamentally the success of the Interim Commission in laying the foundations for the FAO derived from his talents in mediating between opposing viewpoints. His own hopes were straightforward: an international body that would help in feeding a hungry world. The aim was laudable; but the means of achieving it caused divisions. Churchill, for example, did not even bother to read the

Hot Springs resolutions. His adviser Lord Cherwell recommended acceptance of the Hot Springs recommendations because they had no short-term impact and would not interfere with the ability of the British to get food before others did. Cherwell admitted he had not read the relevant memorandum on Hot Springs but said that it seemed "to be mainly concerned with pious intentions to raise the standards of nutrition everywhere by giving advice on the production, distribution and choice of food".[22] The British were suspicious that the Americans would use the new organization as a device to break down tariff barriers and impose their free-market system upon the world. Their ambition was to limit the organization to a technically and scientifically oriented institute that would not affect policy in any form. The Americans, on the whole, had a broader view (as did "Dickie" Law at Hot Springs), which envisioned an organization that took a direct role in feeding the world. Reflecting the "welfare internationalism" of Henry Wallace, the most active American delegates argued that at Hot Springs "What had heretofore been just the United States program during the New Deal now became worldwide – better living for farm people, more and better food for farm people and others, [and] participation by farm people in deciding on programs." The skeptical, not to say cynical, Dean Acheson mocked this approach as a "hot meal for every Hottentot", and some other Americans shared his opinion. Other nations held various viewpoints, depending upon whether they were producers or consumers. The Soviets, testing the waters at their first international conference, maintained a conspicuous silence.[23] For Mike, the challenge was obviously great.

Mike met regularly with his committee over the next two years and drafted the constitution for the FAO. By this time the United Nations itself had taken form, and the FAO was to be closely integrated with it. As Mike wrote later, the preparatory work was "well and honestly done", but it must be added that the vision of an organization that would take a direct role in world food distribution atrophied during the many committee meetings. The political questions were thorny; the Americans and the British were often divided; the Soviets were increasingly sullen. Mike's reputation as a shrewd conciliator was nevertheless established in his FAO work. His technique, however, drew some criticism. His colleague Escott Reid reflected this view in a diary comment: "I now realize better Mike's ability to rise in favour. He is agile at quitting a position when he finds that the powers don't like it." Mike did "quit positions" when holding them seemed futile. In the case of the FAO, however, a tenacious defence of a broader program would probably have shattered the chance of any U.N. organization dealing with the most fundamental problem of how humans can eat nutritiously and sufficiently.[24]

The Quebec Conference of October 16 – November 1, 1945, brought together most of the United Nations to christen the new FAO. At the conference's opening, the head of the American delegation, Agriculture secretary Clinton Anderson, rose to nominate Mike Pearson to chair the conference. Mike's name was the only name considered, Anderson claimed, and he went on to laud the "extremely fair, immensely interested" efforts of Mike on the Interim Commission. By all reports, Mike handled the conference effortlessly, although he did not succeed in having the FAO locate its permanent home in Quebec City, as local Quebec politicians embarrassingly requested. Nor did he manage to persuade the increasingly prickly Soviets to sign the FAO constitution. Their delegates apparently wanted to sign, but Stalin never sent the instructions. The Soviets, however, did not object to the proposal that Mike be appointed the FAO's first director general. Mike did, and wisely so, realizing that the FAO's future rested in the arcane sciences of biology, agronomy, and nutrition, and that he could hardly represent an organization whose activities he could neither explain nor understand. His final eloquent speech to the Quebec conference offered the hope that future generations would reap the harvest of this research. His own role would come in constructing the political, not the scientific, ladders for mankind to reach the new heaven.[25]

The FAO experience underlined for Mike how difficult the construction of international organizations would be in a world of sovereign states. He had no hesitation in stating his conclusion derived from that experience to a University of Toronto audience in February 1945: "Power in the conduct of international relations must be related in some way to responsibility. Absolute equality would probably mean absolute futility." "Sovereign equality" was a lot of nonsense: post-war international agencies should be determined on a "functional basis".[26]

"Functionalism" became the key word for Canadian diplomats after 1942, and in simplest terms it meant that each state was entitled to some share in decisions affecting it and a greater share if it was especially affected. In the insightful mind of Hume Wrong, this straightforward concept was artfully sculpted to create a Canadian foreign policy that for the first time had corporeal existence. The previous chapter described the shock that Canadian diplomats and politicians experienced after Churchill and Roosevelt ignored Canada in the planning of the war after Pearl Harbor. Wrong, with his long Washington experience, realized that more resentment would accomplish nothing; indeed it would further undermine Canada's position. In a series of brilliant memoranda and initiatives, Wrong made tactical assaults upon the combined boards from which the Americans and the British had excluded Canada and upon UNRRA. His ammunition was logic; his weapons were Canadian diplomats, most notably Mike Pearson. In fighting for this cause, their excellent academic training, their strong feeling of Canadian nationalism, and, not least, a new sense of camaraderie made them extraordinarily effective. By 1943 even Mackenzie King, whose annoyance with Wrong had filled many diary pages, was confessing that Wrong was doing excellent work. Indeed, as historian Jack Granatstein has said, he was giving Canada a foreign policy that had flesh and bones.[27]

Wrong, Robertson, and Pearson sorted out the tactical details of how to apply theory to practice. Mike's role, it was tacitly agreed, was to be the idea's salesman. He was superbly fitted for the task. In his mid-forties Mike looked much younger. Newspaper stories referred to his "boyish face", "engaging grin", "unruly hair", "easy manner", and even "rock-ribbed physique". His face was redder, the jowls less firm, but Mike remained pleasantly handsome, and one must not minimize this quality in a North American society that increasingly valued physical attractiveness. Moreover, Mike knew both American and British officials well, and it was they who had to be convinced of "functionalism's" merit. Between 1943 and 1944, Mike gave more public speeches to larger and more prestigious audiences than ever before. By early 1945 Canadian papers could simply refer to him as "Pearson" without further identification. He had become a public figure. His FAO work contributed mightily to this recognition, but his efforts to get Canada a place on UNRRA's councils marked him as functionalism's front-line general and identified him as a liberal and a nationalist, stances that Canadians much prized in those times.[28]

Initially, in the summer of 1942, UNRRA seemed to Mike to be more "a headache than an opportunity". Mike's position in Washington left him exposed to angry telegrams from Ottawa demanding a larger voice in UNRRA, and American irritation when he expressed those demands. Canadians knew by 1942 that their post-war economic position would be second only to that of the United States and that Canada therefore would and should play a major part in post-war relief. And yet the Central Policy Committee of UNRRA had no place for Canada, only the Big Four (the United States, Britain, the Soviet Union, and China). Here was fertile terrain for a functionalist assault. On February 26, 1943, Mike, at Ottawa's behest, "got off a letter to the State Department, Litvinov, the Chinese Ambassador, and the British Embassy, [saying] that unless Canada was put on the Policy Committee we would not play at all." "This will certainly bring matters to a head with a vengeance," he wrote in his diary. And it did. He got a call the same afternoon, proposing a compromise whereby a Canadian would be named to chair the important Suppliers Committee, and this Canadian chairperson would sit on the Policy Committee whenever supplies came up (which was invariably). In fact, the Big Four would agree only to the words "participate in" rather than "be a part of" the Policy Committee. This solution satisfied Mike but was not good enough for Ottawa and especially not for the powerful deputy-minister of finance, Clifford Clark, who demanded that Canada take a stand on no taxation without representation.[29]

The account in Mike's memoirs is full and accurate, and there is no need to repeat its detail here. We should only note that Mike in Washington was more inclined to understand the American and Soviet viewpoints than were his colleagues and political masters in Ottawa who had quaffed copious potions of the heady brew of nationalism and functionalism. In Washington Mike had to deal with Dean Acheson who suffered Canadian fools especially badly (perhaps because of his own Anglo-Canadian background, perhaps because his close friend Hume Wrong told him Canada bred so many of them). Ottawa, Acheson wrote later in his memoirs, "raised the matter to the plane of high principle upon which the Department of External Affairs prefers to rest Canada's more mundane interests." His account bristles with sarcasm as he quotes a Canadian note that said, "These difficulties are a challenge to statesmanship (in this case, apparently, to American statesmanship)...." In fact, the British had difficulties too, and in trying to help they managed to confuse the situation by suggesting that they might even consider giving up their seat on the Executive Committee for Canada, in which case Canada would represent the British Commonwealth among the great powers. The notion attracted McCarthy, but Mike told him that "there was no use trying to argue that Canada would act for the Commonwealth or the U.K. act for Canada on any of these organizations." The British proposal was "generous", Robertson told King, but it was unsatisfactory and a bad precedent.[30]

In the end, the Americans worried far more about troubles with the Soviet Union, which objected to Canada's presence on the committee because they thought it meant simply another British vote. (The Soviets were even more convinced that this was the case than were the Americans.) Mike knew that the Canadians were doing well to be offered the compromise: in Washington in the early spring of

1943 Moscow was being courted and its concerns mattered most. Britain even encouraged this courtship because Churchill and Eden rightly feared that the Americans were tending to see the Pacific War as "their war". By keeping American attention on Moscow and post-war arrangements, the American contribution to Europe was assured.[31] Privately, Harry Hopkins, Roosevelt's closest confidant at this time, had little patience with British or Canadian requests that Canada's interests be recognized. He told Roosevelt that the United States should resist any efforts to seat separate delegations from Canada or Australia at the U.N. conferences. "We should put our foot down in the very beginning," Hopkins advised Roosevelt. Fortunately, in the case of UNRRA, the Americans lifted it a bit. Mike was much relieved.[32]

Both Acheson and Mike were "delighted" when Ottawa accepted the compromise on April 8, 1943. "I hope we play our cards right now and put a good man on the Supplies Committee," Mike wrote in his diary that evening. The "good man" Ottawa chose was Mike, and his prediction that the Supplies Committee would have much significance was largely but not wholly justified. From his first UNRRA council meeting in Atlantic City in November 1943 to his fifth in Geneva in the summer of 1946, Mike took part in UNRRA's deliberations and became known as a skilful negotiator and chairman.[33] The Supplies Committee had twelve members, including the four great powers, with the others chosen on "functional" grounds. In this work Mike became even more closely associated with Brooke Claxton, the Montreal MP who was quickly acquiring a reputation as a political spokesman for the "functional" principles and for Canada's place at the peace table. It was a valuable link for Mike, and they quickly discovered how compatible their political views were. Canada, Claxton wrote in 1944, "is the fourth industrial power, the fourth naval power, and the fourth air power in the free world."[34] These new facts justified new approaches, and, among Canada's diplomats, Mike came to personify these approaches, which emphasized Canadian sovereignty and the economic and social aspects of international organization. Politically, they sold well; practically, they placed Mike upon a podium where his utterings represented not merely Canada but also Canadians' hopes for a better world. As Acheson had sarcastically noted, Canada managed to have its "mundane interest" coincide neatly with international high principle – at least for a while.*

That "high principle" was the belief that multilateral approaches alone could assume future peace and prosperity. UNRRA, the FAO, the Chicago civil-aviation negotiations, and the post-war financial negotiations at Bretton Woods were part of the reconstruction of the shattered world economic and social system. Most important, however, were the negotiations leading towards the creation of a new world organization to succeed the discredited league. The great powers' so-called Moscow Declaration of November 1, 1943, removed any doubts that such an organization would be created. But as the vision of a United Nations acquired brick-and-mortar reality, Mike was disturbed by parts of the design. In the Armstrong lectures at the University of Toronto in January 1942, he had expressed what he himself described as an "idealist" view of world politics, and his approach, as Peter Gellman has recently suggested, was "reformist".[35] In March 1943 he argued strongly that there should be a full-scale United Nations conference that would set a path for the "technical" conferences to follow. Such a meeting, Mike told Robertson, "would emphasize the unity of purpose of the United Nations in a way which no statement from any single United Nations conference could." The Canadian and American governments both thought the proposal premature, and the food and relief conferences followed, as did the Moscow declaration with its joint American-Soviet request that other countries, apart from the four great powers, should simply "adhere" to the declaration. As Hume Wrong put it, that proposal

---

* Functionalism, in Canada's view, emphasized suppliers rather than recipients, producers rather than consumers. In the post-war era its justification diminished quickly as "consumers" asserted their sovereign rights as well. In a sense, "functionalism" was a Canadian attempt to exaggerate the significance of a small nation in a fashion that contradicted the liberal, democratic, and universalist notions on which a true world government would have to be based.

was no more than "an invitation from the big boys to the little boys to sign on the dotted line".[36]

The tactics of the "big boys" bothered Wrong, concerned as he was about Canada's place in the post-war world; their principles troubled Pearson, focused as he was on how that international organization could assure international security. Although several scholars have asserted that there was "little disagreement" among the Canadians in their aims for the new world organization, strong agreement on tactics concealed subtle yet important differences in beliefs.[37] Pearson's willingness to describe himself as an "idealist" in 1942-3 reflects an explicit rejection of the "realism" made academically fashionable by Hans Morgenthau's brilliant *Politics Among Nations* (which Mike probably did not read) and Walter Lippmann's 1943 classic *U.S. Foreign Policy: Shield of the Republic* (which Mike and millions of Americans certainly did read).* Lippmann's "realist" critique of the "one worldism" of Wendell Willkie and its "abstract theory of our rights and duties" called for an American policy emphasizing a great-power condominium and spheres of influence. The only world organization that could work was one based upon power and national sovereignty. The league failed because the fog of Wilsonian idealism clouded its vision; it had thus failed to see clearly when danger threatened. Whatever Mike had believed in the 1930s, he dissented strongly now from such opinions.

Robertson and Wrong were not so sure and neither was Mackenzie King whose diary reveals that, despite public statements of internationalist faith, his commitment to a world organization based on collective security was wobbly indeed. Pearson and Escott Reid fought against great-power domination because they were, in Reid's own words, utopians; Wrong, King, and, to a lesser extent, Robertson, did so because they wanted Canada's national interests recognized and represented. As Reid says in his book on the U.N.'s formation, the difference was not really recognized until the dust of battle

---

* This book was serialized in *Reader's Digest* and wondrously transformed into seven pages of cartoons in *Ladies' Home Journal*.

settled in 1946. Then Reid realized that he and Pearson had fought on the same side as their Ottawa colleagues, but under a different banner. Both Reid and Pearson were less willing, as John Holmes, a witness himself, has written, "to temper their conceptions of an ideal world order with a recognition that the willingness of all great powers to participate was of over-riding importance."[38] Mike was more pragmatic than Reid but their views of the purposes of international organization were similar.

The Dumbarton Oaks proposals for a world organization did not reflect the vision of an organization Canada held. The great powers alone sketched out the plans for the new United Nations and naturally their place in that organization was larger than "middle powers" – as Canada and nations of similar rank were now called – had wanted or expected. Mike was kept informed of great-power bargaining and he passed on the details to his Ottawa masters, with increasingly less enthusiasm. The British emphasis on a "regionally based organization" that Churchill thought could maintain the Empire and a British pre-eminence in Western Europe found little favour with Canadians who believed it would condemn Canada to either North American isolation or an orphan status in the post-war world.[39] But what was the alternative?

In mid-January, Mike and Reid went to the State Department to convey Canada's views on the Dumbarton Oaks proposals. As the American report on the meeting noted, Canada's greatest difficulty was the classification of nations as "great powers" and all others as equal but lesser. Mike and Reid argued that it was "unrealistic not to recognize that the potential of power which could be contributed by Canada and other secondary powers was not much less than that possessed by, say, China, and not to recognise the immense gap between such nations as Canada and nations such as Luxembourg and Panama which could contribute no increment of power whatever." There should be special recognition for middle powers such as Canada and Brazil. The State Department reply to Canada's queries and objections was, in Mike's words, "short, vague and not particularly enlightening". In fact, the reply made it clear that the State Department did not welcome Canadian initiatives that challenged great-power pre-eminence in the United Nations.[40] In a speech at the University of Toronto one month later (when he received an honorary LL.D.), Mike's increasing doubts were most apparent. After listing the difficulties in the path of post-war international co-operation, he said that he was "not one of those who view the future with any exaggerated optimism; or that I get much comfort out of the kind of advertising which shows a gaunt, deep-eyed, suntan-cheeked soldier looking out of a devastated landscape into a sunrise in which there seem to be floating pretty wives, lovely children, handsome homes, ice-cream cones, helicopters and nylon stockings."[41]

Mike is usually described as one of the architects of the United Nations, and yet his direct influence on Canadian policy and on Canada's work at the San Francisco conference was not great. Indeed, his more effective work may have been his pre-San Francisco efforts to make Americans more receptive to the idea of a United Nations that would, however little, limit the sovereignty and independence of that instinctively isolationist nation. Mike paid special attention to Senator Arthur Vandenberg of Michigan who he feared would lead an attack against the United Nations as Henry Cabot Lodge had done so effectively against the League of Nations. James Reston of *The New York Times,* then a young reporter, also worked on Vandenberg, and he and Mike jointly tried to steer recalcitrant American politicians and bureaucrats towards the responsible internationalism both wanted. Vandenberg's celebrated conversion to internationalism in January 1945 cleared away most doubts that Canadians and others had about the American commitment to internationalism. Mike helped in promoting Canada's interests, but at San Francisco, Norman Robertson was the Canadian team's general manager, Hume Wrong its canny coach, and Mike, a brilliant player on the specialty squad.[42]

Mike's duties at Washington, which was recovering from the shock of Roosevelt's death and Truman's accession, did not permit him to be absent long or to spend much time on preparations. He travelled to San Francisco by a special train that left Washington on

April 20. He quickly developed a headache that was not helped by Australia's Herbert Evatt who "kept bobbing in" to Mike's compartment, all the time denouncing the Dumbarton Oaks arrangements and the refusal of the great powers to accept any amendments to that scheme. Each time he tried to read the Dumbarton Oaks papers, his headache returned and so he contented himself with reading Hugh MacLennan's new novel, *Two Solitudes,* which he very much liked. At San Francisco, the conference organization was "hopeless", his luggage was lost at the station, and huge throngs crowded the St. Francis Hotel's elegant lobby to see the "celebrities" and made that old hotel's service thoroughly chaotic. The atmosphere was peculiar. After the first week, Mike wrote in his diary: "I don't know whether it is because we are too absorbed by Conference activities, or whether we have become numbed by repetition to the imp of great events. Whatever it is, however, the fact remains that headlines such as 'Hitler Dead,' 'Mussolini Hanged by the Feet,' 'Berlin Captured,' 'Nazis Collapse Completely,' all leave me about as cold as the headline, 'Yanks Win Two Games.'"[43] Mike, who was obviously tired, focused on two areas: limiting the independence of the great powers on the Security Council and the role of the economic and social agencies. His attitude was pragmatic: "On important questions of principle, on which we have already submitted amendments, we must fight through to the end. On other questions, we should not press the Big Four if they in fact attach importance to them."[44]

Mike knew the conference could be only a beginning; the events of 1944 and early 1945 had dashed many dreams for a stronger international organization. The debate droned on, petty politicians fussed over trivialities, and a droll humour pervaded all. Mike asked Charles Ritchie, who had caught measles on his arrival, how so many incompetents could have become foreign secretaries of their countries: "He said, from the look of them, in many cases, it must have been through the boudoir." The well-informed Ritchie added that, "in his experience, a boudoir led not to a Foreign office, but to a blind alley."[45] There seemed too many blind alleys at San Francisco, as Mike explained the Canadian position on each issue every morning to the press, and then moved on to a committee meeting where once again he was the Canadian spokesman. His frustration – and Canada's – came from the general instructions they had been issued: the delegates had to do nothing to endanger American, Russian, or British acceptance of the charter. Retreat, therefore, was frequent. Pragmatic though he was, Mike sometimes thought that Canada went too far, and he developed a grudging respect (not shared by his colleagues) for the aggressive Evatt. When, for example, the conference chairman Edward Stettinius broke his promise to the Canadians that there would be only three speakers at the closing session of the steering committee and then opened it up to several others but not Mackenzie King, Mike was infuriated and expressed his irritation to Jack Hickerson. Hickerson explained it away, but to Mike it was pure "bunk". The Australian response was stronger: Evatt sent a note to Stettinius saying the list was "a bloody outrage". Mike also admired Evatt's courage when he stood up after one of Senator Connally's "roaring, raving and gesturing" performances and said that if the senator ever lost his senate seat he could always get a job with the Ringling Brothers' circus. Evatt did go too far but Mike knew that he, not the Canadians, had won the affection of the smaller nations. Their gratitude was expressed when they elected Australia, not Canada, to the new Security Council in January 1946.[46]

Canada had worked to preserve the great-power unity that the war had forged with such difficulty. The result was a less public role for Canada than many Canadians had anticipated. The work of Robertson and Reid in drafting the charter, work done quietly and most effectively out of the public eye, represented the major contribution of Canada to the conference. Mike had the highest admiration for their work and for the pre-conference planning over which Wrong had presided. And yet he, like the other Canadian delegates, was disappointed with the conference. King and the Canadian politicians had to leave to fight the election in the middle of the conference, and their education in the "new internationalism" was not so complete as the bureaucrats had hoped. "Canada" spoke only twice in public session, and Mike's skills were not employed so fully as he had hoped.

The Soviets profoundly disappointed him and the other Canadians, not least because Canadian hopes for near great-power status so often collapsed when confronted with Soviet obstinacy.[47] It boded ill for the future.

What that future would be became even less certain in August 1945 when the atomic bombs fell on Hiroshima and Nagasaki. That month Mike was in Europe for an UNRRA council meeting, and he went over to the continent to witness the devastation six years of war had wrought. Seeing the shattered city of Berlin and the ruins of the Thousand-Year Reich, Mike became "depressed and distressed and saw little light for the future...." He returned with these images to North America where he learned the astonishing news that a cipher clerk in the Soviet Embassy in Ottawa had defected and had exposed a spy network whose tentacles extended into the Canadian civil service and scientific establishment. Like Robertson, Mike was especially troubled by the civil servants' betrayal of their oath and office. For them, public service was a calling, and the sins of a very few would reflect upon all those who wore the same cloth – and it did. King and Robertson went to Washington at the end of September to tell the Americans what had occurred. Mike himself briefed Acheson, but the Canadians proceeded cautiously, concerned because a legal case against the accused spies was not ready and because the revelation of spying could have a devastating impact on the fragile relationship between the Soviet Union and the West.[48]

The most sensational aspect of the case surrounded the atomic-bomb secrets, although at first President Truman's reaction to the Gouzenko revelations was cautious just as King's had been. Then attitudes hardened, and British prime minister Clement Attlee and Truman decided to meet in Washington, along with King, to discuss what controls could and should be placed on atomic questions. In wartime, Canada, because of its extensive atomic research, served with the Americans and British on a combined policy committee, which supposedly assured collaboration among the three nations in that field. Roosevelt and Churchill had agreed that wartime collaboration would carry over into the peace. But as in so many other areas, the coming of peace brought new strains, and Truman refused to be bound by the pledges his predecessor had made in different times.[49] Mike had said at San Francisco that the pace of events had numbed him and others around him. The pace had not slowed, but the numbness vanished when Mike was asked to summarize Canadian policy on atomic energy. King, Truman, and Attlee were to meet in Washington in early November 1945; the Canadians recognized the meeting's importance immediately.

The atomic bombs, the viewing of European destruction, and the spy scandal strengthened Mike's internationalist sentiments, which though present at San Francisco had not had a sense of extreme urgency. Mike had served in the place of C.D. Howe as the Canadian representative on the Combined Policy Committee and was familiar with the political and, to a lesser degree, the scientific issues surrounding nuclear energy. Moreover, his service as the departmental specialist on disarmament in the early 1930s had established some foundations for understanding arms control. Indeed, in 1934 he had told an Ottawa church group that "we get almost into the realm of the fantastic when we consider the release of atomic energy as a destructive force". This remarkably prophetic remark was followed by another, which seemed less valid once fantasy became reality in 1945: "If that energy is ever released ... and applied to destructive purposes, we would doubtless have world peace because the world would be blown to bits."[50] But "deterrence", which this view logically and theoretically supports, was definitely not the best choice in the fall of 1945.

The explosion of the atomic bomb was, in the words of the leading student of the early impact of the bomb, "a psychic event of almost unprecedented proportions". Nor surprisingly, the "dominant immediate response" was "confusion and disorientation". The bomb had defeated the hated Japanese but its implications were so much greater. *The New Republic* reported that a malaise had gripped Washington as parents in the capital considered what future their children might have. *Time* said all the great events of the year were insignificant compared to the meaning of the mushroom clouds over Hiroshima. Bob Hope said that there would be no more "Roses are red, violets are blue". In the atomic age, the verse would read: "Will you be my little geranium, until we are both blown up by uranium?" The strained humour reflects the anxious mood which led public opinion towards a strengthened internationalist sentiment in the fall of 1945.[51]

Aware of the need to take advantage of that public mood, Mike drew up his memorandum on "atomic warfare" hastily in the first week of November 1945. It is a remarkable document. The eminent diplomatic historian James Eayrs has said that it "deserves a place among the great diplomatic state papers" because of its brilliant analysis and prescience. His aim was to convince his political master, Mackenzie King, that, in the memorandum's words, "any constructive solution of this problem of the war use of atomic energy, must be international – not national. There is, in fact, no national solution." Mackenzie King marked this passage and several others on his personal copy. Another passage he marked came where Mike quoted Truman's comment that the United States regarded the bomb as a "sacred trust" that "thoughtful people" knew would not be violated because of the U.S.'s known "love of peace". Mike archly commented: "'Thoughtful people' are not likely to include Soviet officials in the Kremlin...." King agreed. He also agreed with Mike's conclusion that the significance of the bomb could not be exaggerated: "It presents us with the greatest threat to man's existence ever conceived, and, paradoxically, the greatest opportunity for world peace." That kind of peace could best be shaped if the bomb forced the United Nations to become "an effective association for peace". This was not a passage marked by King.[52] Perhaps he was even less a U.N. man than at San Francisco; Mike certainly was more.*

Mike urged a bold course upon King. He recommended that the

---

* The King diary entries for this period (Nov. 10-Dec. 31, 1945) are missing. This missing section probably contained the comments on the Gouzenko spies. Its disappearance, in my view, is probably explained by King's suspicions about some public servants or colleagues. Such comments about Skelton's son "Sandy" Skelton, for example, are found in the existing diary. King's mind was suspicious, and his imagination may have run wild. Who destroyed it? King or a friend of those he suspected? We almost certainly will never know.

three leaders issue a statement of principles upon which an international agreement might be based, followed by an announcement that this proposed agreement would be submitted for discussion at the U.N. General Assembly. Because of the significance of the announcement, all radio stations in Britain, Canada, and the United States should give free time for this announcement. The radio program might begin with short statements by King and Attlee, followed by a "ten or fifteen minute statement" by a scientist of world repute "who in the most dramatic and impressive fashion possible ... would drive home to listeners the implications for human existence of atomic warfare." Then Truman would conclude the program by presenting the principles of the international agreement and announcing that he was presenting that agreement to Congress for ratification and for other governments to follow. This imaginative proposal unfortunately had little impact on what followed when the leaders of the English-speaking world met in Washington.[53] There was an anti-British mood in the American air that November, and the British, for their part, resented the rapid American withdrawal from Europe and, particularly, the American assumption that their economic ways would prevail in the post-war world.[54] There was altogether too much suspicion, and Mackenzie King was too tired and too timid to prod the two new leaders towards the bolder course his aides had urged.

After a ceremonial beginning, the tripartite talks began in earnest on November 11. After King, Attlee, and Truman laid wreaths at 11:00 a.m. at Arlington Cemetery's Tomb of the Unknown Soldier on a damp and misty morning, the three leaders boarded the presidential yacht, the *Sequoia,* and sailed upon the Potomac until nightfall. Mike, as ambassador, was the only Canadian to accompany King. There were only seven others and one of them, the crusty and not very competent American secretary of state James Byrnes, insisted that no record be kept. For the first time Mike was asked by an American president for his opinion on an important political question. Seated around the yacht's dining-table, each leader and his adviser told Truman what he thought should be done to assure that atomic energy would never be used again for destructive purposes. It is unclear what Mike said or how long he spoke but his opinion was clear: the atomic bomb must be placed under international control.[55] Talks continued with more advisers, including American scientists, and finally a committee was struck to produce the final declaration. The distinguished American scientist Vannevar Bush;* Sir John Anderson, Lord Privy Seal in Great Britain; and Mike drafted the declaration that incorporated the British and American drafts and Canadian amendments thereto. The declaration proposed an atomic-energy commission to be set up under the new United Nations organization. This commission would work by stages towards the elimination of nuclear weapons from all national arsenals. But there was to be no sharing of secrets with the Soviets nor was there to be a public statement that the United States, Great Britain, and Canada would continue to co-operate in the field of atomic energy. The proposed commission became a reality in January 1946, and Canada, in perfect functionalist fashion, joined the five permanent Security Council members as the sixth. In the end, what came forth from this meeting was mainly "fine words and noble sentiments". Writing in 1970, Mike sombrely reflected on those events: "There was a solemn warning in [those words and sentiments] but there was to be little effective action to follow. Have they become merely the expression of another 'might have been' of history.... Today the answer seems to be 'yes' and it could mean humanity's greatest and final failure." As the hopes for international control of atomic energy under the United Nations faded, Mike lost some faith in the U.N. and much faith in great-power co-operation. He nevertheless remained convinced that Canada's fate would be decided not in Ottawa but beyond the nation's boundaries. The disappointments did not dim his vigour in international gatherings; indeed, they strengthened it.[56] This commitment brought busy times.

---

* Bush was the head of the Office of Scientific Research and Development during the war years. In 1949 he published *Modern Arms and Free Men*, in which he minimized the impact of the bomb. However, he did admit that its first use in 1945 had "overwhelmed our calm reason for a time".

In October 1945, Robertson called in American ambassador Ray Atherton and told him that Canada could not possibly participate in all the international conferences in which such participation was expected.[57] The Canadians were ubiquitous at the many conferences in that critical year, and no Canadian was so prominent as Mike. His stay in Washington had cast him in a major part in a drama that was truly being played out upon a world stage. Occasionally jealous of the spotlight, Mackenzie King had none the less come to admire Mike's talents. "Read splendid review of Canada's war effort by Mike Pearson," King wrote in his diary of January 10, 1943. "Listened to Pearson's address on Canada's war effort.... Excellent speech, with light touch," he wrote the next day. The canniest judge of political talent had spotted a promising recruit. The next day they had a chat. Over the next two years, Mike became a public figure, and his broad grin was increasingly familiar to ever more Canadians and Americans. He appeared on radio quiz shows (and did very well on "Information Please" against the writer Clifton Fadiman and the self-proclaimed *savant* Oscar Levant). His speeches were both numerous and widely noticed. "A forceful speech", "an excellent speech", normally caustic British officials minuted on one of his speeches. In response to rumours in 1945 that Mike might be sent to Tokyo on the Far Eastern Advisory Commission, Mike's old friend and British Labour politician Philip J. Noel-Baker expressed despair at such an appointment: "It is little short of a disaster. Such men are rare and should not be sterilized in their prime." In fact, this period may have been Mike's most satisfying and creative as he moved from conference to conference, from podium to microphone, from chancery to Canadian Club, putting forth his nation's and his own arguments for an international structure more lasting than the league.[58]

Mike's work with the FAO first captured attention, and his name quickly surfaced as a possible FAO chairman. He was not a scientist, the FAO's future was uncertain, and he quickly dismissed the idea in 1944. When discreetly asked about the post however, Mike "let slip that if he were offered a post in any future world political organization he might well take it."[59] That opportunity appeared quickly in

1945 when world leaders considered who should be the first secretary general of the United Nations. Mike's part at San Francisco was less impressive than that taken by Robertson and, to some extent, Wrong, but his personality attracted more attention than that of either. Conference chairman Edward Stettinius, of whom Mike thought poorly, told Mike that his "constructive outlook, energy, and good humour [had] helped to resolve many difficulties".[60] As the British and the Americans debated where the new United Nations should be, they also considered who should direct it in its first years. Stettinius seems to have been the first to bring forward Mike's name, although Noel-Baker, now British minister of state for United Nations affairs, also seems to have thought of Mike as soon as the question was considered. Norman Robertson was also mentioned and seems, most interestingly, to have been the first choice of Dean Acheson and Jack Hickerson, the State Department officials with whom Mike had worked closely during his Washington years. Both thought Robertson's appointment would serve U.S. interests better, and Hickerson frankly thought Robertson the better man, possessing more "character" and "ability". These reservations are not surprising; Mike himself had developed reservations about Acheson and Hickerson. There was a *bonhomie* among the three, but never real friendship.[61] The suggestion of Robertson was extraordinary despite his exceptional talents. His shyness and public reticence were severe handicaps for a first secretary general. In any event, when Stettinius asked King about Pearson and Robertson, King quickly and correctly suggested that Robertson would not be interested. He then spoke highly of Mike, who emerged as a strong candidate for the position if the U.N. were to be located in Europe. An American site made him less likely but not improbable. He had strong support from the British where Noel-Baker's influence was great, from Wellington Koo of China, and at times from the Americans. The Canadians at the U.N. meeting in London did not push Mike's case, but neither did they oppose it.

On January 21, 1946, the eleven-member Security Council met, and eight members favoured Mike and three favoured a European.

Among the three opposed was the Soviet Union, and Andrei Gromyko let it be known that the Soviets would veto Pearson. The Americans gave way and accepted the compromise candidate, Trygve Lie of Norway. Hume Wrong summed up what happened for Robertson: "Pearson was strongly pushed by the British and supported by the Americans as their first choice. The Russians, however, were unyielding in their insistence that the Secretary General should not come from 'the Anglo-Saxon bloc,' with the headquarters in the United States and this Assembly in London." Wrong thought Mike was "well out of it", telling Robertson that he doubted that the "best man on earth" could enhance his reputation as secretary general.[62] Wrong cabled Mike immediately: "Congratulations on your narrow escape. It was a close thing and they have not nominated the better man. You have been spared many trials and our service has been spared an irreplaceable loss." Mike, however, did not see matters quite that way.[63]

Although Mike too despaired for the future of the U.N. in that bleak midwinter of 1946, he recognized, as he told his cynical friend Maurice Pope, that "a venture of this kind is the only possible approach to world peace". The secretary general would have to be a "great man" to succeed with all the troubles the young organization faced.[64] Mike told Wrong and Pope that he was relieved, but his tone betrays his disappointment. In truth, he wanted to face the challenge of being a "great man". He had indicated to Mackenzie King that he would take the job if offered, a judgment that King, whose skepticism about the U.N. was growing, thought faulty. It was especially ill-conceived, King believed, since Pearson "had very much in mind entering Canadian public life."[65] One way or another Mike was ready for the "Big League", as he put it to a fellow baseball fan. The $30,000 per year salary was surely an additional attraction. His experiences in Washington had drawn him from the diplomat's desk to the public podium. There was now little that was quiet about his diplomacy. Memoranda were less frequent, and long-term considerations often gave way to urgent and messy necessities. Graham Greene once said that a political mind possesses an intelligence of the second order. Mike's career does suggest that weaker critical faculties may indeed be a prerequisite to, and the result of, a public life. In the scarce time available to Mike after 1944 his linking of goals and means inevitably became less detailed, and his critical spirit not so pronounced. Nevertheless, his experience had given him rich resources upon which to draw. In the summer of 1946 Mike returned to Ottawa to replace a tired Robertson as under-secretary, and rumours abounded that Mike's return was a final step before his entry into politics. The prime minister, now seventy-two, was in his final years; public life beckoned and Mike was ready to heed that call. Nothing about this future task seemed of the second order to Canada's best-known diplomat.[66]

The war's end brought international disappointments as well as personal success. The intensity of that time allowed few moments of private pleasure but there were some touches of humour. Costin, his old tutor, wrote him to tell him that he had been elected an honorary fellow of St. John's, an honour he shared with twelve other notables such as the former governors of Burma and Nigeria, the Bishop of Oxford, and the architect of Guildford Cathedral. Rising to unaccustomed heights of sentiment, Costin reminded Mike, "I gave you at your marriage Blake's picture of a young man rising like the dawn. You have risen to the meridian. May you long shine with the power of light and heat to the general good of your own country, the Commonwealth and this poor distracted world." The sentiments "amused and moved" Mike, who told his fellow St. John's alumnus A.D.P. Heeney that no honour had pleased him more "apart from the 2nd vice-presidency of the Young Temperance League" in Peterborough in 1910. Then, as in 1946, it was important that Mike keep his balance. In this poor distracted world it was becoming ever more difficult, but he was managing well.[67]

CHAPTER TWELVE

"A SORT OF ARMAGEDDON"

I can hardly tell you how strongly I feel that it is absolutely necessary for our party to go full out in regard to the threat of communism, both from the domestic and international point of view, and to be critical of the government for its carelessness in dealing with so serious a situation.

– George Drew, premier of Ontario, to John Diefenbaker, MP
(1946)[1]

THE COLD WAR cast its malign spell upon the world in the winter of 1946, and the malignancy quickly spread to internal organs of government. It was not only George Drew who saw the "threat of communism" as both domestic and international. The Gouzenko incident had convinced Mackenzie King that the new enemy attacked the heart and the mind as well as the body. As 1946 passed, his gloom deepened, reaching its nadir in November. Canadians, the prime minister told his cabinet, were "headed into an inevitable conflict ... with Communism versus Capitalism or Atheism versus Christianity. The war will be in the nature of a religious war as well as a class struggle and may result in a sort of Armageddon."[2]

King's language was archaic, but the opinion was contemporary, and Mike Pearson helped to shape his prime minister's beliefs. King lectured to the cabinet just after he received an appreciation of Canada's defence position from his new under-secretary. The cabinet and the prime minister had to decide whether the international situation warranted accepting the so-called 35th Recommendation of the Permanent Joint Board on Defence, a recommendation that, if accepted, would lead to unprecedented peacetime military co-operation between Canada and the United States. The decision would be historic, and, in Mike's view, there could be little doubt where history should lead.

By November 1946, Mike had given up on the United Nations (U.N.) as an instrument to attain "peace and co-operation" among the great powers. "We know," he told King, "that little confidence can be placed in the ability of the United Nations to guarantee security, until it can reflect friendly relations between the Great Powers themselves. We should, of course, continue to work for a strong United Nations, with every member nation making its contribution to the preservation of peace by international action." The U.N.'s failure was the sad corollary of Soviet-American confrontation. The Americans, Mike argued, might be sometimes "aggressive and provocative", but they would certainly not provoke a conflict. "But what about Russia?" he asked. "Is it possible for the western democratic world to work out, if not a friendly, at least a tolerable relationship with a state, organized on a police basis, governed by ruthless despots, inhabited by millions of fighting men to whom life is hard and cheap, and with a dynamic communist ideology?" The question, of course, was rhetorical.

"My own view, for what it may be worth, is that without some fundamental change in the Soviet state system and in the policies and views of its leaders, the U.S.S.R. is ultimately bound to come into open conflict with western democracy.... We should not make the mistake we made with Hitler, of refusing to take seriously the words these leaders utter for home consumption," Mike went on in the memorandum to King. The next war would be "short, nasty and brutish," and in the age of "atom bombs, bacteria and guided missiles" Canada no longer occupied a fireproof house. It now must join with the United States, the bulwark against Soviet domination, to defend itself.[3]

Professor Denis Smith, in his history of Canada and the cold war, has correctly described this memorandum as an attempt to ginger "the prime minister's thoughts with a renewed dose of fear". Certainly the memorandum abounds with cold-war rhetoric, and the Soviet threat is perceived as principally ideological. Similarly, political scientist Reg Whitaker has claimed that "virtually all the anti-Communist stops" were pulled out by Pearson as he rallied Canadians to confront the Soviet challenge.[4] Mike's rhetoric was unusually bellicose, and his appreciation of the early cold war was far distant from that of such "realists" as Walter Lippmann, who deplored talk of spiritual struggle and argued that a more rational policy could be framed if one recognized that the threat came from the Russian army, not Soviet communism. However, for Mike, the key to the struggle was "spiritual" because "the crusading and subversive power of communism has been harnessed by a cold-blooded, calculating, victoriously powerful Slav empire for its own political purposes".[5] This 1948 speech used exceptionally strong language, but the perception was quite similar to that expressed in his 1946 memorandum. The language has not worn well and the intellectual appreciation of the Soviet threat to Canada and the West seems distorted, especially in the view of the revisionist historians who have cast a critical eye on the anti-communist rhetoric and practices of the late 1940s. Two complaints have been made: the harsh rhetoric against the Soviet Union led to a repression of domestic political radicalism, and the focus on the Soviet enemy accompanied a blindness to the economic imperialism of the United States. In the derisory formulation of the Canadian historians Robert Cuff and Jack Granatstein, "Corporal Pearson willingly enlisted in the Acheson volunteers" as they marched off to extend American power by fighting the evil empire of Soviet communism.[6]

How strange it seems then to read in John Costello's bestselling *Mask of Treachery* that Mike Pearson may have been a "member of a Soviet network".[7] Costello draws this conclusion mainly from the work of Professor James Barros on Herbert Norman, the Canadian diplomat who committed suicide in April 1957 after he was named as a Soviet agent by witnesses before an American Senate investigating committee. In his book on Norman, Barros alleges that Norman was a Soviet "agent of influence" and argues strongly that Mike Pearson, as secretary of state for External Affairs, "covered up" Norman's early association with communist agents at Cambridge University in the 1930s and other evidence suggesting Norman was a serious "security risk", as the U.S. congressional committees suggested. Since the book's publication, Barros has been more open about his "suspicions of the political behaviour of Lester Pearson", and in response to criticism of his comments has written: "Specifically, however, suspicions about Pearson in Washington surfaced on August 14, 1951, when the American Elizabeth Bentley, who had defected from a Russian spy ring, gave sworn testimony in secret testimony before the Senate Internal Security Subcommittee. During the war, a communist agent she was running in the Canadian Legation, Hazel [*sic*] Sise, told her that the sensitive and secret information he was giving her for transmission to Moscow came from Lester Pearson." Barros admits that Bentley "made it clear in her testimony that that was only what Sise alleged." Peter Worthington, a noted Canadian journalist, shares these suspicions. He has claimed in his memoir, *Looking for Trouble,* that "in his book, *Special Counsel,* former lawyer for the U.S. Senate Security subcommittee, William Rusher ... identifies Pearson, though he doesn't name him, as a suspected Soviet sympathizer.... Elizabeth Bentley ... identified Pearson as one of the Soviet contacts in the Canadian Embassy in Washington." He adds, nevertheless, that the American government "took it seriously", and that Pearson's "antics" at the time of the Korean War, his defences of Norman and other actions of his, lent support to the suspicions.[8]

Norman and Mike's defence of Norman do not concern us here (they will in Volume 2 of this biography), but the allegations concerning Pearson's relationship with Sise and the passing of information to Moscow obviously do bear upon the subject of his view of the Soviet Union in the 1940s. And there is other evidence that those who regard Mike as, at best, "soft on communism" and, at worst, an "agent of influence" might add to their circumstantial case, based on his early 1930s article on the Soviet Union; his strongly pro-republican views in the Spanish Civil War; his meeting with Fred Rose, which led to the release of imprisoned Canadian communists; his request to become Canadian minister in Moscow where he would have joined Clark Kerr, the British ambassador who was suspiciously enthusiastic about the Soviet Union; and his silence about many of these events later.

Elizabeth Bentley gave more than one hundred names of individuals whom she alleged were Soviet agents or sympathizers. The credibility of this Vassar graduate, who became a courier for communist underground networks in the United States between 1938 and 1945 when she gave her information to the FBI, has been much debated. However, an objective observer must agree that some of her allegations have had additional support from other sources and, on a broader level, there can be no doubt now that her suggestion of a large Soviet network in the Anglo-American democracies is accurate. Assessing the evidence, the distinguished American diplomatic historian John Gaddis has claimed that "it is now a matter of record that during the 1920s and 1930s the Russians had mounted an extraordinarily ambitious effort to recruit agents, chiefly in Great Britain but also in the United States, who might over time rise to positions of influence or even authority in those countries. The sheer scope of this operation is astonishing in retrospect." There was Soviet espionage and therefore Soviet agents: only numbers, names, and motives remain in doubt.[9]

Bentley's testimony about Mike Pearson was given on August 14, 1951 before the U.S. Senate Judiciary Committee Subcommittee to Investigate the Administration of the Internal Security Act and Other Internal Security Laws. Subcommittee counsel Robert Morris asked Bentley whether she or any of her communist associates had "any particular connection with the Canadian Legation". She said that Fred Rose, Tim Buck (Canadian communist leader), and Sam Carr (a leading Canadian communist) gave them names of "any

Canadians who came to the United States and were in a position to help us". Her testimony,* which Senator Joseph McCarthy had been invited to hear, continued:

> Bentley: As a result of this, in 1942 Mr. Hazen Size, S-i-z-e [*sic*], came down and was promptly turned over to us. He brought a letter signed, I think, by Fred Rose.
>
> Morris: He was a conscious, direct agent, is that right?
>
> Bentley: Yes, he had quite a background of Communist activity and had fought in Spain besides.
>
> Morris: Would you say his Communist background was open and notorious?
>
> Bentley: According to him he was fairly open. I don't know how open that would be.

After identifying Sise as part of the "Canadian Film Board", Bentley says Sise's "most valuable material came from Mike Pearson".

> Morris: Who is Mike Pearson?
>
> Bentley: That is really his nickname, it's really Lester Pearson, and he was second in charge of the Canadian Legation during that period, which would be from 1942 to 1943 when I lost Hazen Size.
>
> Morris: Was he a councilor to the Canadian Legation?
>
> Bentley: I don't know the precise title, but Hazen said he was the top man in the Legation. I understand from Hazen that Pearson knew Hazen was a Communist and was willing to

---

* The testimony remains closed, but I located a copy in the John Diefenbaker papers where it seems to have been passed on by a Canadian journalist with Washington sources. Such a "leak" was not unusual, and it seems incorrect to suggest, as Barros does, that the document could have been "made available" to Diefenbaker only "on the very highest authority of the American government." Barros, "Letter", *International Perspectives* (March / April 1989), 24. Diefenbaker does appear to have taken the allegations seriously and he is said to have thought Pearson was sympathetic to the Soviets.

help. Pearson by virtue of his position used to sit in on American functions, particularly British ones re British policies, all of which was super hush-hush.

Morris: Then he used to give the information he obtained to Hazen Size?

Bentley: That is correct, and he passed it on to me.

Morris: Do you have any question now that Hazen Size was a Communist?

Bentley: Hazen Size said [Pearson] knew.

Morris: Nevertheless he was giving this information to Hazen Size?

Bentley: This is correct.

Morris: Hazen Size turned it over to you?

Bentley: That is correct.

Morris: What did you do with it?

Bentley: That was turned over to [Jacob] Golos during his lifetime, and later on to his succeeding agent.

Morris: And it went on to the Soviets?

Bentley: This is right.

Chairman: I would like to ask a question. What was the nature, the manner, in which the information was conveyed to you? Was it by documents or by microfilm or how was it?

Bentley: No, Mr. Hazen Size made notes and turned the notes over to me. Once in a while he would forget to make notes and would remember it and I would write it down, but he generally wrote notes.

Morris: Your relations with Size were over a long duration?

Bentley: Roughly two years. As a matter of fact, he only dropped him because he was starting to go to a psychiatrist. In espionage you don't trust a person who goes to a psychiatrist and your orders are to drop him. I immediately dropped him when he started going to a psychiatrist.

After Bentley's testimony ended, Morris introduced the testimony of Edward C. Carter, which linked Mike with the "Washington

chapter" of the Institute of Pacific Relations, a group that received
much criticism for its leftist associations from Senators McCarthy,
McCarran, and other senators.[10]

Mike did know Hazen Sise, having met him in London in 1936.
Sise, an architect, had studied with Le Corbusier and was deeply
influenced by Walter Gropius and the Bauhaus School that the Nazis
had recently closed down. His father, Charles Sise, a wealthy Canadian businessman of American origins, had founded Bell Telephone
in Canada. The events in Europe deeply affected the "lanky, shy"
Sise, as they did many architects of the modernist school who became
profoundly anti-Fascist in the 1930s. Sise met Norman Bethune in
1936 and was immediately captivated, volunteering to follow him to
Spain to serve in Bethune's famous medical service. Sise explained his
decision and his beliefs to his father just before his departure to
Spain:

> I am not a Communist, but have been very close to their way of think-
> ing both by the logic of their beliefs and by the trend of events, which
> every day go more and more to justify their position – Now the only
> difference between Communists and that great mass of Left opinion
> which hopes for Socialism is that the Communists know very well that
> we will never get it unless we are willing to fight for it – that, indeed,
> we will not be able even to preserve Democracy in the face of the
> threat of Fascism unless we are willing to organize to impose disci-
> pline on ourselves to fight.

Mike did not discourage Sise in his decision to go to Spain; indeed he
helped him obtain identity papers and told him that he should hope
for little help for the Republicans from Britain because its government would "do nothing to imperil their precarious neutrality".[11]

Sise served briefly in Spain, returned to Montreal via London
where he expressed to Mike an interest in External Affairs, and after
his return argued strenuously with his Canadian socialist friends who
wanted Canada to remain neutral in any European war. When war
came, his bad health prevented him from enlisting, but he managed,

as Bentley said, to get a position as the film officer attached to the Canadian embassy in 1942-3. He left Washington in July 1944. There can be no doubt that Mike spoke with him often, and he admits he did so in his memoirs where he describes Sise as "a rather radical young man". Sise's papers do reveal that he regarded himself as a person of the left, and it is likely that in Washington, as elsewhere, he would be in contact with like-minded individuals. When confronted with Bentley's testimony, Sise denied it emphatically, but did not deny knowledge of Bentley. One other consideration is relevant: Mike had little regard for confidentiality. The distinguished journalist Bruce Hutchison recalled in amazement how "though many men were much closer to him, often on returning from London or Washington he would tell Dexter and me the top secrets of the British and American governments, his conversations with a prime minister or president, even military secrets which both of us promptly put out of our minds and wished we had not heard."[12]

Bentley's testimony resulted in an FBI file on Mike of 243 pages that is labelled "Espionage – R", a designation that means the FBI considered it possible that Mike was a spy. Most of the file has been released, and the contents are revealing. On August 21, seven days after Bentley's testimony, L.L. Laughlin of the FBI reports that he has learned that "Pearson was to be named very shortly as a *member* [italics added] of the Communist Party, presumably by some committee of Congress". Someone (the name is blacked out) was reported to have some information about Mike, but the New York agent noted that the last time they contacted this person "a story appeared shortly thereafter in the *New York Journal-American*" indicating the FBI was investigating that person. Such a story, it was suggested, might lead to criticism of the FBI. Moreover, a check of the files on August 16 revealed that, in her original 1945 testimony and her later comments, Bentley had never mentioned "any information ... concerning Pearson". Bentley was confronted with this fact and said "she apparently was in error since it was her recollection that she had made this information available to Bureau agents". And so, in late

August 1951 began the FBI file on "Lester (Michael) Pearson, highly placed Canadian government official" and the entries piled up until he left public life seventeen years later.

The FBI interviewed Bentley about her congressional testimony, and she initially said that Mike "had moved in left wing circles before World War II" and that in 1943 he had "attended all top level meetings with British diplomats". She did admit, however, that she "never had any direct contact with Pearson". At this point, a senior State Department official, H. Freeman Matthews, deputy undersecretary for Political Affairs, intervened and requested of J. Edgar Hoover that his agents ask Bentley whether Mike knew that Sise was giving her information.* Bentley became defensive: she admitted that "she was only guessing but that she was of the opinion that Pearson either knew ... or that he was simply stupid". In her next interview her case was further weakened. In her 1945 testimony she had simply described Sise's information as "principally gossip overheard in the Canadian and British Embassy [that] could be characterised as the names of prominent British officials who were coming to the United States" and some details on Canada's war effort – hardly "top level policy discussions". Under more intensive questioning Bentley retreated, claiming that Pearson was a "left-winger" because he moved in the "same circles" socially as Sise. That is untrue; they had no contact after their London meeting, until Washington. She also admitted that she never discussed with Sise that what he said was being "delivered to the Russians". She also changed her date of her first meeting with Sise to 1942. Her case against Mike began to crumble when she was interviewed again on September 26, 1951 with "New York newspapers" already making not-too-discreet enquiries about what Bentley had said to the Senate subcommittee. Under intensive questioning she again conceded that "this information [told to her by Sise] was principally gossip that Sise had overheard

---

* The State Department was required to pass the information on to the Canadian government. It did so but first warned Mike that St. Laurent was being informed. St. Laurent dismissed the information as nonsense.

and that she could not state definitely whether Pearson was conscious that he was supplying information to Sise." The FBI agent handling "the case" recommended that "in view of the above facts and since it appears no further investigation is to be conducted ... it is recommended that this case be closed." J. Edgar Hoover initialled "OK" beside that recommendation but then added "but also send memo to A.G. briefing him on Pearson's background in case matter comes up at cabinet". The FBI, the memorandum concluded, had no "derogatory information" regarding Mike in its files.

But Mike later annoyed the FBI, Hoover, and the congressional committees by hesitating to grant Igor Gouzenko permission to testify before a congressional committee and by denying that Canada had given information to the United States about the alleged Soviet ties of the American public servant Harry Dexter White. Word of Bentley's original testimony "leaked out" in 1953, and press stories appeared suggesting Mike was one of three Canadians in Washington in wartime who supplied "information to a Communist spy ring". Robert Morris, the subcommittee counsel who had questioned Bentley, refused to comment. Mike denounced the rumours as "false to the point of absurdity". But he had annoyed Hoover and his congressional allies such as senators Joseph McCarthy and Pat McCarran who had elicited Bentley's testimony. ("Pearson had better stop mouthing his half truths as pertain to the FBI," an angry Hoover scrawled on a memorandum in November 1953.) Mike thus joined many other scoundrels in Hoover's bulging files. Other rumours surfaced about "violently uncomplimentary remarks" Mike allegedly made in the NBC studios. If there were tapes, a senior FBI officer wrote in 1957, they should be obtained from NBC "to put Pearson in his proper light". When Mike became prime minister in 1963, Hoover warned Attorney General Bobby Kennedy of "important security evidence" regarding Canada's new leader.[13]

Put in its proper light the evidence is flimsy, the allegations wishful thinking. Bentley could not spell Sise's name; the FBI thought "Michael" to be Mike's given name for the first two years of its file. Mike did speak with Sise. Why should he not? Sise was an officer of the Canadian government working in an area of government-information policy where Mike had official responsibility. Secondly, Sise probably did have many lunches at L'Escargot with Elizabeth Bentley, and in 1942-3 his sympathies for the Soviet Union, at that time *the* major force against the Fascism he detested, were undoubtedly strong. He would not hesitate to lunch with a woman with pro-Soviet sympathies and discuss what both would regard as the common front against Fascism. Moreover, Bentley herself said that she never told Sise she was passing on information to the Soviets. She was also incorrect in her allegation that Sise and Mike were "close friends", and they certainly did not travel in the same "social circles". Even more tellingly, she brought up Pearson's name only in 1951 when Mike was being criticized for comments he had made about American policy in the Korea War and when he was prominent and she was seeking publicity. He had offended the anti-communist right and the timing is surely not coincidental on the part of the Senate subcommittee. Finally, even though Sise was *not* privy to information being passed to the Soviets and Mike had *no* knowledge that Sise was even talking to Bentley, would it have mattered? In 1943 an astonishing amount of intelligence material was being passed officially to the Soviets by the British, the Americans, and the Canadians. After all, they were allies, and the Soviet Union's "friends" in 1943 included not only Bentley and Sise but even Henry Luce and Mackenzie King. Even advanced military technology was shared by Canadians with the Soviets after 1942. Soldiers from both countries, one must recall, had the same targets for a time.[14]

The controversy over Mike's attitude towards the Soviet Union does raise a fundamental question about his personality and character. For those who seek to categorize, Mike Pearson is remarkably elusive, even to those who knew him well. The prominent civil servant Arnold Heeney, who correctly believed that Mike admired him, wrote in his diary in 1955 a comment that has often been used to illustrate the problem: "LBP in fine form.... He continues to be consistently vigorous and interested and stimulating and cheerful – but over the years, although consistently friendly and satisfactory with me, he is increasingly impersonal – a deep one whose secret self very few if any can know." Bruce Hutchison spoke, accurately, of the close relationship among himself, fellow journalist Grant Dexter, and Mike but, like Heeney, noted how Mike was "candid in fact [and] in appearance" but that a "compartment of his mind was hermetically sealed. His personal credo, his view of life and death, his ultimate conception of the universe, the choice between belief and disbelief that every man must make – this region, the only one that matters finally, was never shared with us, if it was shared with anybody, even by a passing hint." Others who worked closely with Mike are more critical; Tom Kent and Walter Gordon, for example, have expressed frustration with Mike's reticence and equivocation. One former colleague put it bluntly: "nailing Pearson down was like stabbing a sponge".[15]

In the case of his attitude towards the Soviet Union and communism, a topic on which even the most rigorous intellectuals, such as the historian-diplomat George Kennan, could appear contradictory or even confused, it is not so surprising that Mike's attitudes could be subject to the wildly different interpretations described above. We have seen earlier how private he was, refusing to talk about his religious beliefs, taking refuge in anonymity when he wrote articles for publication long before his official position required him to do so, and employing witty or clever escapes when confronted with theological or ideological controversy. He was, in more ways than he ever realized, the son of the genial parson with a first-rate academic record who shunned theological disputes and whose sermons were dedicated to improving his parishioners' everyday life. And, like Ed Pearson, Mike responded to events and persons in a manner normally emotional and intuitive rather than intellectual or theological. In the case of the Soviet Union, this tendency is especially pronounced.

In the 1930s his first memoranda on the Soviet Union were attempts at dispassionate analysis; none the less, they betray a fascination with the Soviet experiment. It is not that he has seen the future and it works, but that, as in the case of his attitude to the United States in the 1940s, he recognizes where the future agenda is being created and he knows he and Canada must address it. He made his frankest comments about the Soviets to Harry Crerar in 1938. He began with a lament about the Munich pact and admitted to being pessimistic about the future. He then continues: "my conviction that there is soon to be another outburst is lightened somewhat by a feeling that it may result in a Slav-Teuton war. If the Latins will only stop snarling at each other, or at least restrict their unfriendly activities to snarls, that wouldn't be too unhappy a development. God knows, I would be delighted to see the sub-human Nazis and the equally sub-human Bolsheviks batter themselves to pieces against each other, while the Anglo Saxons held the ring."[16]

"The sub-human Nazis and *equally* sub-human Bolsheviks" suggests why Mike so quickly transferred his wartime loathing of Hitler to Stalin when it seemed the Russian dictator was smashing the Allied plans for peace. In forming his attitude, which changed most considerably between August 1945 and the fall of 1946, Mike relied upon his intuition and his feelings rather than upon his reason. In his memoirs and elsewhere, he describes the major influences that underlay his increasingly hostile attitude towards Soviet communism. "Stony-faced" Molotov and the infuriating Vyshinsky personified its inscrutability and suspicious character that he came first to distrust and then to loathe. The final meeting of the United Nations Relief and Rehabilitation Administration Council took him to Europe in 1946. Jan Masaryk of Czechoslovakia sat beside him at the meetings and whispered too loudly "about the price which he and other Czech democrats would have to pay for collaborating with Czech communists who had already their own plan for a takeover". In Poland, a Polish communist told him at a bend of the Vistula River that, at that very spot, the Soviets had halted their forces to allow the Nazis to wipe out the Polish resistance in Warsaw. And in the nearby village he saw, as he had in Heidelberg many years before, little children pathetically marching by, dressed in the colours of their parents' political faith. The sight repelled him, for these coloured shirts and blouses "were merely the symbols of that political and ideological division which had had so much to do with the ruin of their own village and all the other thousands of cities and towns and villages that once made up Europe". In 1946 Soviet rhetoric became more ideological, its denials more fantastic, its assertions more outrageous. The West too raised its voice. Churchill's Fulton speech, on which Mike exercised some editorial skills, surprised Mike with its strong language but, fundamentally, he welcomed its message and influence, which he believed would effectively counter the erratic and hesitant foreign policy of Harry Truman. In the first year of the cold war the British took the hard line; the Americans were conciliatory. The Fulton speech marked a turning-point. The speech, its most rigorous analyst claims, accomplished two things: it clarified "the distinction between Soviet totalitarianism and a Western democratic outlook" and it invoked "the geopolitical combination of American power and British connections which alone in this period offered the West the prospect of security and general democratic renewal."[17]

By September 1946 the Americans, whom Mike since his earliest diplomatic days had regarded and feared as "natural isolationists", had become willing, in the words of a memorandum given to the president just before Mike left Washington for Ottawa, "to join with the British and other Western countries to build up a world of our own".[18] For Canadians such as Wrong, Robertson, and Pearson, this American commitment had been long and earnestly sought and was richly treasured. Although there was a price in terms of the unpredictability of American leadership, the unity of the democracies was a precious good that their experience led them to cherish. It was, to be sure, a unity based too much upon fear, but as Denis Smith has suggested, "the generation that had lived through a devastating world war was accustomed to alarm as the basis for policy." It would be unrealistic to expect otherwise. But there was much hope too, a positive sense that derived from the triumph of the democracies over autocracy (few would have bet on the democratic side in 1940) and from the sense that the experience of the 1930s and of the war had illuminated the superiority of democratic values. In toasting Robertson, Wrong, and Mike in the fall of 1946, Escott Reid claimed that the reason they created disciples was that they were liberals. Their liberalism, Reid suggested, was that of Cyril Connolly in *The Unquiet Grave*. "As we relive the horrors of the Dark Ages, of absolute States and ideological wars, the old platitudes of liberalism loom up in all their glory, familiar streets as we reel home furious in the dawn." It was not the liberalism of the nineteenth century with its idea of progress and its faith in human nature but of the mid-twentieth century where hope was tempered by memories of previously unimagined horrors. It was a liberalism after the fall of man.[19]

Mike intuitively recognized the opportunity the post-war mood and structures offered Canada and he fully recalled the 1930s' follies. His responses to the Soviet Union were, characteristically, emotional and not the product of a protracted study or of the Cartesian logic that later prime ministers allegedly employed. He was thoughtful, perceptive, and very intelligent, but he was not an academic in approach: he was rightly amused when he discovered that Mackenzie King had referred to him as a scholar. His intelligence, background, and the company he kept have created misunderstandings. Mike, for example, is so often linked with Hume Wrong and Norman Robertson, a "Trinity in Unity" Escott Reid called them. All three were determined secularists and they shared many opinions. However, Robertson and Wrong constructed their analyses through a reasoned assessment of the information they possessed and the experiences they had had. Their faith derived largely from the workings of their reason; Mike's came from his senses and his heart. In truth, Mackenzie King was closer to Mike in intellectual temperament, and his instinctive judgment that Mike would be "the best of any successor to myself" reflects an awareness of that similarity. The frustrations of friends, colleagues, and historians who try to discover what motivated Mackenzie King have a striking parallel with those who have sought to find, in Heeney's words, Mike's "secret self". Both men scanned the surface with political antennae of exquisite sensitivity, and their feelings largely shaped their deeds.[20]

"As Pearson came into the office," King wrote in his diary on September 4, 1946, the day he resigned as secretary of state for External Affairs, "I was struck by his fine face and appearance." The soon-to-be-appointed under-secretary told King that "he was sorry to begin his work in the Department of External Affairs without [King] at the head" and that he had "learned a great deal" from King. Mike was being polite rather than candid. In fact, as he later admitted, King's departure from External made the return to Ottawa far more palatable.[21] He was aware that one might manipulate King through flattery and fear: his comments on September 4 are an example of the former, and his November memorandum about the Soviet Union an example of the latter. Such activities, though essential, were not to Mike's taste, nor were they always effective. He was therefore delighted when King persuaded Louis St. Laurent to accept the External Affairs portfolio. King, who had served twenty years in the portfolio, had become even more crotchety and opinionated. He did not share his younger diplomats' support for internationalism and remained suspicious of British attempts to centralize the empire and of American efforts to contain Soviet communism. If King's mind was crammed with prejudices, memories and, to be fair, knowledge about Canadian diplomacy, St. Laurent's was a much cleaner slate, although certainly not a *tabula rasa*. A devout Roman Catholic who had had a distinguished career at the Quebec bar, St. Laurent came to Ottawa to serve as King's "Quebec lieutenant" after the death of Ernest Lapointe in 1941. He stayed with the government through the Conscription crisis of 1944, and his political standing was much enhanced with the Liberal victory in the 1945 election. He had wanted to leave politics after the war but King pleaded with him to remain, and the offer of External Affairs, which had become the prized portfolio, was the web to trap him in Ottawa.

St. Laurent's decision was a godsend for Mike. Although St. Laurent was of Irish and French-Catholic extraction and thus disposed by heredity to distrust the British, he was not an isolationist. His wartime experience at international conferences such as Bretton Woods and his exposure to foreign policy issues when he served as acting secretary of state for External Affairs had inspired a strong faith in international solutions. Moreover, like many French Canadians, he lacked the English Canadians' traditional suspicions of the

United States. He did possess the conservative Roman Catholic's distrust of communism, so much so that his lawyer's respect for civil liberties was not reflected in his treatment of Canadian communists. He was, finally, a corporation lawyer, at home in the richest board-rooms, and an impressive advocate of the rights of the corporate sector of Canadian life. He had lost his savings in the Wall Street crash, and wartime prosperity was therefore especially welcomed by him as a lawyer, an investor, and a North American. He was an odd blend, but one to the taste of the times.

Patrician and very much the seigneur of Quebec's Grande Allée, St. Laurent seems to have possessed extraordinary charm and presence. Certainly Mike respected and liked him immediately, and his comments on St. Laurent in his memoirs are unusually affectionate. Mike had reason for bias because St. Laurent certainly favoured him.* Yet even those who often disagreed with St. Laurent, such as Paul Martin, echo Mike's high regard, with Martin describing St. Laurent as the ablest prime minister of the four under whom he served.[22] He was astonishingly quick to understand a memorandum and had the outstanding lawyer's gift for simplicity in explanation. When one contrasts St. Laurent with the unpredictable, often ill-mannered, and complicated King, one can understand the relief of External Affairs officers when their new minister took over in September 1946.

Fortune was Mike's concubine upon his return to Ottawa. King had left External, and Wrong and Robertson, who had so dominated the department during wartime, were departing, respectively, to Washington and London. Both were Mike's friends, but his freedom was greater with both absent from Ottawa. There were subtle differences among them that would have been more starkly exposed had

---

* St. Laurent's francophone origins were a great benefit in Mike's view. In 1945 he had argued that if "Canada is to play its part in international affairs, it must be a united Canada, standing above petty squabbles of its lesser citizens who would degrade it to the level of separate and competing groups and races". St. Laurent made this vision possible. An anglophone leader would have found the task more daunting.

either Robertson or Wrong remained. Wrong, for example, devoted much time to policy planning, but Mike on his return let such activities end. He was much more the pragmatist and, in the flurry of daily tasks in post-war Ottawa, planning the future died as a regular departmental activity.[23] Wrong also had an administrator's mind and had, so far as it was possible in wartime Ottawa, brought order out of departmental chaos. Mike had joined Wrong in lamenting Skelton's failings as an administrator in the 1930s but Mike was not much better. There were too many opportunities in the post-war world, and Mike as under-secretary was all too eager to take advantage of them. One of the best young officers of the time, John Holmes, later recalled that his colleagues in the 1940s were "constructivists by nature. At the drop of a gavel they would conceive a new international organism."[24] Some organisms aborted, others survived and flourished intermittently, but Pearson and his career-diplomat colleagues, free at last of King's penchant for international inactivity (if not celibacy), were determined to be present at the creation of the post-war international system.

Mike's first weeks in Ottawa were frantic. Writing to Robertson on November 5, 1946, a few weeks after his assumption of office, Mike bemoaned the sickness of some officers, the absence of others, and the regular phone calls from Mackenzie King, but he made clear to Robertson he was where he wanted to be: "I have had about the busiest three weeks of my life, but I am enjoying it."[25] Neither the pace nor the enjoyment lessened over the twenty-three months he served as under-secretary. His wartime work habits persisted in peacetime, and his private life became ever more entangled in his public duties. For Mike it was exhilarating; for Maryon, it was often frustrating, for Ottawa remained a man's town.

On their return to Ottawa the Pearsons rented an old farmhouse at 243 Augusta Street in the Sandy Hill district, not far from Laurier House, the Liberal shrine where King dwelt. They liked the Augusta Street home much less than the Rockcliffe home they had foolishly sold when Mike was appointed to Washington. Sandy Hill lacked Rockcliffe's elegant patina but it was comfortably upper middle class with a scattering of small stores. There was little grass to cut, and the East Block, which still housed External Affairs, was a brisk fifteen-minute walk away. Ottawa was becoming ever more a government town and the traces of the old timber town ever more vestigial. Rideau Hall was no longer the "court" for Ottawa's social set and, in proper post-imperial fashion, entertainment had become more democratic. Mike grumbled about the new expenses he would incur for entertainment and even hinted to King that a special fund should be established for him comparable to the one several millionaires had established for King. King was sympathetic, but the idea came to naught. Mike and Maryon, like many other senior Ottawa civil servants, did take advantage of the European disorder to hire a refugee servant, an Estonian named Magda, who stayed with them for a couple of years until whispers began about so-called liberal people taking advantage of European refugees.[26]

Mike and Maryon entertained foreign dignitaries at home, but not often. The house was mostly quiet, with the children away at school and Mike frequently at conferences or the United Nations. Maryon's appointment books for the period recall an age of many cocktail parties and bridge games, and diplomatic comings-and-goings. The Pearsons did renew old friendships with Graham and Molly Towers, Bill and Ethel Harris, and David and Mary McKeen, but increasingly Mike, who rose before Maryon to make breakfast, went to bed early to leave the others to their frolics. Maryon, who loved dancing and who lamented the lack of social occasions in Ottawa compared to London or Washington, organized a dance club for junior foreign-service officers. In a democratic flourish, Maryon through Mike deliberately excluded the heads of missions. The club was a great success in a capital that lacked good theatre, restaurants, and movies but whose winter made indoor activities all the more treasured.

Mike's work came first, but he did find relaxation with Patsy and Geoff when they came home and at baseball games. In those days of the great Yankee and Brooklyn Dodgers teams, the U.N. General Assembly happily coincided with the World Series, and Molotov in the U.N. was never a match for DiMaggio in Yankee Stadium. Mike also played tennis, and had an unusual capacity to simply relax and forget while on his brief holidays at Murray Bay with the Towers or at a cottage in the Gatineau Hills, north of Ottawa. The photographs of the period, especially those of the family together, evoke a sense of gaiety and playfulness. Mike seems more assured and content than ever before. Those who dealt with him then or even in his office were struck by his ease, affability, and informality.*

A British diplomat recalled that "most people after a discussion with him, left his room with a lighter heart and a brighter outlook than when they had entered". Certainly the British diplomat was correct in his suggestion that there was "nothing phoney" about the manner. Yet, as Arnold Heeney noted, the public face increasingly concealed the private self. It also concealed the intensity that his constantly jiggling foot beneath the table betrayed. After 1946 Mike had very little private life as most Canadians would have defined it. As he became a public person, Maryon became more private and increasingly resentful of the costs of public life. She remained fiercely supportive of Mike's causes but, in fact, she shared them less than she had before.[27]

Of his causes, none mattered more to Mike than the strengthening of the bonds among the North Atlantic democracies. His senior departmental colleagues shared his goals. It is worth noting that the External Affairs "trinity" of Robertson, Wrong, and Pearson had had diplomatic postings only to London and Washington (Wrong endured a brief and largely unwanted stay in Geneva in the 1930s). Since their school days (all were Oxford men) they had lived within the North Atlantic triangle. For them theatre meant London's West End or New York's Broadway, and foreign offices meant London's

---

* Mike and Maryon were often described in the Ottawa press. Maryon quickly adopted Dior's "New Look" and was invariably described as "slim and elegant". Mike's long hours took their toll and by the end of 1948 he was deemed "chunky" by a social columnist. His reaction, noted on the scrap-book clipping Maryon kept, was two large exclamation points and a question mark.

Whitehall and Washington's Foggy Bottom. Their experience reflected Canada's major interests, and it gave them the personal contacts and diplomatic skills to advance those interests expertly. Nevertheless, Eastern Europe where the cold war germinated was *terra incognita* for them, and Dana Wilgress, Canada's first minister to Moscow, who did know Eastern Europe well, worried, with some justification, about how the United States and, by implication, his colleagues seemed "bent on humiliating" the Soviet Union.[28] It would have been helpful to have known more about Eastern Europe. Similarly, East Asia, where the cold war's greatest casualties were to occur, was not directly known, and its future violence and power were quite unimagined. Although Mike and his colleagues had a North American attitude towards the end of European colonialism, probably the most important development of international history since 1945, their understanding of the forces that were shaking the foundations of European rule was weak. Their liberalism in international politics, as Escott Reid later said, emphasized political freedom, the most cherished ideal of the West, but tended to overlook the tensions between political democracy and economic inequities.[29]

These were limitations that hindsight illuminates, but they were not the ones that troubled most Canadians in the post-war years. In his hardening attitude to the Soviet Union and his desire to form a "common front" with Western Europe against Soviet communism, Mike and his colleagues in External Affairs were not in advance of public opinion. Indeed, if popular opinion had an influence on Canada's diplomats in their response to Soviet communism, "it was as a spur, rather than as a brake". Conversely, public-opinion polls suggest that Canadians' trust and confidence in the United States, as expressed in responses on such questions as free trade, were also in advance of the politicians'.[30] The divisions of the 1930s about Canada's foreign policy had largely dissolved. Fascist sympathizers had disappeared; communists were shunted to the side by the post-Gouzenko security measures and by the force of the new consensus. As under-secretary Mike realized the consensus produced a rare opportunity to strengthen the position of External within Ottawa's bureaucracy and of Canada in the multitude of international organizations the war had spawned. By December 1948 the department had 1,213 employees, including 216 foreign-service officers. The number contrasts sharply with the 474 employees and 72 officers the department had had in 1944.[31] At a time when most government departments were reducing the bloated wartime bureaucracies, External Affairs continued to swell. In the glow of wartime triumph, foreign policy mattered more than ever to Canadians. Mike and his colleagues were determined to make Canada, which they believed was as instinctively isolationist as the United States, thoroughly and lastingly ensnared in the web of international organizations. They did not trust Canadians to continue to look outwards; their work would make them do so.

With such protean tasks, Mike never had the amount of assistance he thought he needed. Escott Reid gave exceptional assistance in Ottawa but the range of tasks had exhausted him by late 1947. Gerry Riddell, like Mike a former history professor at Toronto, was an exceptional speechwriter and gave a philosophical coherence to Canadian foreign policy in a period when the department was actively seeking to shape public opinion. But the many new posts and the extraordinary (some would say ridiculous) number of conferences (97 in 1946 and 86 in 1947 as compared to only 25 in 1945) used up the best people.[32] Nevertheless, the Canadians made their contribution, even if some conferences, such as the Paris Peace Conference of 1946, reminded one Canadian delegate, Charles Ritchie, of Sartre's play *Huis-clos* where the situation was frozen and the delegates could "only repeat endlessly the same arguments and the same gestures". The Russians, with their "nerves, stomachs, and constitutions of iron", sat stoically through the debates but the Westerners had not sufficiently "streamlined their lives" to avoid distractions. In Ritchie's view, it was hardest on the young diplomats who "must have time to sleep with their wives or someone else will do it for them".[33] Mike could do little about conjugal relations, but he did try to streamline the department by reorganizing it into more divisions with more precise authority. However, it proved almost impossible to fit the department into regular patterns and "streamlining" remained a vision not a reality.

If the department remained ill-formed, Mike himself was now "streamlined": 1947 was a year of continuous meetings, conferences, and fateful decisions with crisis a constant companion. The winter of 1946-7 was dreadful, as German children begged American soldiers for food; as Great Britain, the supposed victor, struggled to warm its people in the coldest winter in memory; as refugees huddling together in vast camps desperately craved new homes in North America; and as angry diplomats failed to agree how to make peace with Germany and Japan. The story of the Marshall Plan and European reconstruction is both complicated and well known and cannot be retold here. That there was "fire in the ashes" – Theodore White's memorable image of European reconstruction – did not seem at all obvious in that terrible winter. Hindsight may suggest that there was more strength in the Western European economies than anyone realized or, as some American historians have recently suggested, that the Marshall Plan of 1947 and American policy represented mainly an effort to create in Europe a capitalist economy that served American economic corporatist interests.[34] However, both views seem reductionist. Reading Canadian newspapers, private journals, and diplomatic despatches, one is struck not by such longer-term aims but by a sense that Europe was in terminal throes, that its precious civilization was doomed, and that North America had to respond.

Our knowledge of what Mike thought is not precise. He no longer kept a journal, and his despatches are both rarer and less reflective. We do know what Mackenzie King thought: he believed St. Laurent and Pearson were throwing caution to the wind and abandoning the precepts that he believed had served Canada, himself, and the Liberal party so well. If Mike was wary about the depth of Canada's commitment to internationalism, he knew all too well how shallow the prime minister's commitment was. Mike's "gingering" of Mackenzie King's fears about the cold war is best understood in this light: it was necessary to assure King's support for External Affairs' policies of active participation in international affairs. Mike recalled Hume Wrong's mocking 1930s portrait of the ideal Canadian diplomat *sans* face, *sans* voice, and *sans* thought, and was determined that in the post-war world they would speak often, thoughtfully, and with a sense of a prosperous and responsible nation that they represented. Commitments, of course, brought danger, but Mike and St. Laurent had no hesitation in running the risk. Their ambitions terrified Mackenzie King.

King, not surprisingly, found it difficult to remove his hand from the External Affairs department that he had manipulated so long. Mike, as under-secretary, wriggled to avoid his grasp and, during most of 1947, he managed to do so – partly because King was often absent and preoccupied with the Liberal succession and partly because St. Laurent's eminence sheltered him. St. Laurent, with the assistance of the talented Gerry Riddell, had set out his view of what the principles of Canadian foreign policy should be in January 1947, and the statement, the so-called Gray Lecture, was generally well received. St. Laurent did follow the King tradition in asserting that "national unity" was the pre-eminent concern for Canadian foreign policy-makers, but the remainder of the lecture expressed a far more activist stance for Canada.[35]

The first problems with King came when Mike, recalling the shabby living conditions of many Canadian diplomats, set out to build new residences for them in the many capitals they now served. King, whose miserliness was legendary and whose fear of public criticism of his expenditures made him force his poor chauffeur to list some of King's personal expenses as his own, grumbled bitterly about the ostentation but eventually allowed purchase of properties where Canada had excessive credits, as in the sterling bloc. The resulting purchases were probably the best investment the Canadian government ever made, as international property values soared in following decades.[36]

The differences over buildings were a minor skirmish; the major battles came as Mike in 1947 moved to extend Canada's range of international interests. King did not quarrel with the notion of greater North Atlantic unity, which he regarded as within the historic tradition of Canada's international interests and as a useful method of counterbalancing the predominance of the United States, whose designs for Canada's future he increasingly distrusted. The conflicts developed over the United Nations, which King, after a brief and modest embrace, began to regard as as "great a menace as the League of Nations".[37] He specifically objected to Canada's involvement through the U.N. systems in distant countries and in conflicts over which King believed Canada had no reason for concern. Mike, who had once said that a bomb dropped in wartime in China could be heard on the St. Lawrence, obviously disagreed and in 1947 he aggressively promoted his viewpoint by seeking a seat for Canada on the Security Council of the U.N. and by participating actively in U.N. attempts to settle dangerous problems in the Middle and Far East, areas that Canada traditionally had shunned.

Palestine was, in King's eyes, a British problem. The Holocaust, the stream of Jewish refugees, and the interest of the U.N. in the bitter antagonism between Arab and Jew made Mike regard Palestine as a Canadian concern. Emotions played a part too: he wrote in his memoirs, Palestine was "the Holy Land – the land of my Sunday School lessons". Moreover, he saw the developing differences on the issue between the United States and the United Kingdom as potentially dangerous for Canada; nevertheless, it also offered a diplomatic opportunity that he quickly grasped. Mike became directly involved when the U.N.'s First (Political) Committee set up the U.N. Special Committee on Palestine (UNSCOP). Mike and St. Laurent were hesitant to accept when the Americans tried to nominate Canada as one of the seven members of UNSCOP, but their resistance was weak. Mike had placed Canada in the forefront of the issue by expertly chairing the First (Political) Committee, and, although King would certainly have refused UNSCOP membership and would not have been embarrassed to do so, Mike and St. Laurent saw an opportunity for Canada to assert its mediatory role. Indeed, Mike was even willing to let his name stand as a possible chair for a special committee on Palestine. Mackenzie King quickly vetoed that.[38]

Mike believed in partition of Palestine to create an Arab and Israeli state, and he held this view so tenaciously that he even fought J.L. Ilsley, the respected official head of the Canadian delegation to the U.N., who opposed it, and the Americans who were reluctant to consider the question of administrative responsibility during the partition period. The British mandate over Palestine was quickly expiring, and chaos loomed. The Canadian delegation was divided, but by November 1947 Mike had asserted full control of Canadian policy. *The New York Times* lauded his efforts as "tireless" on the Palestine issue. His dedication to the internationalization of issues was obvious, as was his fear of the growing chasm between American and British views on the subject. He complained to Massey about his work: "Here I am in the middle between an obstinate Russian and a not too skilful American, and it has been about the most exhausting experience of my life". Massey knew Mike well enough to know that such exhaustion was exhilarating. Mike finally got approval from the working group on Palestine on November 18, 1947 for a plan that called for mandate termination by August 1, 1948, with partition to follow. A U.N. commission would supervise the partition. For Mike, such a commission would be a precedent for international policing, one he desperately wanted to establish. The U.N. General Assembly supported the plan, but events did not, and peace did not follow in the benighted Holy Land.[39]

Mike's activities nevertheless attracted attention and praise, not because his plan succeeded but because he showed through his "tireless efforts" how the U.N. could be at the centre of an international issue despite the superpower impasse. John Holmes later wrote that it was "the Canadian performance, or more particularly Lester Pearson's performance, over Palestine in 1947 that might be regarded as the beginning of Canada's role [and] reputation as a moderate mediatory middle power." Mackenzie King, however, watched the performance with increasing discomfort although other issues managed to distract him, and External Affairs deliberately kept him uninformed. King was not the only one troubled by the performance.

Bruce Hutchison, who was at the U.N. that fall, and who was in awe of Mike's deft manipulation of issues and personalities at Lake Success, where the U.N. General Assembly was held that year, saw that Mike – the "hockey player", he appropriately named him in his private letters – was "running everything on his own". He reported the comments of Senator Norman Lambert, who said that Mike "might clear with St. Laurent. No one knows. But in any case he goes out and lays down policy and commits Canada to anything he pleases without telling Ilsley or [Lambert]. They never heard of the Canadian plan for Palestine till they read it in the papers. The hockey player is so very able and so nice that no one would think of checking up on him or asking him anything. If he succeeds in such gambits as Palestine, fine. He and Canada will get full credit. If he fails on somewhere else he and Canada may get into trouble."[40]

Troubles soon came when King returned to Ottawa on December 4, 1947, and discovered that Dr. G.S. Patterson had been named a member of the U.N. Temporary Commission on Korea (UNTCOK). In Britain, Ernest Bevin, the Labour foreign secretary, and Winston Churchill had terrified him with their talk of an imminent war. It did not help when, in an "automatic writing" session with his favourite spiritualist, Geraldine Cummins, Franklin Roosevelt warned him to pay attention to the "Far East" where war was likely in a year".* The debate about the influence of the spirits on King does not belong here, but his reaction could have been predicted in the absence of divine intervention.[41]

King's explosion was memorable, the greatest Mike had ever seen, and he felt the heat of the blast. When, on December 18, St. Laurent asked cabinet permission for the appointment of Dr. Patterson, King refused to agree and clearly expressed his grounds for opposition which applied not merely to the Korean case but to Pearson and St. Laurent's general approach.

---

* Mike later claimed that Cummins's advice (or Roosevelt's, some might say) was a major influence on King. Others, however, disagree. King, after all, had already expressed many doubts about Mike's activism at the U.N.

> I felt [King wrote] a great mistake was being made by Canada being brought into situations in Asia and Europe of which she knew nothing whatever, of interfering with Great Powers without realizing what consequences might be.
>
> ... I asked why should we attempt to go in and settle a situation as had arisen in Korea. Have our country drawn into or possible consequences that would come from war.... We knew nothing about the situation and should keep out.

When St. Laurent objected that Canadian membership in the U.N. and its Security Council brought obligations, King replied that the U.N. "counted for nothing so far as any help in the world was concerned". It had been at best impotent and at worst a Soviet propaganda tool. King tried to find the villain and he fastened quickly on "Pearson, [who] with his youth and inexperience and influenced by the persuasion of others around him, had been anxious to have Canada's External Affairs figure prominently in world affairs and has really directed affairs in New York when he should have been in Ottawa, and without any real control by Ministers of the Crown."[42]

External Affairs tried to answer King's complaints with a memorandum that illustrated only how little the departments understood the mentality of the prime minister. The memorandum argued that Canadian membership was necessary to maintain Canada's position at the U.N. and to satisfy an American request that Canada accept lest the Soviet Union be given "an opportunity to exploit the situation". These comments, not surprisingly, made King feel "more strongly than ever that we should not proceed with that appointment". Neither St. Laurent nor Pearson would back down, even when King threatened "to go out on a crusade [himself] against the United Nations and let the people see the mistake that was being made".[43] To avert this action, St. Laurent suggested to King that Mike go to Washington to tell the president about the prime minister's views. On New Year's Day 1948 Mike left for Washington on "one of the most difficult assignments" he had ever been given.

He met President Truman and expressed Canada's uneasiness

about membership on UNTCOK when neither the Soviet Union nor the United States was a member, and Canada was the most prominent or, as Truman said, "the most respectable" member. Truman's response would have chilled King: "Don't worry, you won't get into any trouble over there, and if you do we are behind you." Otherwise, Truman was "aimless and amiable" and thoroughly uninformed on Korea. (Mike, it should be said, was never the admirer that so many American historians have become of the man from Missouri.) Truman did write a letter to King, but it did not change his mind. Mike speculated about King's motives. Could it be that he was trying to force out St. Laurent and Ilsley who backed St. Laurent in order to put in place another successor, or was it simply that King's mind had "fallen back into its accustomed pre-1939 pattern of isolation and suspicion of commitments". On his side King confessed that "this whole business has shaken my faith in Pearson's judgment."[44]

When Mike saw King's strongly worded reply to Truman's letter on January 7, he himself was shaken. He realized that if it were sent either King or St. Laurent and Ilsley would resign. Mike moved deftly and, it would seem, not too candidly in that he told King, according to King's account, that "he would take no exception to the wording of the letter or to the statements that were in it". He wondered, however, if the cabinet should not see it before it was sent. King disagreed but agreed to let St. Laurent see it. That night, after a dinner at Laurier House in the darkened second-floor library, St. Laurent threatened to resign. King, who had himself used that threat expertly, refused to budge and said that he would regret St. Laurent's resignation but did not care if Ilsley left. In the end, King agreed to Canada serving if St. Laurent and the U.N. accepted that the commission would "only act where it could act over the whole of Korea, which would mean that it would be acting with the consent of the Russians as well as the consent of the Americans".[45] This meant, of course, that it would not act at all, and it did not.

Neither side won, but King was old and leaving soon. St. Laurent's succession was assured. A little more than two years later

King died, and St. Laurent as prime minister and Mike as secretary of state for External Affairs planned Canada's entry into the Korean War on King's funeral train. In a sense, perhaps, the old lion's last roar had an echo and some vindication.[46]

During the Korean dispute, King and Mike argued about their positions vehemently. While King harked back to the 1930s (in his diary he frequently slips and calls the U.N. the "League") to justify his caution, Mike argued that the situation was different from that of 1938-9. "At that time, many people in Canada thought that we could remain aloof from the approaching struggle, and that our participation arose in part, through our membership in the Commonwealth. Now the pressures were all from Washington, not London, and it would be extremely difficult for us to isolate ourselves from United States policies because of continental considerations. On the other hand, as the enemy this time would be Russian Communism, feeling in Canada would be united in opposition to that enemy." King, however, saw the Americans, like the British before them, dragging Canada into commitments that were not in its interests and regarded Mike as "much too ready to be influenced by American opinion".[47]

These differences were starkly illuminated in 1948 when Canadian and American negotiators were negotiating a free-trade arrangement between the two countries. Attempts to restore British trade had collapsed, Europe's prosperity seemed a forlorn hope, and in a world awash with inconvertible currencies, a free-trade agreement seemed the best solution for Canada, which had major problems acquiring sufficient American dollars to satisfy Canadian consumers' pent-up desires for houses, cars, and appliances. By March 1948, Canadian and American trade officials had developed a free-trade plan and had informed King who, according to Canadian negotiator John Deutsch, initially reacted favourably. Mike was an immediate supporter, especially when free trade was linked with the notion of an Atlantic security pact. Free trade, of course, was a Liberal ideal; King had gone down to defeat fighting for Reciprocity in the 1911 election. But King had become increasingly wary of the Americans and their diplomacy. Moreover, he had "a quite extraordinary experience which [he] took to be perfect evidence of guidance from Beyond". An old study of colonial nationalism by British statesman Sir Richard Jebb, which he fortuitously spotted on his library's shelves, rekindled his British soul, and he became suddenly aware that supporting free trade "as the last act of [his] career would be to absolutely destroy the significance of the whole of it", a significance that he found in the balance he had maintained between continental and imperial pressures. Immediately he decided that he would no more countenance fighting for free trade than he "would of flying to the South Pole".[48]

The day after the decision, March 28, 1948, he lunched with Mike, who had come to argue that Canada should press forward with the negotiations (about which he had only recently learned). King told him his decision, which evidently disappointed Mike. He did not give up: at a meeting on April 21, he said he thought it would be "unfortunate if the Americans got the impression that they had made an offer and were turned down". King, correctly, pointed out no offer had been received. Mike sent yet another memorandum to King on May 5, 1948, suggesting the matter was still open. King called in Mike and hammered the final nails in free trade's coffin (until a Conservative government exhumed it in the 1980s). He warned Mike that "he would never cease to be a Liberal or a British citizen and if I thought there was a danger of Canada being placed at the mercy of powerful financial interests in the United States, and if that was being done by my own party, I would get out and oppose them openly."[49] The matter was closed.

Those who seek the elusive skills that made Mackenzie King the greatest Canadian political leader of this century should consider that, in August 1948, a few months after these stormy disagreements with Mike, he urged his successor, St. Laurent, to bring Mike into the cabinet as secretary of state for External Affairs. He held few grudges. In one of the few letters Maryon kept, King wrote graciously on August 28, 1948: "It was such a pleasure ... to have the privilege ... to be seated at your side at dinner, and seeing our distinguished Undersecretary of State". Indeed, King "favoured"

Pearson's entry very strongly. When St. Laurent hesitated, claiming it "would be a big responsibility as Pearson had no guarantee for the future", King replied: "That was the real test of the man." He had no doubt Mike would meet the test and wrote in his diary that evening: "My own view, though I did not express it, is if Pearson does come in, he will succeed St. Laurent when he gives up the leadership whether in office or in opposition. I would like Pearson to come in, and think him quite the ablest man for that post. Indeed if he could have been induced to come in at the present time, that would have been all to the good in many ways but I am glad to have St. Laurent, above all others succeed me."[50] The press, and Mike, talked, then and later, about how he was conscripted for politics. King must have chuckled for he knew better than anyone else that the wooing of Mike was not necessarily conscription.*

Mike, as King predicted, moved quickly to guarantee his future. At a dinner party with his wealthy friends Walter and Liz Gordon, he raised the problem of his last civil-service pension and the risks of politics. Gordon and Wynne and Beryl Plumptre, who were also guests, told him that the situation demanded his entry into politics. Gordon promised him that he would assure that there would be no financial problems, and he held to it. Mike owed a lasting debt to Gordon, one that troubled him later.[51]

A seat was found in Algoma East as Tom Farquhar, in time-honoured fashion, was appointed to the Senate. This vast Northern Ontario constituency of about 20,000 square miles abounded with what Mike called "Liberal worthies". Everyone knew Tom Farquhar, and as Mike and he went along Highway 17 Mike followed Farquhar's advice to "wave to everybody". At the end of the first day of campaigning, Mike saw a farmer walking home across a field and waved. Farquhar's arm remained limp as he wryly said: "You can stop

---

* The notion of the necessity of French-English alternation in Liberal leaders was obviously not King's. It is, in fact, an accident of history and a recently invented tradition.

waving now, we're out of the constituency." In any event, Mike had few worries then or later.* The by-election, on October 25, which the Conservatives did not contest, was not an overwhelming victory over the CCF and the Social Credit candidates, but 1,236 votes was a satisfactory margin. Mike had waved often and well.[52]

Mike, the Conservative *Ottawa Journal* declared, was the Liberals' "golden boy", surely an appropriate description for an MP from northern Ontario. The glitter, however, derived not from any spadework in Algoma East but from his "performances" in London, Washington, and New York, and Canadians saw only the surface of the ore, not its core. Time has exposed what lay beneath and many have found inconsistencies and impurities in Mike Pearson's diplomacy of the 1940s. No doubt he failed to recognize the linkages between economics and politics, and like liberals from Adam Smith and Richard Cobden to Cordell Hull, he accepted too easily that closer economic and personal contacts make war less likely. His support for free trade and his lack of concern for closer economic ties with the United States derived from his belief that such an increase in personal and business contacts, especially when extended to Western Europe through the Marshall Plan, would quell the darker spirits of the world. These are, John Gaddis has written, "pleasant things to believe, but there is remarkably little historical evidence to validate them."[53] Most wars, unfortunately, are fought between people who know each other well, and interdependence does not lead inevitably to concord.

Similarly, while Mike brilliantly represented the cause of political freedom in the 1940s and illuminated as well as any political leader how intolerable the repression of individual rights became as Stalin spread his web from his own tragic land over Eastern Europe, he did not grasp how passionately much of the world desired economic as well as political equality. While he favoured the end of colonialism,

---

* The constituency has been Liberal since 1935 and has been represented by only three members: Farquhar, Pearson, and Maurice Foster. Its Liberal record is unique.

he could not foresee in the 1940s that economic justice, as much as political liberty, fired anti-colonialism. The Third World's "tilt" against the West he therefore could not have anticipated. On the Macedonian plains, he had looked with despair upon the "wretched" souls without education and without hopes, but apart from the granting of political rights, neither then nor in the 1940s could his imagination comprehend how their lives might be made longer and materially richer. In 1940 George Grant, then more Red than Tory, told his mother that he did not share her high regard for Mike Pearson because Mike could not understand why the New Deal was important and why Roosevelt must defeat Willkie. Mike's liberalism, which was real, was fundamentally political and that passion for equality or redistribution that animated such Canadians as Frank Scott and J.S. Woodsworth he neither shared emotionally nor comprehended intellectually. He instinctively favoured the welfare state whose building-blocks fell into place during the 1940s in Canada, but he showed surprisingly little interest in its construction or in the manner in which the resulting structure would alter the social contract. His liberalism maintained the flavour of the small-town manse and was relatively untouched by the potent spices added by T.H. Green, John Maynard Keynes, and even his friend Frank Underhill that so altered its taste in the twentieth century.

These faults, however, were, in so many ways, his nation's, and by looking only through their perspective one reduces a complex man and his times. Mike Pearson was born into an Anglo-Canadian society that hoped to build its future upon the pillars of imperialism and Christianity, which, in the mind of believers such as Ed Pearson, his young sons, and his large and prosperous congregations, balanced exquisitely the claims of power and prosperity against those of conscience and service. By the time Mike reached his majority, both pillars had decayed irreparably, and their fragments lay scattered about him. When he lay in the hospital ward with Clifford Hames, who would die in the war's last months, he realized how the world he expected to live in had been made still-born by the events of 1914-18. He stumbled for a while in the new terrain, and his breakdown of

1918-19 deeply affected him, forcing him to limit his range and to resist close emotional ties with others and with faiths or ideologies that demanded intense commitments. It is absurd to imagine Mike becoming a strident atheist or embracing the tenets of Marxism. Both stances demanded too much; hence he simply turned away.

What he lacked in the range of experience, he made up for in the intensity with which he began to search for the fragments of the past that would be most valuable in modern times. He was a prospector of extraordinary skill and intuition. Tolerance, universalism, and responsibility were, for him, the richest legacy of his tradition, and they were values that he found too rarely in Canada in the 1930s and 1940s with its Padlock Law, its anti-Semitic school texts, its puritanical tastes, its suspicion of the foreign, and its small-town ways. These were the fragments of Western imperialism and religion that he thought should remain in the rubble. By 1948 he had extracted from that rubble some of the finest specimens and had shaped them together into a political form that Canadians could recognize as their own. This very private man, whose adult years were mostly spent outside of Canada, who often found its atmosphere stifling, who distrusted emotionality yet depended upon his intuition in reaching judgments, had through intense effort and an act of will cast an increasingly brilliant image of what Canada could become. His personality and his deeds thus were transformed into something larger than himself and became emblematic for his nation, an expression not of what it was but what it might yet be. Pearsonian diplomacy, as it came to be called, was not merely a product of foreign offices and conferences. It was, at its core, a political metal of the highest value, and the open, vital, and self-confident human face imprinted upon it represented a generation in the life of Canada.

NOTES

CHAPTER 1: BEGINNINGS

1 L.B. Pearson, *Mike: The Memoirs of the Right Honourable Lester B. Pearson. Volume 1: 1897-1948* (Toronto: University of Toronto Press, 1972), 1.

2 *Mike, I:* 3, and E.A. Pearson Scrapbook, MG 26 N12 (NAC).

3 Flavelle quoted in Michael Bliss, *A Canadian Millionaire: The Life and Business Times of Sir Joseph Flavelle, Bart. 1858-1939* (Toronto: Macmillan of Canada, 1978), 88. Bliss's biography is the finest evocation of Methodist Toronto in the 1890s and early 1900s. On Canada's "transformation" the finest study remains R.C. Brown and Ramsay Cook, *Canada 1896-1921: A Nation Transformed* (Toronto: McClelland and Stewart, 1974).

4 E.A. Pearson to Annie Pearson, Nov. 17, 1890; Annie Pearson to E.A. Pearson, Nov. 21, 1890; E.A. Pearson, "A Family Record," n.d. [1890s], Pearson Papers Private (PPP). Also, on Thomas Bowles, *Orangeville Banner*, Mar. 2, 1977; E.A. Pearson Scrapbook; and Pearson, *Mike, I:* 4. On his family record Ed wrote "My Precious Wife, Annie Sarah Bowles, and myself first met one another at about 4 p.m. on the 8th day of November 1890." November 8, 1890, was a Saturday, but Ed says the meeting took place on a Sunday, and it likely did.

5 Ken Reid, "Lester Pearson", unpublished family history, courtesy of the author.

6 Reid, "Lester Pearson"; and Joseph V. O'Brien, *"Dear, Dirty Dublin": A City in Distress* (Berkeley: University of California Press, 1982), 6-11; and D.P. Chart, *The Story of Dublin* (Nendel, Liechtenstein: Kraus, 1971; orig. ed. 1907), 116-18. The Pearson home at 6 Wesley Terrace was valued at 100

pounds sterling in 1842. An 1828 survey indicated that only 1,034 of 17,314 residences had a value exceeding 100 pounds sterling. The Pearsons obviously retained some measure of prosperity among the staggering poverty of Dublin's southwest. U.K. *Parliamentary Papers,* 1833 (XXXV), no. 5. The major study of Ontario's Irish is Donald Akenson, *The Irish in Ontario: A Study in Rural History* (Kingston: McGill-Queen's University Press, 1984).

7 R.P. Bowles, "The Tipperary Bowles", PPP; and James O'Shea, *Priest, Politics and Society in Post-famine Ireland: A Study of County Tipperary 1850-1891* (Dublin: Wolfhound, 1983), 9-43. Tipperary emigration is studied in Bruce S. Elliott, *Irish Migrants in the Canadas* (Kingston: McGill-Queen's University Press, 1988).

8 Bowles, ibid.; and Michael Gauvreau, "History and Faith: A Study of Methodist and Presbyterian Thought in Canada, 1820-1940" (unpublished Ph.D. thesis, University of Toronto, 1985), 45-50. On the Canadian Methodist background, see Goldwin French, *Parsons and Politics* (Toronto: University of Toronto Press, 1961).

9 Bowles, ibid.; *Orangeville Banner,* Mar. 7, 1977; and *Canadian Pictorial News Magazine,* v. 1, no. 26 (Dec. 15, 1960), 2.

10 *Toronto Globe,* Dec. 22, 1897; Ronald Haycock, *Sam Hughes: The Public Career of a Controversial Canadian 1885-1916* (Waterloo: Wilfrid Laurier Press, 1986), 31; and E.A. Pearson Scrapbook.

11 E.A. Pearson Scrapbook and press clippings (PPP).

12 E.A. Pearson Scrapbook.

13 *Mike, I:* 6-7.

14 Ramsay Cook, *The Regenerators: Social Criticism in Late Victorian English Canada* (Toronto: University of Toronto Press, 1986), 20; and Gauvreau, "History and Faith", 337. Gauvreau argues that Victoria College managed to deal with the "threat" of scientific history through the adoption of a "progressive orthodoxy" that maintained an optimistic and millennialist thrust for Methodist theology.

15 "Gleanings from Our Pulpits", E.A. Pearson Scrapbook.

16 Quoted in Ann Douglas, *The Feminization of American Culture* (New York: Knopf, 1977), 327. Billy Sunday, like Ed Pearson, first gained renown as a

sportsman. He dubbed a sprained calf a "Charley horse", a term that persists in baseball circles.

17 "Rev. Edwin A. Pearson, D.D.", *The New Outlook,* Nov. 25, 1931, 4. Also *London Advertiser,* Dec. 19, 1927.

18 Sermon preached on appointment to Central Methodist Church, Hamilton, 1911. E.A. Pearson Scrapbook.

19 *Mike, I:* 9.

20 A leading historian of Canadian women has written of the late-nineteenth century: "Although women were having fewer children than had been the case earlier in the century, this did not necessarily lessen women's commitment to the domestic sphere; indeed through an intensification of the mother-child relationship it may have increased it." Wendy Mitchinson, "The WCTU: 'For God, Home, and Native Land': A Study of Nineteenth Century Feminism", in Linda Kealey, ed., *A Not Unreasonable Claim: Women and Reform in Canada, 1880s-1920s* (Toronto: Women's Press, 1979), 153; *Mike, I:* 9.

21 E.A. Pearson Scrapbook. Ed Pearson's income rose continuously, reaching $1,800 by 1911, not including such benefits as the parsonage.

22 Public health deteriorated as Hamilton industrialized. The medical health officer reported in 1910 that the city had to "exercise constant watchfulness if epidemics and high death rates are to be avoided". The "white plague" of tuberculosis was the greatest killer of young adults and infant mortality was the major component of the death rate. The infant mortality rates were higher than in Calcutta in the 1980s. See Rosemary Gagan, "Mortality Patterns and Public Health in Hamilton, Canada, 1900-1914", *Urban History Review,* XVII (Feb. 1989), 161-75.

23 The term "civics lesson" is used by Ramsay Cook to describe Ed's Methodist colleague Dwight Chown's Christianity. See Cook, *The Regenerators,* 230.

24 Sermon at Central Methodist, Hamilton, 1911, E.A. Pearson Scrapbook and PPP.

25 *Peterborough Examiner,* Nov. 18, 1907.

26 This particular service on June 10, 1900, "High Class Toronto Theatres Condemned by Rev. Mr. Pearson", was attended by one hundred members of the Sons of England and the Orange Lodge of Davisville (PPP).

27 "Returns after Extended Trip to British Isles and Europe", E.A. Pearson Scrapbook.

28 Interviews with Charles Ritchie, Patricia Hannah, Geoffrey Pearson, Rev. Frank Morgan, Rev. A.B. Moore, and Escott Reid. Also, A.C. Forrest, "And Now, Mr. Pearson", *United Church Observer,* Apr. 15, 1968, 13.

29 *Mike, I:* 12; Report of Peterborough Collegiate Institute, Mar. 24, 1910 (PPP). E.A. Pearson Scrapbook and Vaughan Pearson Papers (PPP). Lester Pearson wrote the preface to Marjorie Freeman Campbell, *A Mountain and a City: The Story of Hamilton* (Toronto: McClelland and Stewart, 1966), ix.

30 On sports in Canada, see Alan Metcalfe, *Canada Learns to Play: The Emergence of Organized Sport, 1807-1914* (Toronto: McClelland and Stewart, 1987), esp. chapters 2 and 3.

31 *Mike, I:* 6, 8. Family interviews and PPP.

32 Interview with L.B. Pearson, "First Person Singular", Show 1, June 3, 1973, Canadian Broadcasting Corporation, 1973 (PPP).

33 *Mike, I:* 13.

34 "I don't recall very much in the way of discipline. This was a time in society when you obeyed your parents.... I was licked by my father once or twice, but it would be mother who would have to tell him to do it, I think." Interview with L.B. Pearson, "First Person Singular", Show 1. Pearson did recall one occasion on which he defied his father and jumped on the runner of a sleigh: "He really gave me a beating on that one."

35 Neil Sutherland, *Children in English-Canadian Society* (Toronto: University of Toronto Press, 1976); Diana Baumrind, "Rejoinder to Lewis's Reinterpretation of Parental Firm Control Effects: Are Authoritative Families Really Harmonious?", *Psychological Bulletin,* 94 (1983), 132-42; and Neil Semple, "'The Nurture and Admonition of the Lord': Nineteenth Century Methodism's Response to 'Childhood'," *Histoire sociale / Social History* (Mai-May 1981), 157-75.

36 Jerome Kagan, *The Nature of the Child* (New York: Basic Books, 1984), 280.

CHAPTER 2: THE WARS

1 Vernon Scannell quoted in Paul Fussell, *The Great War and Modern Memory* (New York and London: Oxford University Press, 1975), 334.

2 Lester Pearson, *Mike: The Memoirs of the Rt. Hon. Lester B. Pearson. Volume 1: 1897-1948* (Toronto: University of Toronto Press, 1972), 14; E.A. Pearson Scrapbook, MG26 N12 (NAC); Pearson Papers Personal (PPP).

3 *Mike, I:* 15.

4 E.A. Pearson Scrapbook; Victoria College Archives, A-70-025, Box 8, file 50.

5 *Mike, I:* 13; "First Person Singular", Show 1, CBC Television, 8; John Weaver, *Hamilton: An Illustrated History* (Toronto: James Lorimer, 1984). On housing, see Michael Doucet and John Weaver, "Material Culture and the North American House", *Journal of American History,* 72, no. 3 (Dec. 1985), 560-87.

6 E.A. Pearson Scrapbook; *Mike, I:* 15; and L.B. Pearson, "Preface" to Marjorie Freeman Campbell, *A Mountain and a City: The Story of Hamilton* (Toronto: McClelland and Stewart, 1966), ix.

7 Carl Berger, *The Sense of Power* (Toronto: University of Toronto Press, 1970). See also Robert Bothwell, Ian Drummond, and John English, *Canada 1900-1945* (Toronto: University of Toronto Press, 1986), 191.

8 *Mike, I:* 14-15; Patricia McHugh, *Toronto Architecture: A City Guide* (Toronto: Mercury Books, 1985), 7-8; and Claude Bissell, *The Young Vincent Massey* (Toronto: University of Toronto Press, 1981), 80.

9 "Hazing" (A Petition against the practice), Feb. 1, 1888, E.A. Pearson Scrapbook. Hazing and initiation are described in Keith Walden, "Hazes, Hustles, Scraps, and Stunts: Initiations at the University of Toronto, 1880-1925", in Paul Axelrod and John Reid, eds., *Youth, University and Canadian Society* (Kingston and Montreal: McGill-Queen's University Press, 1989), 94-121.

10 *Varsity,* Oct. 7, 1913; E.A. Pearson Scrapbook; "First Person Singular", Show 2; and PPP. Toronto students had a history of lively stunts. See Keith Walden, "Respectable Hooligans: Male Toronto Students Celebrate Hallowe'en, 1884-1910", *Canadian Historical Review,* 68 (Mar. 1987), 1-34.

11 Lester to Annie, Oct. 1, 1913 (two letters) (PPP).

12 "First Person Singular", Show 2; and L.B. Pearson Scrapbook MG26 N12 (NAC).

13 "First Person Singular", ibid.; and Lester Pearson to Geoffrey Pearson, November 1950 (PPP) in which Lester says that he never excelled in sports until he returned from the war.

14 "High Class Toronto Theatres Condemned by Rev. Mr. Pearson", *Peterborough Examiner*, Nov. 18, 1907. Ed and a friend had gone incognito to a "high class" and a "low class" Toronto theatre and had found the former more offensive.

15 *The Chatham Daily Planet,* July 8, 17, and 25, 1914; and Rupert Brooke, *Letters from America* (London: Sidgwick and Jackson, 1916), 82.

16 "First Person Singular", Show 2; Duke Pearson War Memoir, in possession of Mr. Fred Pearson, West Newbury, Massachusetts; and *Mike, I:* 17.

17 *The Chatham Daily Planet,* Jan. 4, 1915; and entry of Jan. 3, 1915, Lester Pearson Personal Diary, in possession of Mr. Geoffrey Pearson.

18 Diary, ibid., Jan. 16 and 19, Feb. 14 and 28, and Mar. 15, 1915.

19 Ibid., Mar.-Apr. 1915 *passim*; and L.B. Pearson Scrapbook.

20 Lester Pearson Personal Diary, Apr. 27-8, 1915; and *Mike, I:* 19.

21 W.A. Dafoe memoir, in possession of author; Lester Pearson Personal Diary, May 15-24, 1915; and *Mike, I:* 20. The quotation in *Mike, I:* 21, "nearing land and in danger – worried", omits "worried" in the original. The remainder of the entry for May 25 is "Nothing doing on ship. Feeling much better. Weather fine. Getting ready to land."

22 *Mike, I:* 21.

23 Lester Pearson Diary, chapter 1, MG26 N8 v. 1 (NAC); and *The Chatham Daily Planet,* July 3, 1915 (letter to parents and Vaughan).

24 *Daily Planet,* ibid.; and Duke Pearson memoir (in possession of Mr. Fred Pearson).

25 Lester Pearson Diary, chapter 2. On the Scottish trip, see *The Chatham Daily Planet,* Sept. 21, 1915.

26 Diary, ibid., chapter 1, and L.B. Pearson Scrapbook.

27 "Cards on the Table", a discussion between Anthony Weymouth and Michael Macdonald (Pearson), July 12, 1938. Pearson Papers, MG26 N1, v. 58 (NAC).

28 L.B. Pearson Diary, Nov. 28, 1915.

29 See *Mike, I:* 23-5; and L.B. Pearson Scrapbook.

30 *Mike, I:* 25.

31 Winston Churchill to J.L. Garvin, Dec. 8, 1915 quoted in Martin Gilbert, *Winston S. Churchill: The Challenge of War 1914-1916* (Boston: Houghton Mifflin, 1975), 605.

32 L.B. Pearson Diary.

33 Ibid. Punctuation as in original but spelling corrected.

34 *The Chatham Daily Planet* clipping in L.B. Pearson Scrapbook, Early Years; Duke Pearson memoir; and L.B. Pearson to parents, Apr. 17, 1916 (PPP). Interview with Mabel Lucas, CBC Radio, "Voice of the Pioneer", June 7, 1987.

35 *Mike, I:* 29 ff; and E.A. Pearson to Sir Sam Hughes, Sept. 6, 1916, Lester Pearson Personnel File, Dept. of National Defence, National Archives Record Centre, Job No. 33.

36 *Mike, I:* 30; Ronald Haycock, *Sam Hughes: The Public Career of a Controversial Canadian 1885-1916* (Waterloo: Wilfrid Laurier University Press, 1986), chapter 15; and Lester Pearson Diary.

37 Diary, ibid.; and Brooke, quoted in Robert Wohl, *The Generation of 1914* (Cambridge, Mass.: Harvard University Press, 1979), 90.

38 On the war poets and the shift in perception, see Fussell, *The Great War and Modern Memory*; and Eric Leed, *No Man's Land: Combat and Identity in World War I* (Cambridge and New York: Cambridge University Press, 1979).

39 "Rev. Pearson has Concluded Work in Church Here", n.d. (PPP); Ed Pearson to Wm. Bull, Apr. 3, 1917 (PPP); and *The Chatham Daily Planet,* Oct. 30, 1916, and Nov. 12, 1915. L.B. Pearson Diary; *Mike, I:* 32-3; "Nominal Role of Afcananzacs" (PPP); and L.B. Pearson Scrapbook *(Times* clipping).

40 *Mike, I:* 32. This account does not mention that Graves collapsed in mid-summer. On Graves, see Martin Seymour-Smith, *Robert Graves: His Life and Work* (London: Hutchinson, 1982), chapter 5; and R.P. Graves, *Robert Graves: The Assault Heroic 1895-1926* (London: Weidenfeld and Nicolson, 1986), 172-3 and 260-1.

41 Vaughan Pearson to parents, Apr. 9, 1917. Vaughan Pearson Papers, in possession of Pearson family; E.A. Pearson to Sir George Perley, June 6, 1917. L.B. Pearson Personnel File, Dept. of National Defence, National Archives Record Centre, Job No. 30; and Perley to E.A. Pearson, July 9, 1917 (PPP).

42 L.B. Pearson Diary; "General Idea" Concert Program, Aug. 1, 1917, and "Afcananzac Liberation Dinner", Aug. 2, 1917, L.B. Pearson Scrapbook, Early Years, MG26 N12 (NAC).

43 *Mike, I:* 28; L.B. Pearson Diary; and Vaughan Pearson Scrapbook (PPP).

44 L.B. Pearson Diary; Duke Pearson memoir (PPP); Hilary St. George Saunders, *Per Ardua: The Rise of British Air Power* (London: Oxford University Press, 1944), chapter 12; *Mike, I:* 33; and on the fascination with speed, see Wohl, *The Generation of 1914,* 226ff.

45 Lester to Mother and Father, Dec. 4, 1917. MG26 N8, v. 2 (NAC). On the crisis, see John English, *The Decline of Politics: The Conservatives and the Party System, 1901-1920* (Toronto: University of Toronto Press, 1977), 186-204.

46 Lester to Mother and Father, Dec. 15, 1917, MG26 N8, v. 1 (NAC); and L.B. Pearson Diary.

47 *Mike, I:* 35-6.

48 Ibid., 35-7; and Pearson to Mother and Father, Jan. 6, 1918 [inaccurately dated 1917], MG26 N8, v. 2 (NAC).

49 Leed, *No Man's Land,* 163. "Report of a Medical Board -- Royal Air Force" (PPP); and *Guelph Mercury,* Apr. 8, 1918.

50 Both documents in PPP.

51 Pearson to Mother and Father, Jan. 6 and Feb. 3, 1918, MG26 N8, v. 2 (NAC).

52 L.B. Pearson Scrapbook; and *Mike, I:* 36-7.

53 Leed, *No Man's Land,* 181. Sir Andrew MacPhail, *Official History of the Canadian Forces in the Great War, 1914-1919* (Ottawa: King's Printer, 1925), 274-6.

CHAPTER 3: RENEWAL

1 Charles Carrington, *A Subaltern's War* (New York: Minton Balch, 1930), 208.

2 The swimming incident is recounted in W.A. Dafoe memoir (privately held). The changes in sensibility and social behaviour had Edwardian antecedents, and current literature emphasizes continuity rather than change in discussing these socio-cultural trends. Nevertheless, the evidence bearing on Lester Pearson's life suggests that his path and beliefs were profoundly affected by his own wartime experience and that of his society. On collegians, see Paula Fass, *The Damned and the Beautiful: American Youth in the 1920s* (London: Oxford University Press, 1977); on the British youth, Martin Green, *Children of the Sun: A Narrative of "Decadence" in England After 1918* (New York: Basic Books, 1976); on generational unity, Robert Wohl, *The Generation of 1914* (Cambridge, Mass.: Harvard University Press, 1979), 204ff. On Flavelle, see Michael Bliss, *A Canadian Millionaire: The Life and Business Times of Sir Joseph Flavelle, Bart. 1858-1939* (Toronto: Macmillan of Canada, 1978), 329-62. On the Methodist conference, see Richard Allen, *The Social Passion: Religion and Social Reform in Canada 1914-78* (Toronto: University of Toronto Press, 1973), 71ff.

3 Carrington, *A Subaltern's War,* 208.

4 L.B. Pearson, *Mike: The Memoirs of the Right Honourable Lester B. Pearson. Volume 1: 1897-1948* (Toronto: University of Toronto Press, 1972), 37.

5 Vaughan to "Mother, father & Les," July 2, 1918. Vaughan Pearson Papers (PPP).

6 "Medical History of an Invalid", May 6 and Sept. 10, 1918, L.B. Pearson Army Personnel File, Department of National Defence, National Archives Record Centre, Job No. 30.

7 *Mike, I:* 37-8.

8 Barbara Wilson, *Ontario and the First World War 1914-1918* (Toronto: University of Toronto Press, 1977), lxviii. On the returned soldiers, see

Desmond Morton and Glenn Wright, *Winning the Second Battle: Canadian Veterans and the Return to Civilian Life, 1915-1939* (Toronto: University of Toronto Press, 1987).

9 See Peter Ackroyd, *T.S. Eliot* (London: Abacus, 1984), 76; and Donald Creighton, *Towards the Discovery of Canada* (Toronto: Macmillan of Canada, 1972), 3-5.

10 Quoted in Bruce Thordarson, *Lester Pearson: Diplomat and Politician* (Toronto: Oxford University Press, 1974), 10.

11 E.A. Pearson Scrapbook and L.B. Pearson Early Scrapbook, MG26 N12 (NAC). *Mike, I:* 38. On the influenza epidemic, see J.P. Dickin McGinnis, "The Impact of Epidemic Influenza: Canada 1918-1919", in S.E.D. Shortt, ed., *Medicine in Canadian Society* (Montreal and Kingston: Queen's University Press, 1981), 447-77.

12 Scrapbooks, ibid. Interviews with Geoffrey and Patricia Pearson. Vaughan Pearson Scrapbook (PPP). Pearson's 1924 comments on sports, which originally appeared in *Acta Victoriana,* are reprinted in his *Words and Occasions* (Toronto: University of Toronto Press, 1970).

13 *Guelph Daily Mercury,* Dec. 27, 1918.

14 "Medical History of an Invalid", Apr. 15, 1919, L.P. Pearson Personnel File, Department of National Defence, National Archives Record Centre, Job No. 30. The statement in the memoirs that he "was now in good physical and mental condition" and that he was "fit for long hours of study" is obviously an inaccurate memory of that time. See *Mike, I:* 39.

15 Pearson's own low estimate of his education is found in Canadian Broadcasting Corporation, "First Person Singular", Show 2, June 10, 1973. Also, L.B. Pearson Early Scrapbook; E.A. Pearson Scrapbook; and *Torontonensis 1918-1919* (Toronto: n.p., 1919), 60.

16 Major [name unclear] to Secretary, Air Ministry, London, Mar. 22, 1919, DND Army Personnel Files, Reel No. 104, Job No. 30 (Public Archives Record Centre). Pearson pay rates have been calculated from records in this file.

17 Dafoe memoir; L.B. Pearson Scrapbook; and "Ontario Alpha of Phi Delta Theta", Mar. 8, 1919 (PPP).

18 L.B. Pearson Diary, No. 1, MG26 N8 (NAC). On Underhill, see Douglas Francis, *Frank H. Underhill: Intellectual Provocateur* (Toronto: University of Toronto Press, 1986). On the classics and British soldiers, see Paul Fussell, *The Great War and Modern Memory* (London and New York: Oxford University Press, 1975), chapter V.

19 Pearson's dance card for the Senior Class dance on Mar. 28, 1919. L.B. Pearson Scrapbook. On Mary Endicott, see Stephen Endicott, *James G. Endicott: Rebel Out of China* (Toronto: University of Toronto Press, 1986), 239-42. On the events of 1919, see Greg Kealey, "1919: The Canadian Labour Revolt", *Labour / Le Travail*, 14 (Fall 1984), 11-44.

20 *Mike, I:* 39-40.

21 Ibid. *Guelph Daily Mercury,* June 20-4, 1918, and May 26, 1919.

22 Canadian Broadcasting Corporation, "First Person Singular", Show 4, June 17, 1973. This account differs slightly from that in *Mike, I:* 40-1. The interview about religion was with Charles Lynch in 1964 (PPP).

23 Carl Sandburg, *Chicago Poems* (Cleveland: World Publishing Co., 1946; orig. ed., 1916), 31-4; James T. Farrell, *Studs Lonigan* (New York: The Modern Library, 1938).

24 Quoted in Finis Farr, *Chicago* (New Rochelle, N.Y.: Arlington House, 1973), 195.

25 Canadian emigration to the United States reached a peak in the 1920s. See Marcus Hansen, *The Mingling of the Canadian and American Peoples* (New Haven: Yale University Press, 1940).

26 E.A. Arpee, *Lake Forest, Illinois: History and Reminiscences, 1851-1961* (Lake Forest: Rotary Club of Lake Forest, 1963). For a fictional description of Lake Forest, see Hobart C. Chatfield-Taylor, *An American Princess* (Chicago: Stone, 1894). On St. Denis, Don McDonagh, *The Complete Guide to Modern Dance* (New York: Doubleday, 1976), 26-34.

27 *Mike,* I: 41-3; "First Person Singular", Show 4; *Chicago Tribune,* May 15, 1920.

28 Church bulletin, St. James's Methodist Church, Apr. 11, 1920. E.A. Pearson Scrapbook.

29 LBP to parents, Feb. 3, 1921 (PPP).

30 *Mike, I:* 42-3. "First Person Singular", Show 4.

CHAPTER 4: OXFORD

1 Lester Pearson, *Mike: The Memoirs of the Right Honourable Lester B. Pearson. Volume 1: 1897-1948* (Toronto: University of Toronto Press, 1972), 44.

2 *Mike, I:* 44; LBP to EAP, May 25, 1921 (PPP); Claude Bissell, *The Young Vibrant Massey* (Toronto: University of Toronto Press, 1981), 102; and L.B. Pearson Scrapbook, Early Years, MG26 N12 (NAC). In his memoirs Mike said he won a Massey Foundation Fellowship but contemporary reports call it an American University fellowship.

3 Jan Morris, *Oxford* (Oxford: Oxford University Press, 1965), 254.

4 *Mike, I:* 43-4; John Betjeman, *An Oxford University Chest* (Oxford: Oxford University Press, 1938), 36; Jan Morris, ed., *The Oxford Book of Oxford* (Oxford: Oxford University Press, 1978), chapter 6; and Evelyn Waugh, *Brideshead Revisited* (Boston: Little Brown, 1946), 26. Also, interview with V.C. Wansbrough, Oct. 1987.

5 LBP to Annie and Ed, Oct. 1921 (PPP). On clothes and Oxford in the early 1920s, see Martin Burgess Green, *Children of the Sun: A Narrative of "Decadence" in England After 1918* (New York: Basic Books, 1976), chapter v.

6 Harold Acton, *Memoirs of an Aesthete* (London: Methuen, 1948).

7 John Betjeman, *Summoned by Bells* (London: J. Murray, 1960); and Louis MacNeice, *The Strings Are False* (Oxford: Oxford University Press, 1965).

8 Betjeman, *An Oxford University Chest,* 143-4; Anthony and Valentine Sillery, *St. John's College Biographical Register* (Oxford: privately printed, 1978), 2-4. St. John's College Records, St. John's College Library; and *Mike, I:* 44.

9 Interview with Costin and Pearson in "First Person Singular", Show 4, June 17, 1973, CBC Television.

10 Pearson's college chits show no charges for liquor. One of his closest friends, V.C. Wansbrough, says Pearson was an abstainer. His strong opposition to liquor is reflected in his anonymous article "At the Heart of the Empire", *Christian Guardian,* Nov. 30, 1921. On Oxford and the temp-

tations of alcohol for another Canadian, see Charles Ritchie, *An Appetite for Life* (Toronto: Macmillan of Canada, 1977).

11 *Mike, I:* 46. Other information from L.B. Pearson Scrapbook, Early Years; St. John's Biographical Register; St. John's College Records; and interview with V.C. Wansbrough. As the vice-president usually gave the toast, Mike must have done so in 1922.

12 Mike refers to the contract with Creighton in LBP to Annie and Ed Pearson, Oct. 1921 (PPP).

13 *Christian Guardian,* Nov. 9, 1921.

14 Ibid.

15 Ibid., Nov. 30, 1921. Leacock's impressions of England on his 1921 tour are found in his *My Discovery of England* (Toronto: J. Lane, The Bodley Head, 1922).

16 "Rules", Oxford University Lacrosse Club (PPP); L.B. Pearson Scrapbook, MG26 N12 (NAC); *The Isis* (Oxford), Jan. 15, 1922; *Mike, I:* 47.

17 *Mike, I:* 47.

18 The invitations are in L.B. Pearson Scrapbook, Early Sports, MG26 N12 (NAC).

19 Roland Michener quoted in Peter Stursberg, *Lester Pearson and the Dream of Unity* (Toronto: Doubleday, 1978), 21.

20 L.B. Pearson Scrapbook, Early Sports; and *Isis,* Jan. 25, 1922.

21 *Christian Guardian,* Feb. 15, 1922.

22 H.O. Hopkins to LBP, Feb. 24, 1922. L.B. Pearson Papers, MG26 N12, file University Souvenirs 1912-23. An earlier letter from Hopkins (Feb. 15, 1922) congratulated Pearson for winning his "half-blue" in lacrosse.

23 Green, *Children of the Sun,* 152.

24 L.B. Pearson Scrapbook, Sports 1922-23, MG26 N12 (NAC); *Baltimore Sun,* Apr. 8-9, 1922; *Mike, I:* 47-8. Interview with V.C. Wansbrough.

25 Interview with V.C. Wansbrough.

26 Interviews with V.C. Wansbrough and King Gordon; V.C. Wansbrough

memoir (privately held); menu and dance ticket, Grand Hotel et Belvedere, Davos (PPP); King Gordon to Lester Pearson, Nov. 17, 1972 (PPP).

27 Interviews with Wansbrough and Gordon. Letters to author from LBP's classmates.

28 *Christian Guardian,* Aug. 16, 1922.

29 Ibid., Oct. 4, 1922. Roland Michener quoted in Stursberg, *Lester Pearson and the Dream of Unity,* 22. On the German inflation, see Charles Maier, *Restructuring Bourgeois Europe* (Princeton: Princeton University Press, 1975), 356-86.

30 The account of the Archery Club and the Sophists comes from V.C. Wansbrough memoir (privately held), chapter 5. R.P. Graves, *Robert Graves: The Assault Heroic 1895-1926* (London: Weidenfeld and Nicolson, 1986), 260. R.P. Graves has a chapter on his father, John, and Robert while John was at Oxford.

31 The Ralegh Club and Colonial Club programs are in L.B. Pearson Scrapbook, Sports 1922-23, and the dance card in L.B. Pearson Papers, MG26 N12, file University Souvenirs. The description of Acton is from Green, *Children of the Sun,* 153. The Waugh quotations are in Morris, ed., *The Oxford Book of Oxford,* 340.

32 Ronald Steel, *Walter Lippmann and the American Century* (New York: Vintage, 1981), 3-4.

33 *Christian Guardian,* Feb. 15 and 22, and Aug. 30, 1922.

34 *Mike, I:* 44, 46-7.

35 *Christian Guardian,* Aug. 30, 1922.

36 Ibid., Feb. 22, 199. Professor John Holmes alerted me to the linkages between Canadian Methodist faith and the liberal view of Empire. I am indebted to him for this insight and for so many others.

37 *Chatham Daily Planet,* Sept. 7, 1916.

38 *Christian Guardian,* Feb. 22, 1923.

39 Quoted in Paul Carter, *Another Part of the Twenties* (New York: Columbia University Press, 1977), 43-4. On church union, see Mary Vipond,

"Canadian National Consciousness and the Formation of the United Church of Canada", *Bulletin* (United Church of Canada), no. 24 (1975), 5-27.

40 In an interview with Charles Lynch in the 1960s, Lynch asked Pearson directly what he had "brought forward in terms of religious outlook". Pearson admitted that he rarely attended church but claimed he had religious feeling, which he associated with "moral views and standards". To Lynch's claim that Pearson "never wore any particular feeling of religion on your sleeve," Pearson replied: "Well, I don't like to wear anything on my sleeve, I don't like to parade things ... the stronger the feelings, I think, the less I was inclined to parade it." Interview with Charles Lynch [1964?] (PPP). On the Methodist influence on Pearson's language, see W. Burton Ayre, *Mr. Pearson and Canada's Revolution by Diplomacy* (Montreal: privately published, 1966), 15-30.

CHAPTER 5: MARYON

1 LBP to Maryon Pearson, N.D. [1956], (PPP).

2 Susan Riley, *Political Wives: Wifestyles of the Rich and Infamous* (Toronto: McClelland and Stewart, 1989), 137.

3 Lester B. Pearson, *Mike: The Memoirs of the Right Honourable Lester B. Pearson. Volume 1. 1897-1948* (Toronto: University of Toronto Press, 1972), 50.

4 Claude Bissell, *The Young Vincent Massey* (Toronto: University of Toronto Press, 1981), 38.

5 L.B. Pearson, "Oxford – Ancient, Yet Modern", *Christian Guardian,* Aug. 16, 1922.

6 *St. John's College Biographical Register* (Oxford, n.d.), 55-63; David Calleo, *Beyond American Hegemony: The Future of the Western Alliance* (New York: Basic Books, 1987) and *Oxford University Calendar 1924.*

7 On Toronto and the historians, see Carl Berger, *The Writing of Canadian History* (Toronto: Oxford University Press, 1976), 34-53. Berger describes the relevant publications of the Toronto group and analyses the debate.

8 Robert Falconer, President, University of Toronto, to LBP, Sept. 14, 1923, MG26 N12, file – University Souvenirs (NAC); L.B. Pearson Scrapbook, MG26 N12; University of Toronto Archives, History Department, A-10-025, Box 7; and V.C. Wansbrough memoir (privately held).

9 Obituary of Dr. A.W. Moody (PPP). Interviews with Herbert Moody and Ruth Reid. C.W. Parker, ed., *Who's Who in Western Canada. Volume 1. 1911* (Vancouver: Canadian Press Association, 1911), 290. Herbert Moody to Patricia Hannah, Feb. 20, 1985 (in possession of Patricia Hannah).

10 Veronica Strong-Boag, *The New Day Recalled: Lives of Girls and Women in English Canada 1919-1939* (Toronto: Clarke Irwin, 1988), 67. On male-female friendships in the 1920s, see Sara Alpern, *Freda Kirchwey: A Woman of the Nation* (Cambridge, Mass.: Harvard University Press, 1987), 50-1. On the Endicotts, see Stephen Endicott, *James G. Endicott: Rebel Out of China* (Toronto: University of Toronto Press, 1980), 62-3; and the Smith president's comment is quoted in Carl N. Degler, *At Odds: Women and the Family in America from the Revolution to the Present* (New York: Oxford, 1980), 413. Statistics on female enrolment and discussion of the youth culture on campus are found in Strong-Boag, ibid., 24-7.

11 Ramsay Cook, *The Regenerators: Social Criticism in Late Victorian English Canada* (Toronto: University of Toronto Press, 1985).

12 On Sherman, the SCM, and Hooke, see Richard Allen, *The Social Passion* (Toronto: University of Toronto Press, 1973), 221 and chapter 19. Also, Maryon to Kirkwood, Sept. 7 and 29, 1923, and Nov. 9, 1924. Kirkwood Papers; R.P. Bowles, "Student Christian Movement", *Christian Guardian,* Aug. 30, 1922; and Paul Axelrod, "The Student Movement of the 1930s", in Axelrod and John Reid, eds., *Youth, University and Canadian Society* (Kingston and Montreal: McGill-Queen's University Press, 1989), 217-8.

13 Maryon to Kirkwood, Feb. 3 and Mar. 13, 1924.

14 Ibid.

15 Interviews with G.P. de T. Glazebrook, Lillian Snider, and Mrs. N. Stade.

16 Maryon to Kirkwood, Mar. 13 and May 21, 1924.

17 Ibid., May 21, 1924.

18 Ibid., Sept. 21, 1924; and *Mike, I:* 55.

19 Ibid., Nov. 9, 1924.

20 Ibid., Mar. 29, 1925.

21 Ibid., July 16, 1925.

22 Ibid., July 16 and Aug. 12, 1925. Newspaper clipping, Pearson Papers Personal (PPP). Also, *Mike, I:* 55, and interview with Herbert Moody (the best man).

23 Maryon to Kirkwood, Aug. 12, 1925.

24 Ibid., Feb. 11, 1926; Toronto *Mail and Empire,* Jan. 11, 1926; and Patricia McHugh, *Toronto Architecture: A City Guide* (Toronto: Mercury Books, 1985), 237.

25 *Mike, I:* 55. Also, Keith Davey, *The Rainmaker* (Toronto: Stoddart, 1986), 16; Tom Kent, *A Public Purpose* (Montreal and Kingston: McGill-Queen's University Press, 1988), 148; J.L. Granatstein, *The Ottawa Men* (Toronto: Oxford University Press), 78; and Riley, *Political Wives,* 136-49.

26 Maryon to Kirkwood, May 21, 1924; and *Mike, I:* 55.

27 Interviews with Charles Ritchie, Herbert Moody, Lord Sherfield, Lord Gladwin, Patricia Pearson Hannah, Paul Martin, Mary Jackman, and Jetty Robertson. Lord Sherfield and Lord Gladwyn met Maryon in 1930 and described her uncomfortable state in the diplomatic world. Martin knew her at college and in Ottawa in 1926. Herbert Moody, Maryon's brother, lived with the Pearsons in 1926.

CHAPTER 6: ACADEMIC INTERLUDE

1 Ernest Hemingway to Sylvia Beach, Nov. 6, 1923, in *Selected Letters 1917-1961,* ed. Carlos Baker (New York: Scribner's, 1981), 98.

2 On the Annex, see Patricia McHugh, *Toronto Architecture: A City Guide* (Toronto: Mercury Books, 1985), 222-4. Also, James Lemon, *Toronto Since 1918: An Illustrated History* (Toronto: James Lorimer, 1985), 51 and 65.

3 Lemon, ibid., chapter 1; Maryon Pearson-Kirkwood correspondence; interviews with George P. de T. Glazebrook and Herbert Moody; and Conn Smythe with Scott Young, *Conn Smythe: If You Can't Beat 'Em in the Alley* (Toronto: McClelland and Stewart, 1981), 74-85.

4 Lemon, ibid., 26ff. On insulin and a humorous account of the Nobel Prize, see Michael Bliss, *The Discovery of Insulin* (Toronto: McClelland and Stewart, 1982), esp. chapter 9.

5 Lemon, ibid., 53-7; Stephen Speisman, *The Jews of Toronto* (Toronto: McClelland and Stewart, 1979), 321; and Michiel Horn, "Keeping Canada Canadian: Anti-Communism and Canadianism in Toronto, 1928-29", *Canada,* Sept. 1975, 35-47. R. MacIver, *As a Tale That Is Told* (Chicago and London: University of Chicago Press, 1968), 89, 96. On MacIver, see Doug Owram, *The Government Generation: Canadian Intellectuals and the State* (Toronto: University of Toronto Press, 1986), 117-21.

6 L.B. Pearson, *Mike: The Memoirs of the Right Honourable Lester B. Pearson. Volume I: 1897-1948* (Toronto: University of Toronto Press, 1972), 53-4. Billy Dafoe worked with Mike on the lacrosse team. He was coach after Mike left Toronto. However, the American tours ended in 1930 because the American teams were bigger, rougher, and, alas, better. Dafoe memoir (privately held).

7 Interview with L.B. Pearson by Charles Lynch [1964?] In 1969, when I was a graduate student at Harvard, I was, as an inveterate fan, to take Mr. Pearson to a baseball game. Maryon was to be taken to the nearby Newberry Street shops for shopping. Alas, Mr. Pearson cancelled.

8 On Creighton and the SCM, and the department generally, see Carl Berger, *The Writing of Canadian History: Aspects of English Canadian Historical Writing 1900 to 1970* (Toronto: Oxford University Press, 1976), chapters 1, 2, and 9. Underhill dedicated *In Search of Canadian Liberalism* (Toronto: Macmillan of Canada, 1960) to Pearson. The department of history is also described in W.D. Meikle, "And Gladly Teach: G.M. Wrong and the Department of History at the University of Toronto" (unpublished Ph.D. thesis, University of Michigan, 1977). Creighton's comments on Brebner and Underhill and, very interestingly, on his father are in Donald Creighton, *The Passionate Observer* (Toronto: McClelland and Stewart, 1980), 94-9, 119-43, 460-70.

9 J.L. Granatstein, *The Ottawa Men: The Civil Service Mandarins 1935-1957* (Toronto: Oxford University Press 1982), 113-15.

10 Charles P. Stacey, *A Date with History* (Ottawa: Deneau, n.d., [1982]), 14; interview with Paul Martin.

11 [L.B. Pearson], "Robots and Robotism", *Acta Victoriana,* 48, no. 5 (Feb. 1924), 32ff. In the April 1924 issue (48, no. 6), the editors thank Pearson for his contribution to the previous issue, "Robots and Robotism". Even

without this confirmation, one could identify the article by its style and references. Wrong's views on students and Americans are described in greater detail in Granatstein, *Ottawa Men*, 114-19.

12 Stacey, *A Date with History*, 15; Paul Martin, *A Very Public Life*, Vol. I (Ottawa: Deneau, 1983), 43; and Donald Fleming, *So Very Near*, Vol. I (Toronto: McClelland and Stewart, 1985), 46.

13 Berger, *The Writing of Canadian History*, chapter 2; "Outline of Work for 1924-5", George Wrong Papers, University of Toronto Archives; W. Stewart Wallace to LBP, Apr. 30, 1925, Wallace Papers, University of Toronto Archives; University of Toronto History Department Records, Box 007, University of Toronto Archives; and on Kennedy, Lewis Thomas, *The Renaissance of Canadian History: A Biography of A.L. Burt* (Toronto: University of Toronto Press, 1975), 97 and 106; and W.P.M. Kennedy Papers, Thomas Fisher Rare Book Room, University of Toronto, Manuscript Collection 105.

14 "Lecture Notes British Empire 1927", L.B. Pearson Diary, MG26 N8, v. 2.

15 W.S. Wallace, "Notes and Comments," *Canadian Historical Review*, (December 1920), 344; and Berger, *The Writing of Canadian History*, 32-4.

16 W.P.M. Kennedy, "Nationalism and Self-Determination", *Canadian Historical Review* (March 1921), 14. This section draws deeply upon Berger's excellent discussion in *The Writing of Canadian History*, chapter 2.

17 Berger, ibid. On the "internationalist mind", see Warren Kuehl, "Webs of Common Interests Revisited: Nationalism, Internationalism, and Historians of American Foreign Relations", *Diplomatic History*, v. 10, no. 2 (Spring 1986), 107-15.

18 *Mike, I:* 52; Berger, *The Writing of Canadian History*, 30; Thomas, *The Renaissance of Canadian History*, 79-102; Maryon Pearson to Kenneth Kirkwood (Kirkwood Collection, private); J.B. Brebner, *New England's Outpost: Acadia Before the Conquest of Canada* (New York: Columbia University Press, 1927); and H.H. Wrong, *The Government of the West Indies* (Oxford: Oxford University Press, 1923) and *Sir Alexander Mackenzie, Explorer and Fur Trader* (Toronto: Oxford, 1927).

19 Quoted in Thomas, *The Renaissance of Canadian History*, 83, 85-7.

20 Interview with Charles Lynch [1964] (PPP); and Report of speech to Ontario Educational Association, *Toronto Mail,* Apr. 9, 1926.

21 Doug Owram summed up the opinion of the intellectual community: "Disdain for Tory imperialism was neatly balanced by hostility to the inaction and record of that apparent ex-intellectual, Mackenzie King." *The Government Generation* (Toronto: University of Toronto Press, 1986), 168.

22 Martin, *A Very Public Life, I,* 54-55. Interview with Paul Martin.

23 Historical Records, University of Toronto Archives, B770019 / 001, file 1915-50 Membership etc.

24 Mike could not seem to remember when his promotion occurred. In his *Who's Who in Canada* biography, he gives 1926 as the date. He states that he never became assistant professor in *Words and Occasions* (Toronto: University of Toronto Press, 1970), 7. He did on June 8, 1927 (University of Toronto Archives, Board of Governors' Minutes, June 10, 1927). On his "dejection", see Thomas, *The Renaissance of Canadian History,* 86. The salary negotiations are found in George Smith to Sir Robert Falconer, Apr. 19, 1927, History Department Records, University of Toronto Archives. On the furniture, see *Mike, I:* 51. He also has the story wrong in his memoirs; see *Mike, I:* 56.

25 "The Game's the Thing," in *Words and Occasions,* 3-6. Stories on Pearson as a coach are found in *The Varsity.* The only story on his work as a professor is about a description he gave about medieval English students begging their way through college; *Varsity,* Dec. 12, 1927. Other information in this section is from interview with George Glazebrook, the surviving member of the history department in that period.

26 Quoted in Thomas, *The Renaissance of Canadian History,* 90, 92. Also, Berger, *The Writing of Canadian History,* 30-1.

27 Thomas, ibid., 90, 97-8. Interview with G.P. de T. Glazebrook.

28 LBP, "The New History", in *Words and Occasions,* 8-10.

29 LBP's aversion to some characteristics of modern historical research is clear in an interview with Charles Lynch in 1964 (PPP) and in a report on his time at Carleton after his retirement as prime minister. See Peyton Lyon and Bruce Thordarson, "Professor Pearson: A Sketch", in Michael Fry, ed., *"Freedom and Change": Essays in Honour of Lester B. Pearson* (Toronto:

McClelland and Stewart, 1975), 2, 4. Also, interview with Norman Hillmer (LBP's assistant at Carleton).

30 LBP, "Some Fathers of Confederation", *New Outlook,* June 29, 1927; and J.L. Granatstein, *Ottawa Men,* 79. In *Mike, I:* 53, Pearson says that at Toronto he was a "British-Canadian nationalist, but with no party allegiance." This description seems correct.

31 "Statement by Dean McLaughlin", Apr. 11, 1927 (PPP).

32 *Mike, I:* 57.

33 LBP to Geoffrey, Sept. 16, 1951 (PPP).

34 *Mike, I:* 56; Thomas, *The Renaissance of Canadian History,* 95; and "First Person Singular", Show 4, June 17, 1973, Canadian Broadcasting Corporation. Pearson erroneously identifies the host of the dinner as Sir George Foster rather than Sir George Perley. Both were rather ancient Conservative politicians.

35 Kennedy to Skelton, Jan. 30, 1927; Skelton to Kennedy, Feb. 1, 1927; LBP to Skelton, Feb. 28, 1927; Skelton to LBP, Mar. 1, 1927; Kennedy to Skelton, Apr. 6, 1927; Skelton to Kennedy, Apr. 7, 1927. Civil Service Commission Records, Historical Personnel Files, v. 536 (NAC).

36 Interview with G.P. de T. Glazebrook, *Mike, I:* 58. On Wrong, see Granatstein, *Ottawa Men,* 116 and 300, n104 and n105. On the history department see Meikle, "And Gladly Teach".

37 Kennedy to Skelton, May 7, 1928; Skelton to Kennedy, May 8, 1928; and LBP to Skelton, May 10, 1928. Civil Service Commission, Historical Personnel Files, v. 536 (NAC); Kennedy to Civil Service Commission, May 18, 1928, ibid.; and *Mike, I:* 59.

38 Civil Service Commission Results, Sept. 15, 1928 (PPP). For fuller details, see J.L. Granatstein, *A Man of Influence* (Ottawa: Deneau, 1981).

39 Civil Service Commission, ibid. Massey to Skelton, July 25, 1928, and Skelton to Massey, July 28, 1928. Massey Papers, University of Toronto Archives (formerly Massey College). Pearson had copies of the Massey-Skelton correspondence in his personal papers.

40 Skelton to LBP, Aug. 10, 1927 (PPP), and *Mike, I:* 60.

41 *Mike, I:* 61-2. *Toronto Daily Star,* Aug. 22-3, 1928.

CHAPTER 7: THE OTTAWA MAN

1 Rev. E.A. Pearson, "Peace in our Time and After", Remarks at a Morning Service at Dundas Street United Church, London, Ontario [1927] (PPP).

2 Ibid.

3 Charles Stacey, *Canada in the Age of Conflict. Volume 1: 1921-1948* (Toronto: University of Toronto Press, 1981), 97-103; Christopher Thorne, *The Limits of Foreign Policy; The West, the League and the Far Eastern Crisis of 1931-1933* (London: Hamish Hamilton, 1972), 114; and Robert Dallek, *The American Style of Foreign Policy* (New York: Knopf, 1983), 101-2.

4 Charles Maier, *Recasting Bourgeois Europe: Stabilization in France, Germany, and Italy in the Decade After World War I* (Princeton: Princeton University Press, 1975), 579.

5 Quoted in Paul Kennedy, *The Realities Behind Diplomacy: Background Influences on British External Policy, 1865-1980* (Glasgow: Fontana, 1981), 244.

6 Canada, House of Commons *Debates,* Feb. 19, 1929, 240-1. These remarks were made in the Kellogg-Briand debate. On Canada's reputation, see Gwendolen Carter, *The British Commonwealth and International Security: The Role of the Dominions 1919-1939* (Toronto: Ryerson Press, 1947), 10, 24ff. The best study of the League of Nations appeal in Canada is Donald Page, "Canada and the League of Nations Before the Manchurian Crisis" (unpublished Ph.D. Thesis, University of Toronto, 1971).

7 King privately held reservations. See Richard Veatch, *Canada and the League of Nations* (Toronto: University of Toronto Press, 1975), 18.

8 Hugh Keenleyside, *Memoirs of Hugh L. Keenleyside Volume I: Hammer the Golden Day* (Toronto: McClelland and Stewart, 1981), 217-18. Interview with H.L. Keenleyside. Mr. Keenleyside kindly gave me copies of the examinations he and Mike tried.

9 Civil Service Commission, Historical Personnel Files, V. 536, Medical Examiner's Report, Sept. 25, 1928. Interview with Michel Gauvin, former ambassador to Greece, commenting on a Pearson visit to Greece in 1970. Interview with V.C. Wansbrough.

10 Keenleyside, *Memoirs, I:* 218-19; [Hume Wrong], "Notes on Personnel", RG25, McKenzie file, v. 2961, file 56 (NAC); interview with Keenleyside.

11 Interview with G.P. de T. Glazebrook.

12 Quoted in Keenleyside, *Memoirs, I:* 245 n5.

13 L.B. Pearson, *Mike: The Memoirs of the Right Honourable Lester B. Pearson. Volume I: 1897-1948* (Toronto: University of Toronto Press, 1972), 59; and Hadow to Whiskard, Apr. 30, 1929, DO 35 / 68 / 06765 (PRO). On francophone entry, see J.H. Hodgett et al., *The Biography of an Institution: The Civil Service Commission of Canada 1908-1967* (Montreal and Kingston: McGill-Queen's University Press, 1972); and Gilles Lalande, *The Department of External Affairs and Biculturalism.* Studies of the Royal Commission on Bilingualism and Biculturalism, No. 3 (Ottawa: Information Canada, 1970), 3-10, 37-44. The British diplomat Hadow thought that the method of appointment and service should be altered but added that Skelton would brook "no outside advice".

14 *Mike, I:* 60. There is a good sketch of McCloskey and McKenzie in Keenleyside, *Memoirs, I:* 229-31.

15 *Mike, I:* 57, 60.

16 Keenleyside diary entry for Nov. 6, 1931, quoted in *Memoirs, I:* 405. Interview with Hugh Keenleyside.

17 RG26, McKenzie File, vol. 2961, file 56. "Note on Personnel". See also J.L. Granatstein, *A Man of Influence* (Ottawa: Deneau, 1981), 38, where he quotes a Wrong comment to his sister of June 1930 that reports that Pearson and Wrong "spend most of [their] spare time reforming our elementary and rather absurd diplomatic service."

18 *Mike, I:* 82, 83. On the British and Canadian perspective, see Carter, *The British Commonwealth and International Security;* and W.K. Hancock, *Survey of British Commonwealth Affairs: Problems of Nationality 1918-1936* (Oxford: Oxford University Press, 1937). These two are classics. The subject is handled very well in G.N. Hillmer, "Anglo-Canadian Relations 1926-1937" (unpublished Ph.D. thesis, Cambridge University, 1974), and E.M. Andrews, *The Writing on the Wall: The British Commonwealth and Aggression in the East 1931-1935* (London: Allen and Unwin, 1987), chapter 7.

19 Stuart Ball, *Baldwin and the Conservative Party: The Crisis of 1929-1931* (New Haven and London: Yale University Press, 1988), 77. Pearson describes the complex diplomatic machinery as "obscure" and indefinite in a letter to F.R. Scott, July 22, 1931, MG26 N Pre-1948, v. 7 (NAC).

20 *New Outlook,* Jan. 5, 1930; *Varsity,* Jan. 16, 1930; and *Toronto Daily Star,* Feb. 4, 1930.

21 Interviews with Lord Gladwyn (Gladwyn Jebb) and Lord Sherfield (Roger Makins). Maryon Pearson Diary (PPP) and L.B. Pearson Diary, MG26 N8, v. 1, file 11 (NAC).

22 L.B. Pearson Diary, Jan. 19, 1930.

23 Maryon Pearson Diary, Feb. 17, 22, 23, 1930.

24 *Times* (London), Jan. 20, 1930. L.B. Pearson Scrapbook, Early Years, MG26 N12 (NAC).

25 *Mike, I:* 85; and L.B. Pearson Diary, May 1, 1930.

26 The Hague Conference on Codification of International Law: Territorial Waters, *Proceedings,* League of Nations Archives, Geneva.

27 LBP to Skelton, Mar. 12, 1930, MG26 N1, v. 2 (NAC). On the proposed amendment to the Covenant, see "Canada and the Convention", RG25 D1, v. 816, file 648 (NAC). Other material dealing with the London and The Hague conferences is found in RG25, D1, v. 766, file 310 (NAC).

28 LBP to Skelton, Mar. 12, 1930.

29 Report of the Inter-departmental Committee on Preparation for Geneva Disarmament Conference, External Affairs Records, RG25, D1, v. 766, file 310 (NAC). Earlier Pearson work on disarmament matters at the league is found in RG25, D1, v. 816, file 648 (NAC). A file in the Ralston Papers reveals that Pearson handled disarmament questions as early as May 1929. See J.L. Ralston Papers, MG27 III B II, v. 6, File "Disarmament". The document setting up the interdepartmental committee lists other members, including Norman Robertson, but one must assume that the absence of their name from the final reports indicates limited participation. See USSEA to High Commissioner, London, June 24, 1931, *Documents on Canadian External Relations. Volume 5: 1931-1935* (Ottawa: Information Canada, 1973) [henceforth *DCER*], 453-4.

30 "Scrutator" (LBP), "The Political Aspects of the Disarmament Conference", *Canadian Defence Quarterly,* IX, 2 (Jan. 1932), 168-9.

31 Ibid., 182-4.

32 LBP to J.L. Ralston, Sept. 29, 1931. MG27 III B2, Ralston Papers, v. 6 (NAC).

33 *Mike, I:* 87-8; SSEA to Dominions Secretary, Jan. 12, 1932 in *DCER,* 5, 464; and W.A. Riddell Diary, Feb. 1932 (York University Archives).

34 *Mike, I:* 86-7; James Eayrs, *In Defence of Canada: From the Great War to the Great Depression* (Toronto: University of Toronto Press, 1964), 262-5, 316ff; and John Swettenham, *McNaughton. Volume 1: 1887-1939* (Toronto: Ryerson Press, 1968), chapter 7. The best account of disarmament work is in Donald Storey, "The Foreign Policy of the Government of R.B. Bennett: Canada and the League of Nations" (unpublished Ph.D. thesis, University of Toronto, 1977), chapter IV.

35 Swettenham, ibid., 266-7. LBP to McNaughton, Mar. 7, 1932. McNaughton Papers, MG30 E 133, Series II, v. 109 (NAC); External Affairs Records, RG25 D1, v. 2961, file 52.

36 LBP to ODS, Feb. 3, 1932, ibid. On the Canadian delegation, see FO / 411 / 15, Public Records Office (PRO).

37 The Japanese had resented the restrictions placed upon them at the Washington and London conferences. They turned towards China, weakened by civil war, and attacked Manchuria in the winter of 1931-2, claiming that they were protecting their interests. This attack was the first major challenge to the league system – and to the notion of disarmament. On disarmament, see Christopher Hall, *Britain, America, and Arms Control 1921-1937* (London: Macmillan, 1987).

38 LBP to ODS, Apr. 1, 1932, Bennett Papers, Microfilm 222, 271155-6 (University of New Brunswick Archives). For Canadian petitions see ibid., 271048ff. For the boredom of Crerar, see Eayrs, *From the Great War to the Great Depression,* 265.

39 ODS to LBP, Apr. 25, 1932, External Affairs Records, RG25, D1, v. 816, file 648 (NAC).

40 For the pre-1935 period, it is certainly not accurate to state, as the most recent work has, that Skelton had "little use for the League" (John Thompson with Allen Seager, *Canada 1922-1939* [Toronto: McClelland and Stewart, 1985], 306). In a private exchange with N.W. Rowell, Skelton deplored what was occurring in East Asia. Although he indicated that he was opposed to

sanctions, he stated that he was willing to consider them if the Japanese continued to threaten China and thus the League Covenant. The exchange in Feb.-Mar. 1932 is in Rowell Papers, v.8, 6056-66 (NAC).

41 *Mike, I:* 92; and "Talk to Departmental Officers on Mussolini's Proposal to Revise the League Covenant", External Affairs Records, RG25, D1, v. 1685 (NAC). Mike's views were set out at greater length in "The Problem of Security and Sanctions in Light of Recent Developments at Geneva", June 20, 1933, R.J. Manion Papers, v. 81, file Miscellaneous Subjects (50) (NAC).

42 See Philip Noel-Baker, *The First World Disarmament Conference and Why It Failed* (Oxford and New York: Pergamon Press, 1979).

43 Obituary, "Rev. Edwin A. Pearson", *New Outlook,* Nov. 25, 1931; and interview with Patricia Pearson Hannah.

44 Riddell Diary (York University Library).

45 LBP to Evans, June 12, 1931; LBP to Brown, June 16, 1931; LBP to D.A. MacGibbon, June 17, 1931, MG26 N Pre-'48, v. 8, file Royal Commission on Grain Futures (NAC); and *Manitoba Free Press,* June 5, 1931.

46 G.V. Ferguson to LBP, June 3, 1931, Pearson Papers, MG26 N Pre-'48 file, Royal Commission on Grain Futures (NAC).

47 Keenleyside, *Memoirs, I:* 224.

48 Gordon to LBP, 1972 (PPP); and *Mike, I:* 79-80, for the Bennett speech story.

49 On Stevens and the inquiry, see Richard Wilbur, *H.H. Stevens 1878-1983* (Toronto: University of Toronto Press, 1977), 6, and chapters IV and V. For an indication of the public feeling see R.B. Bennett Papers (University of New Brunswick Archives), microfilm 227, 277500-613.

50 Two Pearson documents from the 1930s make fascinating reading in light of his work on the constitution as prime minister. In the first "The Contract Theory of Provincial Rights", written in April 1931, Pearson dismisses the "contract" or compact theory as "almost absurd" and strongly supports the pre-eminence of the federal government. A 1937 article disputes the interpretation made by Judicial Committee of the Privy Council regarding the so-called Bennett New Deal. It was published anonymously in *The Fortnightly Review.* See "The Privy Council and Canadian Federalism", MG26 N9, V. 1, file 30 Nov. 1930 to 3 Aug. 1941 (NAC).

51 LBP, "Address to Ottawa Study Club", June 1, 1934, MG26 N Pre-'48, v. 10 (NAC).

52 Commission Members to Bennett, Apr. 15, 1935. Bennett Papers, microfilm 227, 277607; *Mike, I:* 77; and "The Apprentice 1928-1939", "First Person Singular", Show 5, Canadian Broadcasting Corporation. Treasury Board Minutes, T159147B, Aug. 10, 1935. RG25, v. 839 (NAC).

53 *Mike, I:* 77-8. Mike very oddly, spells Bennett's name incorrectly (as "Bennet") in his letters to him. See, for example, LBP to Bennett, Jan. 22 and June 13, 1941, Bennett Papers, Microfilm 473, 0602073 and 0602078. These are handwritten letters; Mike's secretaries were better spellers.

CHAPTER 8: THE LONDON SEASON

1 Charles Ritchie, *The Siren Years: A Canadian Diplomat Abroad* (Toronto: Macmillan of Canada, 1974), 35.

2 Robert Graves and Alan Hodges, *The Long Weekend* (London: Faber and Faber, 1940).

3 Corelli Barnett, *The Audit of War* (London: Macmillan, 1986), 192. Unemployment figures for Scotland, the northwest, and South Wales were, respectively, 16.8, 17.7, and 25.9. More detail on the uneven nature of British "improvement" in the 1930s is given in A. Booth and M. Park, *Employment, Capital and Economic Policy* (Oxford: B. Blackwell, 1985).

4 Extract of letter from Hadow, Jan. 3, 1930, Admiralty Records ADM 116 / 27M; and E.J. Machtig to P.A. Koppel, Mar. 10, 1932, with minutes. FO 371 / 15879. A 1521 / 1521 / 45. Public Records Office (PRO). Machtig did complain about Pearson's remarks about the Liquor Convention where he suggested revision of the convention.

5 Interview with Lord Gladwyn. Mike also passed on information to Americans. Pierre Boal to Secretary of State, Dec. 15, 1932. State Dept. Records 893.01 Manchuria / 720 National Archives (NA).

6 LBP, "To a Church Group in Ottawa", Apr. 11, 1934, in *Words and Occasions* (Toronto: University of Toronto Press, 1970), 14-15.

7 Quoted in R.A. MacKay and E.B. Rogers, *Canada Looks Abroad* (Toronto, New York, London: Oxford University Press, 1938), 269.

8 The so-called Cahan incident is described in detail in Donald Storey, "The Foreign Policy of the Government of R.B. Bennett: Canada and the League of Nations, 1930-1935" (unpublished Ph.D. thesis, University of Toronto, 1977), chapter V.

9 Riddell's interpretation of sanctions, for example, went well beyond what Skelton accepted. See Riddell to Secretary General, League of Nations, Apr. 29, 1935. League of Nations *Official Journal* (July 1935), 909.

10 Clippings on Ferguson's series of speeches are found in External Affairs Records, RG25 D1, v. 797, file 495 (NAC). An American who did watch "Fergie" wrote: "It used to give him an awful pain at Geneva to hear some little fellow, representing some little nation, and speaking some language other than English get up and talk for an hour or so, and to know that the little fellow had the same right as he did to cast a vote." Herbert S. Goold to Norman Armour, U.S. Minister Ottawa, State Dept. Records 842.00 / 499-1 / 2. National Archives

11 Ferguson to Bennett, Aug. 17, 1935, Bennett Papers, Microfilm 120, 140701 (University of New Brunswick Archives); and L.B. Pearson Diary, Jan. 1, 1936, MG26 N8, v. 1 (NAC). Pearson's official appointment to London came in PC2900 on Sept. 18, 1935. Civil Service Commission, Historical Personnel Files, v. 536 (NAC). The thought of sending Pearson to London had occurred to Skelton as early as 1933. See W.A. Riddell Diary, Feb. 7, 1933, Riddell Papers (York University Archives).

12 Interview with Lester Pearson by Robert Bothwell, April 1970; and L.B. Pearson Diary, ibid.

13 The Peace Ballot was organized by the British League of Nations Society in 1934-5. An astonishing twelve million voted. Seventy per cent agreed with military sanctions and higher percentages favoured other sanctions and the league itself. See Martin Ceadel, "The First British Referendum: The Peace Ballot, 1934-5", *English Historical Review* (October 1980), 810-39. Ceadel points out that public opinion and governmental opinion diverged greatly because the politicians were aware how overextended British interests were. Others have seen the ballot as pacifist but the evidence suggests otherwise. Canada had no such ballot but there was a poll at Dalhousie which, like the Oxford King or Country debate of 1933, is open to various interpretations. The poll, to which roughly half of the student body responded, indicated that most (254 to 205) favoured military measures against an aggressor

nation. On the other hand, most (277 to 177) opposed Canada's participation in such military measures and a distinct minority (157 out of 334) would bear arms in such a conflict: *Toronto Mail,* Oct. 14, 1935.

14 Peter Ackroyd, *T.S. Eliot* (London: Abacus, 1984), 226; Arnold Toynbee, *Survey of International Affairs 1935* (London: Royal Institute of International Affairs, 1936), 50 (Baldwin); Keith Fe, *The Life of Neville Chamberlain* (London, 1946), 265, 268-9 (diary extracts); and on the cynicism of the politicians, see David Carlton, *Anthony Eden* (London: A. Lane, 1981), 59ff.

15 Pearson to Claxton, Aug. 29, 1935; and Claxton to Pearson, Aug. 30, 1935. Claxton Papers, MG32 B5, v. 20 N.P. (NAC). For Rowell, see exchanges with Skelton in Rowell Papers, MG27 II D13, v. 8, file 40.

16 In 1933 Mike had summarized Canada's position as one which held that the "League must remain consultative and not executive. The teeth must be kept out of Articles X and XVI." He had a more activist view in 1934 (that is, after a year of Hitler and a year more of Mussolini and Japanese brutality). See L.B.P. "Delegates and Substitute Delegates to League of Nation Assemblies", External Affairs Records, RG25 D1, v. 765, file 297 (NAC), and compare with "To a Church Study Group in Ottawa", Apr. 11, 1934, in L.B.P., *Words and Occasions* (Toronto: University of Toronto Press, 1970).

17 Meeting of delegates from Commonwealth and Britain, Sept. 24, 1935, Dominions Office Records, DO 35 / 6109A / 22 / 4 / 1707 (PRO).

18 Pearson Diary, Jan. 1, 1936; and LBP, "Report of telephone conversation between Mr. Ferguson – Geneva and Mr. Bennett – Lindsay, Ontario", Oct. 9, 1935. Initialled by Howard Ferguson. Riddell Papers (York University Archives).

19 B. Cockram to H. Paynton, Oct. 7, 1935, Dominions Office Records, DO 35 6109A / 460 (PRO); Ferguson to Bennett, Oct. 10, 1935, External Affairs Records, RG25, D1, v. 1719, file 927 (NAC); and Meeting of Commonwealth and British Delegates, Oct. 8, 1935, Dominions Office Records, DO 35 / 6109A / 22 / 4 / 707 (PRO).

20 This remarkable exchange occurred at 11:05 a.m., October 10, with Bennett in Toronto, Skelton in Ottawa, External Affairs Records, RG25 D1, v. 1719, file 927 (NAC). It was not placed on file until 1954. Story, "The Foreign Policy of the Government of R.B. Bennett", 365. Story contains some additional information from the account in Robert Bothwell and John English,

"'Dirty Work at the Crossroads': New Perspectives on the Riddell Incident", Canadian Historical Association, *Historical Papers 1972,* 265-81.

21 Mary McGeachy to J.W. Dafoe, Oct. 15, 1935, Dafoe Papers, Microfilm M-77 (NAC); and *Mike, I:* 92ff.

22 Pearson was not in Geneva on that date, but it is logical that Riddell would have checked. Pearson does not indicate in his memoirs or in any other document that he advised Riddell. Indeed, a letter of Nov. 22, 1935, from Pearson to Skelton, expresses surprise that newspapers were reporting "that Canada had proposed far-reaching measures for the extension of sanctions". Pearson said he believed that Canada "should not take any lead at Geneva in the application of sanctions". James Eayrs, however, indicates that the unnamed adviser who supported Riddell was Pearson. Riddell indicates that one of his two advisers suggested he make the sanctions proposal. A half-century later the mystery cannot be solved. Pearson to Skelton, Nov. 22, 1935, External Affairs Records, RG25, D1, v. 765; James Eayrs, *In Defence of Canada: Appeasement and Rearmament* (Toronto: University of Toronto Press, 1965), 22; and W.A. Riddell, *World Security by Conference* (Toronto: Ryerson Press, 1947), 123. Riddell's explanation to King and Skelton did not mention Pearson. King Diary, Jan. 30, 1936.

23 See Bothwell and English, "Dirty Work" for fuller details. The quotation comes from Robert Vansittart, *The Mist Procession: The Autobiography of Lord Vansittart* (London: Hutchinson, 1958), 532.

24 L.B. Pearson Diary, Jan. 6 and 9, 1936; LBP to Skelton, Dec. 23, 1935; and Pearson to Skelton, Dec. 23, 1935. External Affairs Records, RG25 D1, v. 1714 (NAC).

25 King Diary, entries for Dec. 18-19, 1935, and Jan. 5, 1936.

26 Gellman bases his analysis on one particular document, a memorandum on the league after Abyssinia. See Peter Gellman, "Lester B. Pearson, the Foundation of Canadian Foreign Policy, and the Quest for World Order" (unpublished Ph.D. thesis, University of Virginia, 1986).

27 L.B. Pearson Diary, Jan. 6 and 9, 1936; LBP to Skelton, Dec. 23, 1935; and, on Pearson's salary, L.B. Pearson, *Mike: The Memoirs of the Right Honourable Lester B. Pearson. Volume I: 1897-1948* (Toronto: University of Toronto Press, 1972), 102, and L.B. Pearson Diary, Jan. 1, 1936.

28 L.B. Pearson Diary, Jan. 18-20, 1936.

29 Ibid., Jan. 20-9; *Mike, I:* 109-11; and on Edward VIII and Mrs. Simpson, see their astonishing correspondence in Michael Bloch, ed., *The Intimate Correspondence of the Duke and Duchess of Windsor: Wallis and Edward Letters 1931-1937* (New York: Avon, 1986), chapters 7-11 especially.

30 This comment belies somewhat the interpretation given in recent works that suggest Mrs. Simpson was reluctantly drawn into marriage. See Bloch, ed., *The Intimate Correspondence of the Duke and Duchess of Windsor,* chapter 9; and Martin Gilbert, *Winston S. Churchill: The Prophet of Truth 1922-1939* (Boston: Houghton Mifflin, 1977), chapter 41.

31 L.B. Pearson Diary, Dec. 31, 1936 (summary of crisis). See also Claude Bissell, *The Imperial Canadian* (Toronto: University of Toronto Press, 1986), 56, which indicates that Massey shared Mike's views.

32 L.B. Pearson Diary, Dec. 31, 1936. On the trade negotiations and the complex set of trilateral negotiations between the U.K., the U.S., and Canada that followed, see Ian Drummond and Norman Hillmer, *Negotiating Freer Trade* (Waterloo: Wilfrid Laurier Press, 1989); and J.L. Granatstein, *A Man of Influence* (Ottawa: Deneau, 1981).

33 Skelton to LBP, Nov. 2, 1935; Wrong to R. Finlayson, Oct. 18, 1935, quoted in History of the Department of External Affairs (forthcoming); L.B. Pearson Diary, Jan. 1, 1936; King Diary, Nov. 29, 1935; and J.L. Granatstein, *The Ottawa Men: The Civil Service Mandarins, 1935-1957* (Toronto: Oxford, 1982), 119-20.

34 Bissell, *The Imperial Canadian,* 56-7; and L.B. Pearson Diary, Jan. *passim* (Wrong letters are quoted in Bissell). Pearson did tell a Canadian friend, however, that Massey was a good high commissioner. Graham Spry to Irene Biss, [July] 1937, Graham Spry Papers, MG30 D297 (NAC).

35 Harold Nicolson, *The Evolution of Diplomatic Method* (London: Constable & Co. Ltd., 1954), 75; Vansittart is quoted in Gordon Craig, "The Professional Diplomat and His Problems, 1919-1939", in *War, Politics and Diplomacy: Selected Essays* (London: Weidenfeld and Nicolson, 1966), 209.

36 Alice Massey to Maude Grant, June 14, 1937, W.L. Grant Papers, MG 30 D20, v. 43 (NAC).

37 James Eayrs, *The Art of the Possible* (Toronto: University of Toronto Press, 1961), 44, 53; and *Mike, I:* 63-4, 108.

38 *Mike, I:* 113-15; and Bissell, *The Imperial Canadian,* 9-10.

39 L.B. Pearson Diary, Jan.-May 1937.

40 Massey to Skelton, Dec. 15, 1936, Civil Service Commission Records, Historical Personnel file, v. 536; Alice Massey to Maude Grant, Mar. 1, 1936, quoted in Bissell, *The Imperial Canadian,* 56; and Vincent Massey to Brooke Claxton, Jan. 17, 1936, quoted in Vincent Massey, *What's Past Is Prologue: The Memoirs of Vincent Massey* (Toronto: Macmillan of Canada, 1963), 228.

41 Wrong to LBP, Nov. 7, 1937, MG26 N1, v. 3 (NAC); Grant Dexter to George Ferguson, Nov. 12, 1937, Dexter Papers (Queen's University Archives).

42 Alan Plaunt to LBP, Jan. 7, 1937, MG26 N1, v. 8 (NAC); and LBP to Plaunt, [Jan. 1937], Plaunt Papers, File 8-4, University of British Columbia Archives. In his diary, Pearson was less enthusiastic than he was to Plaunt. He was "definitely interested", but indicated a promotion and an improvement in the operation of Canada House might keep him in London. L.B. Pearson Diary, Jan. 18, 1937, MG26 N8, v. 1.

43 Granatstein, *The Ottawa Men,* 81-4. In the case of Wrong, who was seeking a university position, King told Skelton that he should be told his resignation would be accepted. He wrote in his diary: "[Wrong] does wonderful work but is an impossible person to work with." He commented on Wrong's job search to the governor general and said Wrong was difficult: "The Governor spoke of how characteristic that was of all the Blakes." King Diary, Feb. 24 and Mar. 18, 1938.

44 A good description of how Pearson, along with his superior R.J. Manion, "broke most of the rules" at Ottawa Conference is found in R.J. Manion, *Life Is an Adventure* (Toronto: Ryerson Press, 1936), 341-2. On Geneva's journalists, see L.B. Pearson Diary, Jan. 1936. He dined regularly with journalists in London, including such well-known ones as Vernon Bartlett and Bruce Lockhart. On Jan. 7, 1937, he dined with the former at Travellers' Club where Bartlett told him how upset the Nazis were over the abdication of Edward VIII. "Bartlett also assured me with a straight face that a very personable young secretary at the German Embassy had been detailed to lay

his body on the altar of The Fatherland by making love to Mrs. Simpson, which he accomplished with complete success," L.B. Pearson Diary, Jan. 8, 1937. On Canadian "public diplomacy" in the 1930s and 1940s and Pearson's later role, see Robert Bothwell and John English, "The View From Inside Out: Canadian Diplomats and Their Public", *International Journal*, XXXIX, no. 1 (Winter 1983-4), 47-67.

45 Skelton to Massey, Feb. 18, 1937, quoted in Granatstein, *The Ottawa Men*, 83.

46 Elizabeth Smart, *Necessary Secrets* (Toronto: Deneau, 1986), 154.

47 See *Mike, I:* 103-04.

48 L.B. Pearson Diary, Jan. 7, 1936; and Michael Davie, ed., *The Diaries of Evelyn Waugh* (London: Weidenfeld and Nicolson, 1976), chapter 4, reports regularly on Boulestin lunches.

49 Philip Ziegler, *Diana Cooper* (Harmondsworth: Penguin, 1983), 193-4.

50 Elizabeth Smart, *Necessary Secrets*, 155. Elizabeth Smart was the daughter of an Ottawa lawyer who was a close friend of Norman Robertson. She dated Graham Spry, a friend of Mike's, for a long time. She became one of Canada's finest poetic novelists, although her personal life was tragic. See the wonderful sketch of Elizabeth's party at Kingsmere in Charles Ritchie, *My Grandfather's House* (Toronto: McClelland and Stewart, 1987), 153-60.

51 Smart, *Necessary Secrets*, 10, 154-5, 159. Interview (telephone) with Alice Van Wart (editor of *Necessary Secrets*); interviews with Charles Ritchie, Jetty Robertson, George and Alison Ignatieff. On men and women's friendships, see Sara Alpern, *Freda Kirchwey: A Woman of the Nation* (Cambridge, Mass.: Harvard University Press, 1987), 49ff.

52 On King and Hitler, see James Eayrs, *Appeasement and Rearmament: In Defence of Canada* (Toronto: University of Toronto Press, 1965), 45-7. LBP to Skelton, Oct. 26, 1935, RG25, V2961, v. 52 (NAC); L.B. Pearson Diary, Feb. 18 and 20, 1936; and Christie to LBP, Dec. 1, 1937, MG26 N1, v. 2 (NAC). On the end of disarmament, Christopher Hall, *Britain, America and Arms Control, 1921-1937* (Basingstoke: Macmillan, 1987).

53 L.B. Pearson Diary, Jan. 19, 1937. On the department's activities, see Christie to LBP, MG26 N1, v. 2 (NAC).

54 LBP to H.D.G. Crerar, May 14, 1936, MG26 N1, v. 1 (NAC); *Mike, I:* 122ff.; and "Cards on the Table: Discussion Between Anthony Weymouth and Michael Macdonald", Oct. 7, 1937, MG26 N1, v. 58 (NAC); ibid., discussion of Dec. 2, 1937, italics in original; and LBP to Skelton, Feb. 19, 1937, King Papers, MG26 J1, v. 240 (Pearson), 206227 (NAC).

55 *Mike, I:* 127; "Cards on the Table", Oct. 5, 1938, MG26 N1, v. 58 (NAC); and Alice Massey to Maude Grant, Oct. 18, 1938, Massey Family Papers, MG30 D59, v. 48 (NAC). See Granatstein, *The Ottawa Men,* 88. For recent archival information that has affected the historiography of Munich, see Gerhard L. Weinberg, "Munich After 50 Years", *Foreign Affairs* (Fall 1988), 165-78. Weinberg's conclusions about the unlikelihood of Canada's fighting in 1938 over the Sudeten Germans are not justified. The evidence in the Canadian archives suggests the opposite although it may be true that the British would not have known that fact. Pearson certainly did as we have seen.

56 LBP to Skelton, Nov. 4, 1938, MG26 N1, v. 2 (NAC). For Skelton's and Wrong's reactions see their memoranda in *DCER,* 6, 1100-3, 1104-10. Wrong's memorandum sees that Canada will go to war and is exceptionally perspicacious.

57 LBP to Graham Towers, Dec. 30, 1938, MG26 N1, v. 2 (NAC).

CHAPTER 9: IN LONDON AT WAR

1 Elizabeth Bowen, *The Heat of the Day* (New York: Avon, 1979; orig. ed. 1948), 81.

2 Quoted in Martin Gilbert, *Winston S. Churchill: The Prophet of Truth 1922-1939* (Boston: Houghton Mifflin, 1977), 1001. Mike's views on rearmament and the navy are found in a "Cards on the Table" discussion of Mar. 3, 1939. The topic of the discussion was "Is England Getting Soft?" MG26 N1, v. 58 (NAC). Pearson's awe of Churchill antedated 1938. See L.B. Pearson Diary, Mar. 24, 1936, and L.B. Pearson, *Mike: The Memoirs of the Right Honourable Lester B. Pearson. Volume I: 1897-1948* (Toronto: University of Toronto Press, 1972), 126-7. A more sympathetic treatment of Chamberlain is found in Ritchie Ovendale, *"Appeasement" and the English Speaking World* (Cardiff: University of Wales Press, 1975).

3 LBP to Frank Scott, Apr. 4, 1939 (PPP). Scott's book *Canada Today* (London, Toronto, New York: Oxford, 1938) had provoked the exchange.

4 Paul Kennedy, *The Realities Behind Diplomacy* (Glasgow: Fontana, 1981), 311; Ebenezer Elliot, "When wilt Thou save the people?" *The Hymnary of the United Church of Canada* (Toronto: Ryerson Press, 1930), 527; LBP to Geoffrey Pearson, Jan. 27, 1939 (PPP); *Mike, I:* 130-1; and LBP to Skelton, Feb. 3, 1939, RG25 D1, v. 767 (NAC).

5 "Cards on the Table", July 12-13, 1938, Pearson Papers, MG26 N1, v. 58 (NAC).

6 Irving Abella and Harold Troper, *None Is Too Many* (Toronto: Lester and Orpen Dennys, 1983); Claude Bissell, *Vincent Massey: The Imperial Canadian* (Toronto: University of Toronto Press, 1986), 100ff. LBP to Annie and Vaughan Pearson, Mar. 17, 1937; LBP to Skelton, Feb. 3, 1939, Mar. 17, 1937, and Apr. 21, 1937, RG25 D1, v. 767 (NAC), ibid.

7 LBP to Skelton, Feb. 23, 1939.

8 Michael Frank Scheuer, "Loring Christie and the North Atlantic Community" (unpublished Ph.D. thesis, University of Manitoba, 1986), 553, 542; and L.C. Christie, "The European Situation", July 19, 1939, *DCER*, 6, 1205-21. The L.B. Pearson Diary indicates that Pearson, unlike Scheuer, believed that Christie wanted to have Canada neutral in September 1939. Christie stayed in the service because he was offered the Washington embassy. Pearson did not approve of the appointment.

9 O.D. Skelton, "Automatic Belligerency", Hume Wrong Papers, v. 3 (NAC). On his view of Toronto "jingoes", see Skelton to Laurier, May 30, 1917, Laurier Papers, v. 709 (NAC).

10 Skelton to Massey, June 8, 1939, in *DCER*, 6, 1194; Massey to Skelton, June 30, 1939, in *DCER*, 6, 1203; and Skelton to Massey, July 26, 1939, in *DCER*, 6, 1124-6. The best analysis of Skelton's attitude is in Norman Hillmer's brilliant article "The Anglo-Canadian Neurosis: The Case of O.D. Skelton", in Peter Lyon, ed., *Britain and Canada: Survey of a Changing Relationship* (London: Cass, 1976). See also H.B. Neatby, *William Lyon Mackenzie King. Volume 3: 1932-1939* (Toronto: University of Toronto Press, 1976), 295. See also C.P. Stacey, *Canada and the Age of Conflict. Volume 2: 1921-1948* (Toronto: University of Toronto Press, 1981), chapter 7.

11 King Diary, May 20, 1939.

12 "Cards on the Table", May 4 / 5, 1939, BBC Empire Broadcast, MG26 N1, v. 58 (NAC); Norman Hillmer, "The Incredible Canadian: Mackenzie King

and the Commonwealth", *University of Leeds Review,* vol. 22 (1979), 83-4; J.L. Granatstein and Robert Bothwell, "'A Self-Evident National Duty': Canadian Foreign Policy, 1935-1939", *Journal of Imperial and Commonwealth History* (January 1975), 212-33; House of Commons *Debates,* Mar. 20, 1939. On the continuity between "old" and "new" policies, see Simon Newman, *March 1939* (Oxford: Clarendon Press, 1976).

13 LBP to Geoffrey Pearson, June 3, 1939 (PPP); Skelton to LBP, Mar. 1, 1939, RG25 D1, v. 767 (NAC); and LBP to Skelton, June 9, 1939, ibid.; and LBP to Annie and Vaughan Pearson, May 5, 1939 (PPP).

14 King Diary, July 15, 1939.

15 Young quoted in Peter Stursberg, *Lester Pearson and the Dream of Unity* (Toronto: Doubleday Canada, 1978), 28; *Mike, I:* 133; interview with Landon Pearson; *Winnipeg Free Press,* July 20, 1939 (weather).

16 Charles Ritchie, *The Siren Years* (Toronto: Macmillan of Canada, 1974), 34 (entry of May 16, 1939); LBP to Skelton, Mar. 24, 1939, RG25 D1, v. 767 (NAC).

17 L.B. Pearson Diary, Sept. 3, 1939; and *Mike, I:* 135.

18 Ritchie, *The Siren Years,* 46; and L.B. Pearson Diary, Sept. 17, 1939, which indicates that Mike saw a fatal accident on the trip out to the Masseys.

19 L.B. Pearson Diary, Sept. 7-13, 1939.

20 Ibid., Sept. 4 and 19, and Dec. 10-11, 1939; King Diary, Sept. 21 and Oct. 24, 1939; and Bissell, *The Imperial Canadian,* chapter 4.

21 L.B. Pearson Diary, Oct. 17-20, 1939.

22 C.P. Stacey, *Arms, Men and Governments* (Ottawa: Information Canada, 1970), 19; L.B. Pearson Diary, Sept. 26, 1939; *Mike, I:* 151ff; Bissell, *The Imperial Canadian,* 137-8; LBP to King, Apr. 24, 1940, enclosing notes of conference at Canada House, King Papers, MG26 J1, v. 292 (NAC); F.J. Hatch, *Aerodrome of Democracy: Canada and the British Commonwealth Air Training Plan 1939-1945* (Ottawa: Department of National Defence, 1983), 12-16, which indicates the gaps in the record but gives credit to Massey. See, however, Cecil Edwards, *Bruce of Melbourne, Man of Two Worlds* (London: Heinemann, 1965), 279. Also, telegram Eden to King, Sept. 26, 1939, *DCER,* VII, 549-51.

23 King Diary, June 10, 1939.

24 A longer extract from Pearson's diary is quoted in *Mike, I:* 157-8, but the original has some differences.

25 L.B. Pearson Diary, Sept. 24 and Oct. 3, Nov. 27-30, Dec. 1-4, 1939; King to Eden, Oct. 8, 1939, *DCER,* VII, 170-1; Eden to King, Oct. 10, 1939, ibid., 176; and King to Eden, Nov. 25, 1939, ibid., 200-4.

26 L.B. Pearson Diary, Nov. 10, 1939; Wrong to McCloskey, Feb. 14, 1940; Granatstein, *The Ottawa Men,* 122-3; and Massey to External, Feb. 12, 1940, RG25 A12, v. 2122 (NAC).

27 Description of Wrong from Ritchie, *The Siren Years,* 195.

28 Massey to Skelton, Jan. 30, 1940, RG25 D1, McKenzie file, v. 2961, file 55 (Wrong) (NAC); and LBP to Skelton, Jan. 15, 1940, RG25, vol. 792 (NAC).

29 LBP to Annie and Vaughan Pearson, Apr. 24, 1940 (PPP); LBP to Geoffrey Pearson, Mar. 20, 1940 (PPP); LBP to Graham Towers, Nov. 22, 1940, MG26 N1, v. 16 (NAC).

30 LBP to Towers, Sept. 20, 1940, MG26 N1, v. 16 (NAC). On Towers in London, see Douglas Fullerton, *Graham Towers and His Times* (Toronto: McClelland and Stewart, 1986), 124-9; on his social life, ibid., 110-15. Other sources for this section include confidential interviews.

31 L.B. Pearson Diary, Nov. 24 and 27-Dec. 4, 1939; and Crerar to Norman Rogers, Dec. 2, 1939, Crerar Papers, MG 30 E157, vol. (NAC).

32 LBP to Skelton, Jan. 15, 1940, RG25 D1, v. 792 (NAC). "Broadcast", Dec. 22, 1939.

33 L.B. Pearson Diary, Apr. 11, 1940.

34 Ibid., Apr. 21, 1940; and J.W. Pickersgill, *The Mackenzie King Record. Volume 1: 1939-1944* (Toronto: University of Toronto Press 1960), 88-91. On Rogers, see L.B. Pearson Diary, June 9-16, 1940.

35 L.B. Pearson Diary, May 11-13, 1940; Ritchie, *The Siren Years,* 51; *Mike, I:* 165ff.

36 Ritchie, *The Siren Years,* 52. L.B. Pearson Diary, May 17-25, 1940.

37 Ritchie, *The Siren Years,* 54-5; *Mike, I:* 178-9; and Richard Collier, *1940: The World in Flames* (Harmondsworth: Penguin, 1980), 165ff.

38 Ritchie, *The Siren Years,* 57.

39 LBP to Maryon Pearson, June 25, 1940 (PPP); and *Mike, I:* 180. That francophobia was common in June 1940 is clear in Sir John Colville's diary; see his *The Fringes of Power: Downing Street Diaries: Volume One. 1939 – October 1941* (London: Sceptre, 1986), 212.

40 LBP to Towers, Nov. 22, 1940, MG26 N1, v. 16 (NAC); for a discussion of Pearson's earlier complaints and their lack of impact, see Stacey, *Arms, Men and Governments,* 141-2. Pearson's best comments are in his diary, Feb. 24, 1941.

41 LBP to Towers, ibid.; and Abella and Troper, *None Is Too Many.*

42 *Mike, I:* 185.

43 LBP to Towers, Nov. 22, 1940, MG26 N1, v. 16 (NAC).

44 Ibid.; Ritchie, *The Siren Years,* 77-9; and LBP to K.A. McCloskey, Aug. 28, 1940, Civil Service Commission Historical Personnel Files, v. 536 (NAC). Interviews with Charles Ritchie and George Ignatieff.

45 Bissell, *The Imperial Canadian,* 116; LBP to "Mother and Vaughan", Sept. 15, 1940 (PPP); and George Grant to Maude Grant, Apr. 20, 1941, W.L. Grant Papers, MG 30 D59, v. 39 (NAC). Interview with Alison and George Ignatieff.

46 E. Greey to *Globe and Mail,* Feb. 22, 1941; and George Grant to Maude Grant, Aug. 31, 1940; Dec. 22, 1940; Apr. 20, 1941; an n.d. [1942], W.L. Grant Papers, MG30 D59, v. 45 (NAC). Also on Mary Greey, Alison Grant to L. Massey, enclosed in Alice Massey to Maude Grant, June 26, 1941. W.L. Grant Papers, ibid., v. 42.

47 Robertson to LBP, Jan. 30, 1941, MG26 N1, v. 2 (NAC); and L.B. Pearson Diary, Feb. 27, 1941. For an account of the Robertson appointment, see J.L. Granatstein, *A Man of Influence: Norman A. Robertson and Canadian Statecraft 1929-1968* (Ottawa: Deneau, 1981), 104ff. Also, confidential interviews.

48 LBP to Robertson, Mar. 4, 1941, MG26 N1, v. 2 (NAC); and King Diary, May 15, 1941. On the Argentine problem, see Robertson to King, Apr. 7, 1941, *DCER,* 7, 55.

49 See *Mike, I:* 187-8. L.B. Pearson Diary, Mar. 26, 1941; and Granatstein, *Man of Influence,* 105.

50 L.B. Pearson Diary, Mar. 29, 1941; "External to High Commissioner," Mar. 28, 1941, MG26 N1, v. 8 (NAC); and King Diary, Feb. 21, 1941, where he mentions Pearson's return.

51 Massey to King, Apr. 2, 1941, MG26 N1, v. 8 (NAC); and LBP to Robertson, Apr. 2, 1941, ibid.

52 L.B. Pearson Diary, Apr. 3, 1941.

53 Graham Spry to Irene Spry, May 7, 1941, Graham Spry Papers, MG30 D297, v. 2, file 2-17 (NAC); LBP, "At a Farewell Dinner in London", in L.B. Pearson, *Words and Occasions* (Toronto: University of Toronto Press, 1970), 35-8; and L.B. Pearson Diary, Apr. 24, 1941.

54 Bowen, *The Heat of the Day,* 79-81; and Programme Notes, "The Heat of the Day", Shared Experience Production, London, 1987. Confidential interviews provided some of this material.

CHAPTER 10: WASHINGTON AT WAR

1 L.B. Pearson Diary, Feb. 8, 1943, MG26 N8, v. 8 (NAC).

2 Richard Neustadt and Ernest May, *Thinking in Time* (New York: Free Press, 1986), especially chapter 14.

3 Neville Chamberlain to Hilda Chamberlain, Dec. 17, 1937, quoted in David Dimbleby and David Reynolds, *An Ocean Apart: The Relationship Between Britain and America in the Twentieth Century* (New York: Random House, 1988), 129.

4 LBP to Claxton, Sept. 19, 1940, MG26 N1, v. 2 (NAC). Claxton had earlier written Pearson, expressing concern about American attitudes towards the war: "It is hardly too much to say that they regard the English as only the better of two evils. I think their attitude of isolation has hardened steadily. A few even face the prospect of Allied defeat without serious concern. All this could change fast enough, but the changes I see are in the wrong direction." Claxton to LBP, Apr. 27, 1940, ibid. All this, of course, did change.

5 L.B. Pearson Diary, Mar. 27, 1941. See also David MacKenzie, *Inside the Atlantic Triangle: Canada and the Entrance of Newfoundland into Confederation 1939-1949* (Toronto: University of Toronto Press, 1986), 55-61.

6 R.R. James, ed., *Winston S. Churchill: His Complete Speeches* (New York: Chelsea House Publishers, 1974), v. 6, 6695. Speech of Nov. 10, 1942.

7 Churchill sent 1,161 written messages and telegrams to Roosevelt and he sent 788 in return. There were also telephone conversations and third-party exchanges. Warren F. Kimball, ed., *Churchill and Roosevelt: The Complete Correspondence* (Princeton: Princeton University Press, 1984), I, 3. Kimball points out how scrupulously Churchill in his war memoirs emphasized the camaraderie and minimized differences. Ibid., 4ff.

8 Dimbleby and Reynolds, *An Ocean Apart,* chapters XII-XIV. David Reynolds develops these views more fully in his *The Creation of the Anglo-American Alliance, 1937-1941: A Study in Competitive Co-operation* (Chapel Hill: University of North Carolina Press, 1984), an excellent overview, which, in my opinion, however, exaggerates the difficulties and the differences. It does not do so as much or as controversially as Ritchie Ovendale, *"Appeasement" and the English-Speaking World: Britain, the United States, the Dominions and the Policy of Appeasement, 1937-1939* (Cardiff: University of Wales Press, 1975). The Americans and the Empire are treated thoroughly in W. Roger Louis, *Imperialism at Bay, 1941-1945: The United States and the Decolonization of the British Empire* (Oxford: Oxford University Press, 1977). Creighton's views are most vigorously expressed in *The Forked Road: Canada 1939-1957* (Toronto: McClelland and Stewart, 1976), especially chapters 3, 4, 7, 8, and 9.

9 On Keenleyside's role see his *Memoirs of Hugh L. Keenleyside. Volume 2. On the Bridge of Time* (Toronto: McClelland and Stewart, 1982), 105-10.

10 LBP to Massey, Jan. 7, 1942, Vincent Massey Papers, unboxed folder (University of Toronto Archives). I owe this reference to Jack Granatstein.

11 Labour people were not happy with Howe at all times but criticism was certainly muted. See Robert Bothwell and William Kilbourn, *C.D. Howe: A Biography* (Toronto: McClelland and Stewart, 1979), 162ff.

12 King Diary, May 19, 1941; *Financial Post,* July 5, 1941; and LBP to Massey, May 27, 1941, MG26 N1, v. 1 (NAC).

13 Keenleyside, *On the Bridge of Time,* 119; L.B. Pearson, *Mike: The Memoirs of the Right Honourable Lester B. Pearson. Volume I: 1897-1948* (Toronto: University of Toronto Press, 1972), 194; and J.L. Granatstein, *A Man of Influence: Norman A. Robertson and Canadian Statecraft* (Ottawa: Deneau, 1982), chapter VII. Interview with H.L. Keenleyside.

14 LBP to Massey, May 27, 1941, MG26 N1, v. 1 (NAC); and LBP to Robertson, Oct. 6, 1941, RG25 D1, v. 799 (NAC).

15 L.B. Pearson Diary, Jan. 28, 1943; Gary Evans, *John Grierson and the National Film Board: The Politics of Wartime Propaganda* (Toronto: University of Toronto Press, 1984), 92-3, 97; and W.R. Young, "Making the Truth Graphic: The Canadian Government's Home Front Information Structure and Programme During World War II" (unpublished Ph.D. thesis, University of British Columbia, 1978), which is the definitive study of Canadian wartime information activities.

16 See Walter Isaacson and Evan Thomas, *The Wise Men: Six Friends and the World They Made* (New York: Simon & Schuster, 1986), 182.

17 On Pearson and Rose, see Merrily Weisbord, *The Strangest Dream: Canadian Communists, the Spy Trials, and the Cold War* (Toronto: Lester and Orpen Dennys, 1983), 112. Norman Robertson to C.J. Mackenzie, Feb. 26, 1942; Thomas Stone to LBP, July 10, 1942; and "History of Examination Unit", Defence Department Records released under Freedom of Information Act.

18 LBP to Robertson, May 26, 1941, RG 25 G2, v. 2397 (NAC).

19 J.W. Pickersgill, *The Mackenzie King Record. Volume I: 1939-1944* (Toronto: University of Toronto Press, 1960), 188.

20 Chester Bloom to J.W. Dafoe, Oct. 20, 1941, Dafoe Papers, v. 12 (NAC). An exception to this rule of disinterest was Adolph Berle although his aim was a relationship between Canada and the United States, where barriers would be no more than state lines. Bruce Hutchinson to Dafoe, ibid. Also, Berle to Sumner Welles, Feb. 28, 1941, State Department Papers 842.20 Defence 162 (National Archives). How difficult it was to make a Canadian case is seen in Leighton McCarthy (Cdn. Minister in Washington) to King, Sept. 26, 1941, RG27c, vol. 5 (NAC). The best brief survey of American views is Robert Bothwell and John Kirton, "'A Sweet Little Country': American Attitudes Towards Canada, 1925-1963", *Queen's Quarterly* (Winter 1983), 1078-1102.

21 Nancy Harvison Hooker, ed., *The Moffat Papers* (Cambridge, Mass.: Harvard University Press, 1956), 369-70.

22 LBP to Massey, Jan. 9, 1942, MG26 N1, v. 1 (NAC).

23 King Diary, Feb. 19, 1941; and LBP, "Memorandum for the Under-secretary", Mar. 4, 1942, MG26 N1, v. 7 (NAC).

24 LBP, "Memo for the Under-secretary", Mar. 6, 1942, Pearson Papers, MG26 N1, v. 7 (NAC) and LBP to Claxton, Jan. 30, 1942, Claxton Papers, MG32 B5, v. 62 (NAC).

25 Confidential interviews.

26 *Mike, I:* 132, 201.

27 Salary Schedule, L.B. Pearson, Civil Service Commission, Historical Personnel Files, RG32 C2, v. 536 (NAC).

28 *Mike, I:* 202.

29 Malcolm Cowley, "Washington Is Like Hell", *The New Republic* (June 1942), 769.

30 On this distinction, see John English and Norman Hillmer, "Canada's Alliances", *Revue Internationale d'Histoire Militaire* (1982), 31-52.

31 L.B. Pearson Diary, Jan. 7, 1943; McCarthy to King, June 9, 1944, King Papers, MG26 J1, v. 364 (NAC); McCarthy to King, July 24, 1944, ibid; and McCarthy to Robertson, July 27, 1944, ibid.

32 Ibid. Also, Massey to King, Apr. 2, 1941, RG25, v. 423 (NAC); Vincent Massey Diary, Mar. 7, 1944; and interviews with George Ignatieff, Escott Reid, Henry Angus, and Charles Ritchie. The Massey Diary reference I owe to Jack Granatstein. On Pearson's reputation as a poor administrator, see James Eayrs, *In Defence of Canada: Peacemaking and Deterrence* (Toronto: University of Toronto Press, 1972), 37.

33 Gordon Skilling, *Canadian Representation Abroad: From Agency to Embassy* (Toronto: Ryerson Press, 1945), 307.

34 L.B. Pearson Diary, Jan. 7, 1943.

35 Ibid., Jan. 30, 1943. In correcting this entry for his memoirs, Pearson corrected the punctuation and removed "Rotarianism" and replaced "political" with "high official". He also omitted the number of film stars and changed "graced 'The head table'" to "graced 'the occasion'." See *Mike, I:* 205.

36 LBP, "An Analysis of the N.R.A.", June 1, 1934, MG26 N1, v. 10 (NAC).

37 On this topic see Robert Bothwell and John English, "The View from Inside Out: Canadian Diplomats and Their Public", *International Journal* (Winter 1983-4), 47-67.

38 L.B. Pearson Diary, Apr. 9, 1945.

39 LBP to McCarthy (copy given to King), Mar. 18, 1943, in *DCER*, 9, 1138-42.

40 LBP to Robertson, Jan. 9, 1945, MG26 NI, v. 2 (NAC). See also LBP to Robertson, Oct. 24, 1944, ibid.

41 L.B. Pearson Diary, Feb. 13, 1943.

42 LBP to Robertson, Sept. 28, 1944, MG26 NI, v. 13 (NAC). Also, LBP to Acting Secretary of State for External Affairs, May 10, 1944, King Papers, MG26 JI, v. 364 (NAC).

43 LBP to Robertson, Oct. 30, 1944, MG26 NI, v. 2 (NAC). On Hickerson, see Bothwell and Kirton, "A Sweet Little Country".

44 LBP to Macdonell, Mar. 21, 1944, External Affairs Records, file 1915-56 (External Affairs Dept.).

45 Quoted in John Gaddis, *The United States and the Origins of the Cold War, 1941-1947* (New York and London: Columbia University Press, 1972), 27.

46 Although increasingly suspicious of Stalin, he continued to respect and sympathize with some Soviet diplomats. L.B. Pearson Diary, Mar. 7, 1945.

47 LBP to Robertson, Mar. 6, 1945, filed in L.B. Pearson Diary. Also see Pearson's comments on March 12, 1945, reporting on United Nations lecture series where four senators spoke but only William Fulbright had something to say.

48 *Mike, I:* 237, 269.

49 See "Official Canadian Comments on Dumbarton Oaks", Feb. 9, 1945. Alger Hiss Papers, RG59 61-D-146, Box 1 (National Archives of the United States).

50 J.G. Parsons, "Canadian Views on Dumbarton Oaks", Jan. 11, 1945, State Department Papers 500-CC / 2-345 FIS (National Archives). L.B. Pearson Diary, Mar. 30 and Apr. 1, 1945. On the State Department poll, see Robert Dallek, *The American Style of Foreign Policy* (New York: Knopf, 1983), 135-6.

51 L.B. Pearson Diary, Apr. 30, 1945.

52 The Soviets were "not a very gracious lot at this conference." L.B. Pearson Diary, Apr. 12, 1945.

53 LBP to Achilles, Apr. 29, 1943, MG26 N1, v. 19 (NAC); and LBP to Secretary of State for External Affairs, June 25, 1943, ibid.

54 John Cheever, *The Stories of John Cheever* (New York: Ballantyne, 1980), preface, ix.

55 L.B. Pearson Diary, Apr. 12, 1945. He added: "Whether they shake your hands or step on your toes the pain is almost equally great."

56 On the Europeans, see H. Stuart Hughes, *The Sea Change* (New York: Harper & Row, 1975). Daniel Boorstin, *The Image or What Happened to the American Dream* (New York: Atheneum, 1962), 3.

57 Verena Garrioch, "Wife of Canadian Ambassador Finds Time to Aid War Effort", Patricia Pearson Hannah Scrapbook (in possession of Patricia Pearson Hannah).

58 *Mike, I:* 203-4. Interviews with Geoffrey Pearson and Patricia Pearson Hannah.

59 Interview of Charles Lynch with L.B. Pearson [1964?] (PPP).

CHAPTER II: THE WORLD STAGE

1 Mackenzie King describing conversation with Grant Dexter, King Diary, Oct. 17, 1946.

2 Charles Ritchie, *The Siren Years* (Toronto: McClelland and Stewart, 1974), 136.

3 LBP, "UNO as Seen from Canada", Address delivered before English Speaking Union, Princeton, N.J., May 13, 1946, MG26 N9, V. 1 (NAC).

4 The Gallup poll revealed that in May 1945, 90 per cent of Canadians favoured joining a world organization to keep the peace. In January, 72 per cent approved of Canada's contributing to a permanent international force to enforce the peace. Quebec was more reluctant than other parts of Canada, but the figures are impressive. For fuller details, see Mildred Schwartz,

Public Opinion and Canadian Identity (Scarborough: McGraw-Hill, 1967), 77-82. On the American figures, which are similar, see Robert Dallek, *The American Style of Foreign Policy* (New York: Knopf, 1983), 132. Both Canadian and American polling results and other international results are given in *Public Opinion Quarterly* for these years.

5 Michael Barkway, "Lester Pearson: Reluctant Politician", *Saturday Night,* Apr. 26, 1952, 13. Barkway points out the somewhat macabre fact that Pearson is the subject of more advance obituary notices in international news-organization files than any other Canadian.

6 Reg Whitaker, "The Myth of Liberal Internationalism", paper presented to Canadian Historical Association Annual Meeting, Winnipeg, 1986. The hymn is by Frederick Hosmer, "Thy Kingdom Come, O Lord", *The Hymnary of the United Church* (Toronto: Ryerson Press, 1930), Hymn 526. Erikson's contributions are described well in Robert Coles, *Erik Erikson: The Growth of His Work* (New York: DaCapo, 1970).

7 LBP to Geoffrey Pearson, June 6, 1945 (PPP).

8 Patricia Pearson Hannah, "My Father, the Prime Minister", *Chatelaine,* September 1963, 28-9, 93-6, and LBP to Patricia Pearson Hannah, Nov. 13, 1940 (PPP).

9 LBP to Patricia Pearson Hannah, Dec. 1940 (PPP).

10 Quoted in "My Father, the Prime Minister", 94.

11 Ibid., 95.

12 Vanier to LBP, July 23, 1943, MG26 N1, V. 11 (NAC).

13 Again broader economic trends and conditions were propitious. The war had forced nations, combatants and non-combatants, to override often the interests of domestic producers and consumers. Moreover, the Allies had to develop international food policies in the Middle East and India, because of military events. See the excellent discussion in Alan S. Milward, *War, Economy and Society, 1939-1945* (London: A. Lane, 1977), 252ff.

14 *FAO: The First 40 Years* (Rome: Food and Agricultural Organization, 1985), chapter 1.

15 L.B. Pearson Diary, Mar. 17, 21, Apr. 5, 12, 27, and entry for May 2-10, 1943; and L.B. Pearson, *Mike: The Memoirs of the Right Honourable Lester B.*

Pearson. Volume I: 1897-1948 (Toronto: University of Toronto Press, 1972), 245-6.

16 L.B. Pearson Diary, entry for week of May 2-10, 1943.

17 Ibid., May 17, 1943. A fuller quotation is found in *Mike I:* 246-7.

18 L.B. Pearson Diary, May 18, 1943; and *Mike I:* 247. A different account is found in John Holmes, *The Shaping of Peace: Canada and the Search for World Order 1943-1957,* Volume I (Toronto: University of Toronto Press, 1979), 47ff.

19 See *Mike I:* 248, where the omission disturbs the sense of what is in the original. Pearson removes the criticism of the Americans' skills. Contrast the later remarks of American delegate Howard Tolley who claims that the conference and its aftermath really amounted to spreading the popular New Deal world-wide. Interview with Tolley, Columbia Oral History Project, Columbia University.

20 L.B. Pearson Diary, May 26-30, 1943; *New York Times,* May 29, 1943; and *Mike I:* 248.

21 L.B. Pearson Diary, June 1, 1943; *FAO: The First 40 Years,* 8-9, and Interview with Howard Tolley, former Chief of U.S. Bureau of Agricultural Economics, Columbia University Oral History Archives.

22 Cherwell to Churchill, Jan. 20, 1944, PREM 4 / 29 / 7 (PRO). He did add that the FAO's staff should not be given diplomatic immunities. "Of course it is very nice to belong to such a body and enjoy all these privileges but it will set a precedent for which there seems little justification."

23 Interview with Howard Tolley, Chief of Bureau of Agricultural Economics, Columbia University Oral History Archives; and interview with P.V. Cardon, ibid.; and "First Conference of the Food and Agriculture Organization", CAB 133177 / 113430 (PRO). The last document points out how Acheson disagrees with the American posture.

24 *Mike I:* 249; Escott Reid, *On Duty: A Canadian at the Making of the United Nations, 1945-1946* (Kent, Ohio: Kent State University Press, 1983); and interview with Escott Reid.

25 F.L. McDougall to Gladwyn Jebb, Nov. 19, 1945, PAG 6 / 1.1, Box 10 (United Nations Archives); W.F.A. Turgeon, on behalf of Quebec govern-

ment, to Jebb, Oct. 3, 1945, PAG 6 / 1.1, Box 9, ibid.; *Toronto Daily Star,* Oct. 18 and 21, 1945; and *Mike I:* 249.

26 *Globe and Mail,* Feb. 24, 1945.

27 The excellent Granatstein account of the development of functionalism is found in *The Ottawa Men: The Civil Service Mandarins, 1935-1957* (Toronto: Oxford, 1982), 124ff. A more theoretical discussion is found in Anthony John Miller, "Functionalism and Foreign Policy: An Analysis of Canadian Voting Behaviour in the General Assembly of the United Nations, 1946-1966" (unpublished Ph.D. thesis, McGill University, 1970), especially 3-32, 75-100.

28 The Canadian move towards left-liberal nationalism is traced in J.L. Granatstein, *Canada's War: The Politics of the Mackenzie King Government, 1939-1945* (Toronto: Oxford, 1975), especially chapters 7 and 8. The famous Gallup poll showing the young CCF party with the support of 29 per cent of the population and the other parties with 28 per cent each occurred in September 1943.

29 L.B. Pearson Diary, Feb. 26-Mar. 4, 1943; *Mike I:* 250ff; and Susan Armstrong, "Canada's Role in the United Nations Relief and Rehabilitation Administration" (unpublished Ph.D. thesis, University of Toronto, 1981), which is the definitive account of the subject.

30 Dean Acheson, *Present at the Creation* (New York: Norton, 1969), 70; Stephen Holmes to Noel Hall, Mar. 18, 1943, FO 371136607 (PRO); LBP to Robertson, Mar. 15, 1943, MG26 N1 V. 12 (NAC); *DCER,* 9, documents 661-715 (UNRRA); Robertson, "Memorandum for the Prime Minister, March 17, 1943", MG26 J4, V. 243 (NAC); and L.B. Pearson Diary, Mar. 14, 1943. See also, Holmes, *The Shaping of Peace,* 38-40; and J.L. Granatstein, *A Man of Influence,* 141-3.

31 Mike wrote in his diary on April 16, 1943: "Extraordinary these days how everybody from the highest to the lowest talks incessantly about Russia, with a mixture of admiration and suspicion." The same year saw the famed issue of *Life* completely devoted to the Soviet Union.

32 Hopkins's comment is quoted in George McJimsey, *Harry Hopkins: Ally of the Poor and Defender of Democracy* (Cambridge, Mass.: Harvard University Press, 1988), 281. On Eden's visit, which played a role in the settlement, see David Carlton, *Anthony Eden* (London: A. Lane, 1981), chapter 7. On the

broader question of the U.S., the U.K., and the attitude of both, see Christopher Thorne's brilliant *Allies of a Kind: The United States, Britain and the War Against Japan, 1941-1945* (London: Hamish Hamilton, 1978).

33 Canada did become a member of the Executive Committee in 1945, as did France.

34 Brooke Claxton, "The Place of Canada in Post-War Organization", *The Canadian Journal of Economics and Political Science,* Vol. 10 (November 1944), 409.

35 *Globe and Mail,* Jan. 17-18, 1942; Peter Gellman, "Lester Pearson, Collective Security and the World Order Tradition of Canadian Foreign Policy" (unpublished Ph.D. thesis, University of Virginia, 1988); and especially the exchange between George Brown and Pearson on idealism in Brown to LBP, Jan. 28, 1942, MG26 N1, V. 2 (NAC) and LBP to Brown, Feb. 9, 1942, ibid.

36 LBP to Robertson, Mar. 11, 1942, *DCER* 9, 866-7; and Wrong, Memorandum to Robertson, Dec. 16, 1943, ibid., 880-1.

37 The description "little disagreement" comes from Granatstein, *A Man of Influence,* 146. John Holmes minimizes differences in *The Shaping of Peace,* 1, but see his comments on pp. 234-5.

38 Reid, *On Duty,* 13-16; and Holmes, ibid., 234-5.

39 Although Churchill is blamed for this concept of regionalism, the British concerns about Canada's place and regional solutions were thought of by others earlier. See Malcolm MacDonald to Viscount Cranborne, Feb. 3, 1942, Macdonald Papers, 12 / 4126, Royal Commonwealth Society.

40 J.G. Parsons, "Canadian Views on Dumbarton Oaks", Jan. 13, 1945, State Department Records, RG59, 500 CC / 2-345 CSIEG (NAC); and LBP to Robertson, Feb. 27, 1945, with enclosure, King Papers, MG26 J1, V. 389 (NAC).

41 L.B. Pearson, "Difficulties in the Way of International Cooperation", Feb. 23, 1945, MG26 N9, v. 1 (NAC).

42 On Reston, Vandenberg, and Pearson, see LBP to Robertson, Oct. 6, 1944, King Papers, MG26 J1, V. 368 (NAC); and L.B. Pearson Diary, Mar. 30, 1945. On Vandenberg's conversion, see Selig Adler, *The Isolationist Impulse:*

Its Twentieth Century Reaction (New York: The Free Press, 1957), 314-16. See on Reston and Pearson, Norman Smith, "Pearson, Press, and People", *International Journal,* Winter 1973-4, 16-17.

43 L.B. Pearson Diary, May 3, 1945. The other information in this paragraph is drawn from the diary. Also, Maurice Pope Diary, Apr. 25, 1945. MG27 IIIF4, V. 1 (NAC).

44 L.B. Pearson Diary, May 10, 1945.

45 Ibid., May 11, 1945.

46 Ibid., June 17, 1945; *Mike I:* 276-7. Reid, *On Duty,* 134-5 (which supports Pearson's opinion of Evatt); J.W. Pickersgill and D.F. Forster, eds., *The Mackenzie King Record, Volume II: 1944-1945,* (Toronto: University of Toronto Press, 1968), chapter 10; and Paul Hasluck, *Diplomatic Witness: Australian Foreign Affairs, 1941-1947* (Melbourne: Melbourne University Press, 1980), 237.

47 Ritchie wrote in his diary on June 19, 1945: "The Soviet delegates have got very little good-will out of this Conference. They use aggressive tactics about every question large or small. They remind people of Nazi diplomatic methods and create, sometimes needlessly, suspicions and resentment." *The Siren Years,* 201.

48 *Mike I:* 256-7; Robert Bothwell and J.L. Granatstein, eds., *The Gouzenko Transcripts* (Ottawa: Deneau, n.d.), 3-21; LBP to Wrong, Oct. 1, 1945, NG26 N1, V. 3 (NAC); and King Diary, Oct. 1, 1945. Many documents that deal with this subject are missing. On Robertson's perception of the civil service and the impact of Gouzenko, see Granatstein, *A Man of Influence,* 174.

49 J.W. Pickersgill and D.F. Forster, eds., *The Mackenzie King Record. Volume III: 1945-1946* (Toronto: University of Toronto Press, 1962), 40ff; Hugh Thomas, *Armed Truce* (New York, 1987), 452ff; and, most important, on Canada's part, Robert Bothwell, *Nucleus* (Toronto: University of Toronto Press, 1988).

50 L.B. Pearson, "To a Church Group in Ottawa", Apr. 11, 1934, in *Words and Occasions* (Toronto: University of Toronto Press, 1970), 14.

51 Paul Boyer, *By the Bomb's Early Light: American Thought and Culture at the Dawn of the Atomic Age* (New York: Pantheon, 1985), 15, 21-2.

52 L.B. Pearson, "Canadian Memorandum on Atomic Warfare", Nov. 8, 1945, MG26 J1, V. 389 (NAC). The document is reproduced in its entirety in J.A. Munro and A.L. Inglis, "The Atomic Conference 1945 and the Pearson Memoirs", *International Journal,* Winter 1973-4, 94-9.

53 Ibid.

54 This subject, American and British views of economic security, has attracted considerable historical debate. Early revisionist work emphasized the economic basis of American international policy, but the recent economic problems of the United States have brought some reassessment. For a good analysis of the literature and of the problems, see Robert A. Pollard, *Economic Security and the Origins of the Cold War, 1945-1950* (New York: Columbia University Press, 1985), especially chapters 1, 9, and 11. On British attitudes in late summer 1945, see Alan Bullock, *Ernest Bevin: Foreign Secretary* (New York and London: Norton, 1983), 193-5, and the Bevin memorandum on which Bullock's discussion is based: FO800 / 478 / MIS / 45 / 14 (PRO).

55 Mike's own accounts of the meeting differ somewhat. See *Mike I:* 259-60; L.B. Pearson, *Peace in the Family of Man* (Toronto: Oxford University Press, and New York, 1969), 12; and the original Pearson memorandum on the subject, which is reprinted in full in Munro and Inglis, "The Atomic Conference 1945 and the Pearson Memoirs", 101-8.

56 *Mike I:* 263; Lewis Clark, U.S. Embassy, Ottawa, to J.G. Parsons, State Department, Nov. 15, 1945, RG59, State Department, 842.00 / 7-2645 (National Archives). Eayrs, *Peacemaking and Deterrence,* 281ff; Margaret Gowing, assisted by L. Arnold, *Independence and Deterrence: Britain and Atomic Energy, 1945-1952,* Volume I (London: Macmillan, 1974), 76; Gregg Herken, *The Winning Weapon: The Atomic Bomb in the Cold War, 1945-1950* (New York: Knopf, 1982); and Robert Bothwell, *Eldorado* (Toronto: University of Toronto Press, 1984), 159ff.

57 J.G. Parsons, Memorandum of meeting, Oct. 19, 1945, RG59, State Department, 711.42 / 10-1945 (National Archives).

58 King Diary, Jan. 10, 11, 12, 1943; "Canadian and Post-War Organisation", Jan. 14, 1945, with attached minutes by P. Falla and Charles Webster. FO371 / 50673 / 117417 (PRO); and Earl of Halifax to Foreign Office, Oct. 11, 1945, with attached minutes by P.J. Noel-Baker, Oct. 15, 1945. FO371 / 45646 / 118688 (PRO).

59 Stephen Holmes, U.K. Embassy, Washington, to Dominions Office, May 17, 1944. FO371 / 40596 / 117417 (PRO).

60 Edward Stettinius to LBP, June 23, 1945, quoted in James Barros, "Pearson or Lie: The Politics of the Secretary-General's Selection, 1946", *Canadian Journal of Political Science,* March 1977, 67. Professor Barros's article is definitive on this topic.

61 Barros, ibid., 77-8. In his diary, Pearson describes Acheson as distant and he found Hickerson often frustrating. His diary does not indicate any of the affection he felt for, say, James Reston or Maurice Pope, the latter an individual with whom he disagreed on many items.

62 This account is drawn from Barros, ibid.; Granatstein, *A Man of Influence,* 155-6; *Mike I:* 280; J.W. Pickersgill and D.F. Forster, *The Mackenzie King Record. Volume III,* 62, 123-4; Boyd Shannon to P.S. Falla, Oct. 3, 1945, with enclosures FO371 / 50885 / 118688 (PRO); Dean Acheson to Edward Stettinius, Sept. 22, 1945, RG59, 500.CC / (PC) / 9-1945 (NAC); Charles Webster Diary, Sept. 1945-Jan. 1946, Library, London School of Economics and Political Science; and Wrong to Robertson, Jan. 30, 1946, MG26 N1, V. 11 (NAC).

63 Wrong to LBP, Jan. 30, 1946, MG26 N1, V. 11 (NAC).

64 LBP to Pope, Feb. 14, 1946, ibid.

65 This comment is not in the Pearson memoirs although the preceding passage is. The result is a misleading impression of Mike's career consideration and his ambitions. See *Mike I:* 281; and J.W. Pickersgill and D.F. Forster, *The Mackenzie King Record. Volume III,* 123-4.

66 See draft of letter to King, Aug. 1946, MG26 N1, V. 7 (NAC); Leighton McCarthy to LBP, Sept. 9, 1946, and LBP to McCarthy, Sept. 13, 1946, MG26 N1, V. 6 (NAC).

67 W.C. Costin to LBP, June 1, 1946, MG26 N1, V. 8 (NAC); and LBP to Heeney, June 22, 1946, ibid.

CHAPTER 12: "A SORT OF ARMAGEDDON"

1 George Drew to John Diefenbaker, Mar. 16, 1946. Diefenbaker Papers, 1940-1956 Series, Box 51 (John G. Diefenbaker Centre, Saskatoon).

2 J.W. Pickersgill and D.F. Forster, *The Mackenzie King Record 1945-1946. Volume III* (Toronto: University of Toronto Press, 1970), 367.

3 LBP to Mackenzie King, Nov. 12, 1946, in *DCER*, 12: 1670-2.

4 Denis Smith, *Diplomacy of Fear: Canada and the Cold War 1941-1948* (Toronto: University of Toronto Press, 1988), 168; Reg Whitaker, "The Cold War and the Myth of Liberal Internationalism", paper presented at Canadian Historical Association Annual Meeting, 1986; and, for an earlier "revisionist" view, R.D. Cuff and J.L. Granatstein, *Canadian-American Relations in Wartime: From the Great War to the Cold War* (Toronto: Hakkert, 1975), especially chapter 6.

5 L.B. Pearson, "Some Principles of Canadian Foreign Policy", in *Words and Occasions* (Toronto: University of Toronto Press, 1970), 68-9.

6 Cuff and Granatstein, *Canadian-American Relations*, 117, 129.

7 John Costello, *Mask of Treachery* (New York: William Morrow, 1988), 580.

8 James Barros, "Letter to the Editor," *International Perspectives* (March / April 1989), 24. Also, James Barros, *No Sense of Evil: The Espionage Case of E. Herbert Norman* (Toronto: Deneau, 1986). Early examples of suspicion about Pearson can be found in "Is Canadian Foreign Policy Aiding the Kremlin?", *The Canadian Intelligence Service* (Jan. 1954), 1-6. Pearson and the allegations are also discussed in Roger Bowen, *Innocence Is Not Enough: The Life and Death of Herbert Norman* (Vancouver: Douglas & McIntyre, 1986), 344-53.

9 John Gaddis, "Intelligence, Espionage, and Cold War Origins", *Diplomatic History* (Spring 1989), 195.

10 "Testimony of Elizabeth Bentley, Clinton, Connecticut", J.G. Diefenbaker Papers, Box 11, 008386-8392 (Diefenbaker Centre, Saskatoon).

11 Hazen Sise to Charles Sise, Dec. 4, 1936, Hazen Sise Papers, MG30 D187, v. 5 (NAC); and Sise Diary, Dec. 1, 1936, v. 9, ibid. On the Nazis and architecture, see B.M. Lane, *Architecture and Politics in Germany, 1918-1945* (Cambridge: Harvard University Press, 1968).

12 Bruce Hutchison, *The Far Side of the Street* (Toronto: Macmillan of Canada, 1976), 249. John Holmes also related to me his surprise when Mike told

others "secrets". On Sise's denial, see Bowen, *Innocence Is Not Enough,* 348. Sise is discussed anonymously in L.B. Pearson, *Mike: The Memoirs of the Right Honourable Lester B. Pearson. Volume 3: 1957-1968* (Toronto: University of Toronto Press, 1975), 167-8.

13 The Pearson file was obtained under FBI Freedom of Information Access request number 262554. I am indebted to Professor William Kaplan for this information. Press reports on Pearson's "communism" include *Washington Times-Herald,* Mar. 18 and Dec. 7, 1953; *Washington Star,* Nov. 23-4, 1953; and *Toronto Daily Star,* Nov. 23, 1953.

14 Bradley Smith, "Sharing Ultra in World War II", *International Journal of Intelligence and Counterintelligence* (Spring 1988), 59-72; Gaddis, "Intelligence, Espionage, and Cold War", 194; and Donald Avery, "Secrets Between Different Kinds of Friends: Canada's Wartime Exchange of Scientific Military Information with the United States and the U.S.S.R.", paper presented at Canadian Historical Association Annual Meeting 1986.

15 A.D.P. Heeney Diary, Sept. 24-5, 1955. Heeney Papers, MG30 E144, v. 2 (NAC); Hutchison, *The Far Side of the Street* (Toronto: Macmillan of Canada, 1976); Tom Kent, *A Public Purpose: An Experience of Liberal Opposition and Canadian Government* (Kingston: McGill-Queen's University Press, 1988); and Denis Smith, *A Political Biography of Walter Gordon* (Edmonton: Hurtig, 1973).

16 LBP to H.D.G. Crerar, Dec. 30, 1938. Crerar Papers, MG30 E154, v. 10 (NAC).

17 L.B. Pearson, *Mike: The Memoirs of the Right Honourable Lester B. Pearson. Volume 1. 1897-1948* (Toronto: University of Toronto Press, 1972), 257-8; Fraser J. Harbutt, *The Iron Curtain: Churchill, America, and the Origins of the Cold War* (New York and Oxford: Oxford University Press, 1986), 285; and Smith, *Diplomacy of Fear,* 232-3.

18 See John Gaddis, *The United States and the Origins of the Cold War 1941-1947* (New York: Columbia University Press, 1972), 321-2.

19 Smith, *Diplomacy of Fear,* 227; John Gaddis, *The Long Peace: Inquiries into the History of the Cold War* (New York and Oxford: Oxford University Press, 1987), 236; and Toast to Robertson, Wrong, and Pearson, Sept. 1946. Escott Reid Papers, MG31 E46, v. 13 (NAC).

20 J.W. Pickersgill and D.F. Forster, *Mackenzie King Record,* III, 372; J.L. Granatstein, *A Man of Influence: Norman A. Robertson and Canadian Statecraft 1929-1968* (Ottawa: Deneau, 1981); George Glazebrook, "Hume Wrong", unpublished memoir; and Reid toast.

21 Pickersgill and Forster, *The Mackenzie King Record,* III, 336; interview with Charles Lynch (1964?); and *Mike, I:* 279ff.

22 Interview with Paul Martin. Numerous colleagues of St. Laurent whom I have interviewed speak in these laudatory terms about St. Laurent.

23 An account of these activities is found in Don Munton and Don Page, "Planning in the East Block: The Post-Hostilities Problems Committees in Canada 1943-5", *International Journal* (Autumn 1977), 687-726.

24 John Holmes, *The Shaping of Peace: Canada and the Search for World Order 1943-1957. Volume 1* (Toronto: University of Toronto Press, 1979), 159.

25 LBP to Norman Robertson, Nov. 5, 1946. MG26 N1, v. 83 (NAC).

26 Pickersgill and Forster, *Mackenzie King Record,* III, 294-5; interview with Geoffrey Pearson; and John Taylor, *Ottawa: An Illustrated History* (Toronto: Lorimer, 1986), chapter 5.

27 Lord Garner, "Mike: An Englishman's View", *International Journal* (Winter 1973-4), 37; confidential interviews; and Douglas Fullerton, *Graham Towers and His Times* (Toronto: McClelland and Stewart, 1986), 107ff.

28 Wilgress to St. Laurent, Apr. 25, 1947, quoted in J.L. Granatstein, *The Ottawa Men: The Civil Service Mandarins 1935-1957* (Toronto: Oxford, 1982), 236.

29 Interview with Escott Reid. See also Whitaker, "The Myth of Liberal Internationalism"; and Victor Levant, *Quiet Complicity: Canadian Involvement in the Vietnam War* (Toronto: Between the Lines, 1986), Introduction. The definitive account of the period is Escott Reid, *Time of Fear and Hope: The Making of the North Atlantic Treaty 1947-1949* (Toronto: McClelland and Stewart, 1977), 234ff.

30 Robert Bothwell and John English, "Canadian Political Parties, Public Opinion, and National Security in the Post-war Period", in David Davies, ed., *Canada and the Soviet Union* (forthcoming).

31 I am indebted to John Hilliker of the Department of External Affairs for this information.

32 Ibid.

33 Charles Ritchie, *Diplomatic Passport: More Undiplomatic Diaries, 1946-1962* (Toronto: McClelland and Stewart, 1981), 6-7.

34 The two major works expressing these different viewpoints are Alan Milward, *The Reconstruction of Western Europe, 1945-1951* (London: Methuen, 1984) and Michael J. Hogan, *America, Britain and the Reconstruction of Western Europe, 1947-1952* (Cambridge: Cambridge University Press, 1987). For a critique of Hogan and his "corporatist" view, see J.L. Gaddis, "The Corporatist Synthesis: A Skeptical View", *Diplomatic History* (Fall 1986), 357-62.

35 The lecture is reprinted in R.A. MacKay, ed., *Canadian Foreign Policy 1945-54: Selected Speeches and Documents* (Toronto: McClelland and Stewart, 1971), 388-99.

36 LBP to St. Laurent, May 21, 1947, King Papers, MG26 J4, v. 241 (NAC).

37 King Diary, Aug. 24, 1946.

38 L.B. Pearson, *Mike: I*, 213. The account here borrows heavily from Anne Hillmer, "Canadian Policy on the Partition of Palestine" (unpublished M.A. thesis, Carleton University, 1981) and David Bercuson, *Canada and the Birth of Israel* (Toronto: University of Toronto Press), 67ff.

39 LBP to Massey, Nov. 16, 1947, MG26 N1, v. 10 (NAC); and LBP to Robertson, Dec. 30, 1947, External Affairs Records, RG25, A12, v. 2093.

40 John Holmes, *The Shaping of Peace: Canada and the Search for World Order 1943-1957. Volume 2* (Toronto: University of Toronto Press, 1982), 63; Bruce Hutchison, "Memo from New York", Nov. 15, 1947. Hutchison Papers, University of Calgary; and King Diary, Oct.-Nov. 1947. *Passim.*

41 J.W. Pickersgill and Donald Forster, *The Mackenzie King Record, 1947-1948. Volume IV* (Toronto: University of Toronto Press, 1970), chapter 4; and Geraldine Cummins, quoted in Gregory Johnson, "North Pacific Triangle?: The Impact of the Far East on Canada and Its Relations with the United States and Great Britain, 1937-1948" (unpublished Ph.D. thesis, York University, 1989), 327-8.

42 *King Record,* IV, 134-6.

43 "Canada and the United Nations Temporary Commission on Korea", Dec. 20, 1947, Privy Council Office Records, v. 84 (NAC); and *King Record,* IV, 136, 138.

44 *Mike, II:* 134ff; and *King Record,* IV, 146.

45 *King Record,* IV, 151.

46 Interviews with Paul Martin and J.W. Pickersgill.

47 *Mike, II:* 139 (quoting from contemporary diary); and *King Record,* IV, 146.

48 *King Record,* IV, 267-8.

49 Ibid., 270-2. Pearson expressed his disappointment to Robertson in a letter of Apr. 22, 1948, MG26NI, v. 13 (NAC). On the negotiations and their background, see especially Robert Cuff and J.L. Granatstein, *American Dollars – Canadian Prosperity: Canadian-American Economic Relations 1945-1950* (Toronto: Samuel Stevens, 1978).

50 *King Record,* IV, 367-8.

51 Interview with Beryl Plumptre.

52 *Mike, II:* 7; and *Ottawa Journal,* Sept. 13, 1948.

53 Gaddis, *The Long Peace,* 224. The University of Michigan's "Correlates of War" project has shown that the ten worst wars between 1816 and 1980 developed out of conflicts between states whose borders were contiguous or who traded heavily with each other.

A NOTE ON SOURCES

A full bibliography will be published in Volume 2 of this biography. It is, of course, impossible to divide the sources neatly between Pearson's life before and after 1949. Nevertheless, some sources were especially useful for this volume. The notes indicate the variety of sources used, but some comments may be helpful.

The bulk of Lester Pearson's public and private papers are deposited at the National Archives of Canada. As one might expect, most of these papers deal with his public career, but, for a biographer, the earliest writings, notably the diary, are invaluable. In addition to the papers at the archives, the Pearson family retains family correspondence, memorabilia, and a few other documents that have assisted me greatly in filling in gaps and in describing Pearson's family life. Patricia and Geoffrey Pearson have been most generous. I have also received material from Fred Pearson and Pamela Phillips, and am most grateful to them. Herbert Moody, Maryon Pearson's brother, helped in explaining the Moody family.

The National Archives was the treasure trove it always is for Canadian historians. Besides the Pearson papers, the following manuscript collections yielded information:

Government Records:

Civil Service Commission Historical Personnel Records

Department of External Affairs Records

Department of National Defence Records

Department of Trade and Commerce Records

Privy Council Office Records
Royal Commission on
  Grain Futures

Royal Commission on
  Price Spreads

Other Papers

Laurent Beaudry
R.B. Bennett
Robert Borden
A.L. Burt
Canadian Institute of
International Affairs
Loring Christie
Brooke Claxton
Donald Creighton
H.D.G. Crerar
J.W. Dafoe
Jean Désy
George Foster
A.D.P. Heeney
C.D. Howe
H.R. Kemp
W.L.M. King
K.P. Kirkwood

R.A. MacKay
A.G.L. McNaughton
Robert Manion
Paul Martin
Massey Family
Arthur Meighen
George Perley
M.A. Pope
J.L. Ralston
John Read
Escott Reid
Norman Robertson
Newton R. Rowell
Louis St. Laurent
Graham Spry
H.H. Stevens
Frank Underhill
Hume Wrong

Other collections in Canada contain some material on Pearson, the most valuable being the Bruce Hutchison Papers at the University of Calgary and the Grant Dexter Papers at Queen's University. The University of Toronto Archives has the history department records and the papers of George Brown, W.P.M. Kennedy, Gerry Riddell, and George Wrong. Trinity College Archives has the papers of George Ignatieff. Victoria College Archives has some material relating to the Pearson family, Lester Pearson, and Maryon Pearson. The University of British Columbia Archives has the papers of three friends of Pearson: Henry Angus, Norman Mackenzie, and Alan Plaunt. York University has the valuable W.A. Riddell Papers. Queen's also has the papers of T. A. Crerar, Norman Lambert,

J.M. Macdonnell, W.A. Mackintosh, Norman Rogers, and John Stevenson. The T.W.L. MacDermot Papers at Bishop's University were disappointing.

The Archives of Ontario has the G. Howard Ferguson Papers and scattered other materials that assisted in tracing the Pearson family background. Kenneth Reid has traced the Pearson family's Irish roots and allowed me to see the essay he wrote. R.P. Bowles wrote a history of the Bowles family that the family kindly provided. Newspapers, especially *The Chatham Daily Planet,* were notably illuminating in giving details on Pearson's early years. *The Christian Guardian* and *Acta Victoriana* yielded some surprising nuggets. Indeed, the amount of pre-1935 Pearson material has been more than doubled by the discovery of unpublished and anonymously published writings by Pearson.

Lester Pearson spent much time outside of Canada, and it is not surprising that information on him is located in archives scattered throughout the Western world. At the Public Record Office in Britain, the Dominions Office, Foreign Office, Prime Minister's Office, and Treasury Records all have Pearson material. At Cambridge University, the University Library has the Stanley Baldwin Papers; Churchill College has the Burgon Bickersteth, Maurice Hankey, and Philip Noel-Baker papers. At Oxford, the college records of St. John's College and the Clement Attlee Papers at University College have material. Malcolm MacDonald's papers were consulted at the library of the Royal Commonwealth Society but have since been moved elsewhere. Charles Webster's papers at the British Library of Political and Economic Science in London have several Pearson references.

Some material was located in the League of Nations Archives in Geneva. The United Nations Archives in New York is not well organized, but I found some material bearing upon Volume 1 (and some valuable material for Volume 2). I was unable to pry material loose from the North Atlantic Treaty Organization's carefully guarded archives.

Pearson gained his initial prominence with his work in the United

States, and it is not surprising that American archives have much valuable material. The records of the Department of State at the National Archives in Washington are frequently cited in the notes. The Federal Bureau of Investigation also has material, and some information was found in the Department of Commerce records. At the Library of Congress, I consulted numerous collections but found Pearson material in only a few, notably the Philip Jessup and Laurence Steinhardt papers. At Columbia University, the oral-history collection has some information as do the Andrew Cordier Papers. Harvard University has the important J. Pierrepont Moffat collection. The presidential libraries of Franklin D. Roosevelt and Harry Truman have a wealth of material dealing with the period Pearson spent in the United States, although neither has much specifically dealing with Pearson.

Interviews have been invaluable in reconstructing Pearson's life and a full list will be published in Volume 2. I have often been given documents during these interviews, and such instances are acknowledged in the preface. I have also benefited from correspondence with Pearson's classmates, colleagues, and friends. Pearson's colleagues were prolific writers; someone once calculated that those who had been members of the Department of External Affairs before 1950 had written fifty books. The total still mounts, with distinguished contributions by such former diplomats as Escott Reid and Robert Ford. These books have helped me greatly in understanding the way in which the department worked, attitudes towards Pearson, and the Ottawa milieu.

Lester Pearson's memoirs have been a source of inestimable value. As Alistair Horne has remarked in his recent biography of Harold Macmillan, one writes memoirs to conceal as well as tell. Like Macmillan, Lester Pearson did not tell all and did not intend to do so. Measured by a different standard, the Pearson memoirs do capture the personality of the author very well. Alex Inglis and John Munro, who edited the three volumes, did particularly well in explaining the significance of events. The omissions are certainly not their fault. In writing this biography, I found the omissions were, in some ways, as important as the content of the memoirs in understanding how Lester Pearson thought. Religion is the best example, but there are many others.

The 1970s and 1980s have been the golden age of secondary works dealing with Canadian foreign policy. My indebtedness will be fully recorded in the next volume, but some mention of the salient works must be made. That most talented and prolific Canadian historian, Jack Granatstein, has written an excellent life of Pearson's colleague Norman Robertson in *A Man of Influence* (Ottawa, 1981) and the best study of the civil service, *The Ottawa Men* (Toronto, 1982). With Robert Cuff, he has also written two valuable monographs: *Canadian-American Relations in Wartime* (Toronto, 1975) and *American Dollars – Canadian Prosperity* (Toronto, 1978). His extensive research and numerous insights have served as beacons for me as I followed Pearson's life. John Holmes understood Lester Pearson better than anyone else. He dealt with only the public Pearson in his important *The Shaping of Peace* (2 vols.; Toronto, 1979, 1982) and explained his public purposes extremely well. The third volume of James Eayrs's *In Defence of Canada* series begins with finely crafted sketches of the world surrounding Pearson in the 1940s. Although Eayrs seems ambivalent towards Pearson, his journalism as well as his historical works are exceptional in their ability to evoke a time and a place, and they have been rewarding reading for me. Denis Smith's *Diplomacy of Fear* (Toronto, 1988) raises troubling questions about the post-war diplomacy that Holmes and others have so highly praised. It is an important book, as are Robert Bothwell's studies of Canada's nuclear history: *Eldorado* (Toronto, 1984) and *Nucleus* (Toronto, 1988). Much of the best research on Canadian history still remains buried in theses. For this volume, I found especially useful the theses of Susan Armstrong, Peter Boehm, Michael Gauvreau, Murray Genoe, Anne Trowell Hillmer, Norman Hillmer, Greg Johnson, Hector Mackenzie, Donald Page, and Donald Story.

Finally, John Hilliker allowed me to read the unpublished first volume of the history of the Department of External Affairs and helped in obtaining departmental papers for me.

INDEX

References to *PS1* through *4* are to photo sections following pages 36, 132, 180, and 276, respectively.